QRP POWER

The Best Recent QRP Articles from QST, QEX and The ARRL Handbook

Published by:

The American Radio Relay League, Inc.
225 Main Street
Newington, CT 06111-1494
USA

Compiled by Joel Kleinman, N1BKE, and Zack Lau, KH6CP/1

Contents

Foreword

Everyone who's operated QRP, the art of transmitting with 5 watts or less of output power, knows the thrill of measuring success by miles per watt in addition to number of countries or sections worked. Some operate QRP to solve an RFI problem, others to be able to use a transceiver they built themselves. Still others simply enjoy the unique challenges of running low power. Making yourself heard over atmospheric noise, uncooperative band conditions and interference from stations running the legal limit is no small feat. Yet QRPers do it all the time!

Now that we've sold out of two printings of the original *QRP Classics*, first published in 1990, we are pleased to present *QRP Power*, the next in what promises to be a continuing series. We've compiled the best articles published in *QST* and *QEX* over the past few years, and have added one impressive article, "Revisiting the 40-40," that has not been published previously.

We welcome your comments on the book, or your suggestions for future publications. There's a handy Feedback Form at the back, or just drop a note to Editor, *QRP Power*, at ARRL Headquarters.

David Sumner, K1ZZ
Newington, Connecticut

Preface

The concept of using extremely low power to facilitate worldwide communications on the amateur bands has been around since the early days of ham radio. It has been only in the last several years, however, that QRP has evolved from a fringe element into a major facet of the radio hobby. Today, QRP is defined as full-blown Amateur Radio using power output levels of 5 watts or less.

QRP enjoyed a resurgence in the early 1970s into the mid 1980s, thanks to people like Ade Weiss, WØRSP, Doug DeMaw, W1FB, The Rev. George Dobbs, G3RJV, Wes Hayward, W7ZOI, Roy Lewallen, W7EL, Chris Page, G4BUE and others. Their pioneering efforts were chronicled in the pages of *QST*, *CQ* and *Radcom*. A selection of QRP articles from *QST* and *The ARRL Handbook* appeared in the ARRL publication, *QRP Classics*, which quickly gained a place in the serious QRPer's library.

QRP Power is a transition from the QRP renaissance period into the 21st century. The articles herein focus on current trends in the field of amateur low power communications. Contributors to this work are some of the best QRP operators on the planet. The circuits and kits presented in this book reflect a dramatic change from the simple direct conversion rigs of the past to more technically superior designs.

Is QRP for everyone? Absolutely not! The world of the QRPer is one in which raw RF power means nothing and operating skills mean everything. To enjoy success, the low power communicator must completely rethink operating strategies. Giving up a 13-dB power advantage quickly underscores the need to dramatically improve operating skills, expand one's knowledge of electronics and antennas, and improve building techniques. Put all these improvements together and you have a more skillful radio amateur.

QRP Power provides a starting point for the neophyte low-power communicator and an idea pool for the advanced QRPer. The object is, quite simply, to further your enjoyment of the hobby. If you're up for a challenge, then welcome to the world of low power communications.

Rich Arland, K7YHA
Wilkes-Barre, Pennsylvania

Acknowledgments

The Editor wishes to thank all the authors whose material appears in the this volume. A perusal of the contents page will show that some prolific authors have several articles represented. It is our hope that by compiling them into one volume, the articles will be made that much more useful to the QRP community.

Special thanks to ARRL Assistant Director L. B. Cebik, W4RNL, who compiled the periodicals list that appears in Chapter 6.

A word of caution: Addresses and telephone numbers were accurate when the articles were first published, but they may no longer be current.

1. How Low Can You Go?

What is QRP?
Rich Arland, K7YHA
From *QST*, October 1994

Hard-Core QRP
Richard H. Arland, K7YHA
From *QST*, September 1995

Low-Power Contesting
Richard H. Arland, K7YHA
From *QST*, March 1996

From QST, *October 1994, p 46:*

What Is QRP?

You've been wanting to try QRP, but you had some questions? We've got the answers!

By Rich Arland, K7YHA

Welcome to the wonderful world of low-power (QRP) communication. In this article I will introduce you to a part of the Amateur Radio hobby that has, for almost 30 years, held enormous fascination for me. I wasn't the only ham enticed by QRP back then. The 1960s saw the beginning of renewed interest in QRP operation by hams, but low-power communications was by no means a new idea.

In the 1920s and 30s, while mainstream Amateur Radio operators embraced higher and higher power levels, low-power pioneers proved that high power was not needed to communicate over great distances. These stalwart experimenters managed great feats of communication, becoming skilled operators in the process. Their experiments with antennas and transmitter efficiency were great contributions to the hobby.

The term "QRPer" comes from the Q signal *QRP*, meaning "please reduce power." QRP power is defined as an output level of 5 W or less. Today's QRPer has the advantage of improved receivers and transmitters, high-gain antennas and a great collective intelligence, in the form of QRP clubs worldwide, that makes QRP operation challenging, exciting and FUN!

The QRP Philosophy

QRP contacts just don't happen, they are the result of careful planning and outstanding operating skills on the part of the operator. For example, experienced QRPers know that they are capable of initiating and maintaining QRP contacts anywhere in the world. This flies in the face of the "more is better" crowd. After all, if 100 watts is good 1000 watts is better, right? Many high power operators' solution to today's crowded, interference-ridden bands is the use of yet more power. This indiscriminate use of power is extremely short sighted, and only increases interference.

QRPers are elitists—make no mistake about it. We are a proud group, who scorn the unrestricted use of power. QRP lends itself to the use of non-polluting energy sources, like solar and wind power. QRP is radio with no harmful side effects!

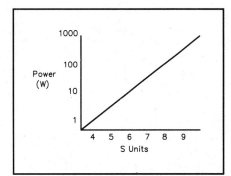

Figure 1—A comparison of power levels and S-meter indications. This graph assumes that an S unit is 6 dB and an indication of S9 corresponds to a power level of 1000 W.

Will QRP Work?

In effect, by reducing your RF output from the normal 100 W to 5 W, you are giving up 13 dB of transmitter power. This sounds like a lot, but, when viewed in terms of S units, things aren't as bad as they appear. This 13-dB difference makes your signal about 2 S units weaker, assuming an S unit is 6 dB. Figure 1 demonstrates this concept. I have arbitrarily assumed 1000 W output from the transmitting station as an S9 signal at the receiving station. Therefore, each decrease of 1 S unit in the receive signal level (RSL) corresponds to an actual power decrease of four (ie, a decrease from S9 to S8 would be obtained by reducing your power output from 1000 W to 250 W). As you can see from Figure 1, the difference in RSL between a 1 kW signal and a 5 W signal is only 4 S units. Our transmitted QRP signal equals an S5 signal at the distant end—solid copy under all but the most congested or degraded band conditions.

We have proven, theoretically, that low-power contacts are possible, so what about the real world? How do you go about becoming active with QRP?

Adjusting Your Rig For QRP Operation

First of all, you don't have to rush out and buy a new rig. Your current HF rig

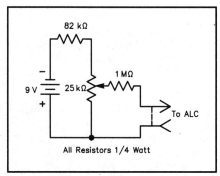

Figure 2—Schematic diagram of an ALC bias supply that may be used to reduce the power output of some transceivers and transmitters.

should do just fine. Since most recent transceivers have a knob to control the RF output, it is a simple matter to adjust them for 5-W output. If your transmitter or transceiver doesn't have sufficient adjustment range, but it does have an ALC (automatic level control) jack, use the circuit in Figure 2 instead. If you can't use this circuit, try the one shown in Figure 3, although you'll have to hunt for some power resistors to build it. You are now ready to try some QRP contacts.

Another Word About Rigs

After owning five Ten-Tec Argonauts, several Heathkit HW 8s and building four commercial kits, I believe that nothing takes the place of using modern commercially manufactured equipment for QRP operation. Performance, especially in the receiver department, is outstanding.

My main QRP rigs are a Kenwood TS-130V (the low-power version of the TS-130 transceiver) and a Ten-Tec Argonaut Model 509 with optional 2.4-kHz 8-pole IF filter. In addition, I have used the Yaesu FT-1000 and FT-890 transceivers, as well as rigs from Icom and Kenwood, all with outstanding success.

Using these modern rigs provides you with an excellent receiver, featuring switchable IF filters, memories, and, in some cases, digital-signal processing—a

Table 1
QRP Calling Frequencies (MHz)

Band	CW	SSB
160	1.810	1.910
	1.843 (Europe)	
80	3.560	3.985
	3.710 (US Novice)	
40	7.040	7.285
	7.030 (Europe)	7.060
	7.110 (US Novice)	
30	10.106	
20	14.060	14.285
15	21.060	21.385
10	28.060	28.385
	28.110 (US Novice)	

far cry from the direct conversion receivers or the simple superhet designs of the early Argonauts.

Homebrew Gear

The excitement and pride you feel while using equipment you have constructed yourself is tremendous. QRP rigs are, by nature, very simple devices. You don't have to be an electronics engineer to build one of the many QRP transceiver kits on the market. The various QRP club newsletters, along with the major amateur radio magazines, offer a wide range of QRP construction projects that can result in a very rewarding experience for the low power communicator. Why not give this facet of QRP a try?

Where To Look

Making QRP contacts is truly exciting. As a matter of fact, it becomes quite addictive. It gets even better when you make a QRP-to-QRP contact. To make it easier to find other QRPers, we look for one another on QRP calling frequencies on each band. Table 1 lists these QRP calling frequencies. When I am puttering around the shack, I leave my receiver tuned to a calling frequency. These frequencies are also prime hunting grounds during QRP contests. Then, you will find many QRP stations stretched out from 10 kHz above to 10 kHz below the calling frequency.

What Modes?

Now a word about modes of operation. CW is the preferred QRP mode. Why? Simply, CW is more efficient than SSB. How much more efficient? According to one source,[1] CW signals can be successfully copied against background noise with only a 3:1 signal-to-noise ratio. A single-sideband (SSB) signal, on the other hand, requires a minimum 7:1 signal-to-noise ratio for successful reception. This means that a CW signal is more than twice as easy to copy than an SSB signal under similar conditions.

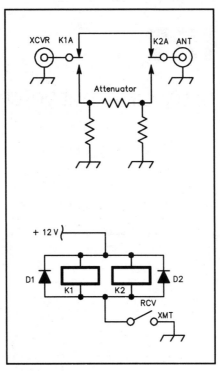

Figure 3—Schematic diagram of a switchable power attenuator that may be used to reduce the power output of transmitters that don't have ALC lines.
D1, D2—1N4001 or equivalent.
K1, K2—High-speed relays, Radio Shack 275-248
R1, R2, R3—Noninductive power resistors. You must calculate the required resistance and power rating.

See the ARRL *Handbook* or *Your QRP Operating Companion* for more information

Single sideband *is* used by QRPers. In my experience, however, low power SSB contacts are much more difficult to make. This is not only due to the RF power disparity, but is also directly related to the more stringent signal-to-noise ratio requirement at the receiving end. The receiving operator's skill also plays a big part in reception of QRP SSB signals. Many sideband operators are not used to having to dig a weak SSB signal out of the background. CW operators, on the other hand, often will make the effort to dig out your QRP signal. This is especially true during contests, where the best CW operators routinely copy QRP signals against a background of 20 dB over S9 signals.

What You Can Expect

Once you start using QRP, you will soon learn the basic facts of life regarding low-power operation. Here are some tips I've collected over the years.

About Calling and Answering CQ

Some QRPers recommend that you not call CQ when running QRP. But if no one calls CQ, it's darned hard to make QSOs, right? If the band is crowded with signals, it's possible that your signal may be lost in the din. If the band isn't very busy, or on the QRP calling frequencies, by all means call CQ.

When answering other stations' CQs, most QRPers assume the other station is running 100 W. If the other station is not very strong, it's reasonable to expect you'll be even weaker. Still, sometimes it pays to take the chance. There are other QRPers out there, and they don't always advertise the fact.

Working DX in Pileups

Breaking a pileup with QRP requires some skill, but your best tool is patience. Take time to study the pileup and get a feel for the other station's technique. Knowing exactly where and when to call won't guarantee a QSO, but calling at the wrong time or frequency sure guarantees you *won't* get through!

One technique, called "tail-ending," requires that you carefully monitor the QSO in progress and drop your call as the other station is signing over to the DX station. Although your signal may be several dB lower than the signing station, the DX operator should hear you relatively free from QRM caused by hundreds of other stations in the pile-up. Adding "QRP" to your call may get the DX station to stand by just for you! You'll find other useful tips in a couple of books available from ARRL.[2,3]

Don't get frustrated if you are unable to work a particular DX station today. Sometimes the propagation just isn't there. If propagation is poor, spend some time with your family. I recommend you learn all you can about propagation, antenna theory and DX operating techniques. Don't become disillusioned if, at first, you have trouble initiating contacts with other stations. The other operator's skills may not be up to par, or his rig or antenna may not be operating well. Just don't give up. Keep trying and you will become successful on a regular basis.

Some More Practical Suggestions

To maximize your enjoyment of QRP, you must develop a special bag of tricks. These suggestions are the result of my almost 30 years of QRP operation.

• Develop good listening skills. Successful QRPers are expert listeners. No other area of your personal operating habits needs as much work as your listening skills. Get on the air often, and use the technique called *band-scanning*. Here, you play detective, looking for clues as to who is on and which areas of the world are open. Concentrate on carefully tuning each band. Start at the low end, and identify each signal you hear as you progress up the band. Practiced often, band-scanning is not only fun, but dramatically increases your knowledge of propagation and band conditions.

In addition, developing careful listening habits helps you spot DX openings. Once you become a better listener, watch your WAC, WAS, DXCC and WAZ scores climb.

• Set realistic goals. Once you get over the initial thrill of making contacts using 5 W or less, you will be tempted to charge off in pursuit of awards and "wallpaper." This is a given. You should, however, temper your newly found enthusiasm with a logical plan to garner the necessary contacts for the various awards. One of the best ways to proceed is to set realistic goals and assign deadlines for completion. Worked All Continents (WAC) in 2 months. Worked All States (WAS) in 12 months. DXCC in two years. Setting goals gives you focus and allows you to easily chart your progress.

• Make It Fun! QRP is a gentle art. It promotes good operating practices over the use of raw RF power. You can pursue QRP at your own pace. For many hams, QRP brings back the good old days when they were first licensed. The thrill of communicating with other amateurs around the world, using RF power that would not illuminate a small light bulb, is rather heady stuff. Every time you make a QRP contact, you will experience the pride of accomplishment.

• Join a QRP club (see Table 2). The QRP Amateur Radio Club International (QRP ARCI) is the world's oldest and best-known QRP organization. The British G-QRP Club is the fastest-growing QRP club in the world, and emphasizes home-brewing equipment. There are many regional QRP clubs that offer local camaraderie, newsletters and competitions. Enter the QRP contests, every year and submit a log to the contest sponsor. This will sharpen your operating skills, and keep your interest peaked.

• Efficient antennas are the key to successful QRP operation. After you start enjoying some QRP contacts, you will want to spend some time (and a little money) maximizing your antenna farm. Replace all coax over three years old with new, low-loss, coax from a reputable supplier. Put your dipoles and wire antennas as high as you possibly can. I used to use RG-8X (otherwise known as mini-RG-8) for all my coaxial runs. Over the last few years, I have changed over to quality RG-213 coax to further reduce feedline losses. Remember, any loss of RF in the coax is wasted power. You want every milliwatt your transmitter puts out to reach the antenna.

If you have a multi-band vertical or triband beam, take it down, clean it up, replace any worn or broken parts, and restore it to its original specifications. Look closely at your ground connections, and clean off any corrosion you find. Good metal-to-metal electrical contact on antennas and in the ground system reduces noise and increases efficiency. Remember, your

---

Table 2
QRP Clubs and Organizations

National and International

G-QRP Club, Stateside contact: Mike Kilgore, KG5F, 2046 Ash Hill Rd, Carrollton, TX 75007. $12 for new membership and annual renewal.

QRP Amateur Radio Club International (QRP ARCI). Contact Mike Bryce, WB8VGE, 2225 Mayflower NW, Massillon, OH 44647. $12 for new membership, $10 for renewal.

Local and Regional

Cleveland QRP ARC, Bruce A. Wright, N8NWL, PO Box 14052, 410 Superior Ave, Cleveland, OH 44114-9998. No dues or membership fees.

Central Pennsylvania QRP Society, Cameron Bailey, KT3A, P.O. Box 173, Mount Wolfe, PA 17347-0173. No dues or membership fees.

Colorado QRP Club, Rich High, W0HEP, 14261 E 4th Ave, No.161, Aurora, CO 80011-8711. No dues or membership fees.

Illinois QRP Group, Vikki Welch, WV9K, 1307H N. Richmond Rd, McHenry, IL 60050-1461. No dues or membership fees.

MFJ-90's Radio Club, Joseph Falcone, AA8HV, 3000 Town Center, Suite 2370, Southfield, MI 48075. No dues or membership fees.

Michigan QRP Club, Membership Chairperson, Michigan QRP Club, 654 Georgia, Marysville, MI 48040. $7 for new membership, $5 annual renewal.

NorCal (Northern California) QRP Club, Jim Cates, WA6GER, 3241 Eastwood Rd, Sacramento, CA 95821. $5 for new membership and annual renewal.

NorthWest QRP Club, Bill Todd, N7MFB, 2418 55th Ave SW, Seattle, WA 98116 $10 for new membership, no annual dues.

NorthEastern Illinois QRP Society, Don Kozlovsky, KE9GG, 28 W 256 Purnell Rd, West Chicago, IL 60185. No dues or membership fees.

Oklahoma QRP Group, Don Kelly, KA5UOS, 703 West 8th St, Edmond, OK 73034. No dues or membership fees.

QRP Club Of New England, Jack Frake, NG1G, PO Box 1153, Barnard, VT 05031. $10 for new membership, $7 annual renewal.

St. Louis QRP Society, Keith Arns, KC0PP, 2832 Penbrooke Ln, St. Charles, MO 63301-0344. $12 annual dues. Membership limited to the Greater St Louis Area.

WI QRP Club, PO Box 111, Brandon, WI 53919-0111. Dues voluntary—$5 to $10 suggested.

Wyoming Valley QRP Commandos, 25 Amherst Ave, Wilkes-Barre, PA 18702. No dues or formal meetings. Membership limited to the Greater Scranton/Wilkes-Barre Area.

---

antenna and ground system can make or break your QRP efforts. The more time you spend on improving them, the better your results.

Spreading The Word

Once you are bitten by the QRP Bug, share your success and excitement with others in the hobby. A good way to do this is to organize a QRP Field Day with your club or group. QRP dovetails nicely with Field Day, where everyone is forced to use portable power sources and less-than-optimal antennas. I have found that QRP Field Days are an outstanding way to show other hams and nonhams that you don't need lots of power to work the world.

Another effective approach to spreading the QRP gospel is to offer to be a guest speaker at club meetings. Once you gain experience as a QRPer, it should be easy to assemble a 30-minute program on QRP operation. There is a lot of interest in QRP, and you'll answer lots of questions. One of the biggest problems I encounter is finding time to field all the questions. You are sure to find one or two converts in the crowd,

not to mention additional operators for an upcoming Field Day!

See You Down The Log

I hope that you've enjoyed this brief look at QRP in the 1990s. One final thought regarding low power communicators: In the early days of Amateur Radio, many amateurs turned to high power in pursuit of the hobby. The "real hams" were experimenting with low power on the HF bands. These radio pioneers relied on superior operating skills to blaze the trail. Today's QRPers share that pioneer spirit. Every day, QRP operators demonstrate to the world that "power is no substitute for skill." Join us and rediscover the thrill and fun of Amateur Radio!

Notes
[1]Jacobs and Cohen, "The Shortwave Propagation Handbook," 2nd edition (Hicksville, NY, CQ Publishing Inc.: 1982), p16.
[2,3]Kearman, The DXCC Companion (Newington, ARRL: 1990); Wells, Your QRP Operating Companion (Newington, ARRL: 1992).

From QST, September 1995, p 66:

Hard-Core QRP

Ultra-low power HF hamming using milliwatts and microwatts.

By Richard H. Arland, K7YHA
PO Box 1782
Shavertown, PA 18708

In a previous *QST* article about low-power operation,[1] I touched on the idea of using milliwatts to communicate between amateur stations. Milliwatting and microwatting (called "hard-core QRP" or "QRPp" by the those who practice the craft) have gained great support over the last several years. Chris Page, G4BUE, world-renowned QRPer and DXer, has written of his success DXing with milliwatts and microwatts in *CQ* Magazine.[2] Encouraged by Chris' article, many low-power communicators have given *ultra*-low-power communication a try.

Exactly what is milliwatting and microwatting? Simply put, it is reducing your transmitter output power down to ridiculously minuscule levels and then make readable radio contact. This is not a new idea, by any stretch of the imagination.

In 1923, Robert Kruse, 1XAM, Technical Editor of *QST*, wrote (in an article titled "Miles Per Watt: An Argument for the Small Set and for Intelligence in Place of Brute Force; Also a New Efficiency Contest"), "...doesn't more credit belong to the man who hauls signals fifty miles per watt

than to the one who has to use greater power to haul them only 25 miles per watt?" Remember, this was in the early 1920s, when Amateur Radio was in its infancy. Regenerative receivers were the order of the day for a "modern" ham shack. Nonetheless, Kruse extolled the virtues of doing more with less, which has become the modern day QRPers' creed.

In his 1924 *QST* series entitled "The New American Amateur," Kruse blasted the "ether busters," "watt hogs" and "thunder factories" that crowded the bands with intense interference. The "New American Amateur," as defined (in 1924) by Kruse and the ARRL, was not satisfied with mediocre station and antenna performance. He sought an efficient station by using low-loss, high-efficiency equipment design and by constantly working to improve his operating skills.

Anyone who practices the art and science of low-power communication can, even today, rightly be considered a "New American Amateur." Kruse would have been proud of today's QRPers. He would be even more impressed with those who communicate using milliwatts and microwatts on the HF bands.

Hard-core QRP is not for the timid. It takes patience, dedication, desire, excellent operating skills, and tenacity to be successful at ultra-low power levels. A very quiet location is also extremely helpful.

The average amateur transmitter emits 100 W of RF energy. This will become our "standard" for the following comparison of power output levels (remembering that $dB = 10 \, Log \, [P_1/P_2]$). The difference between 5 W (true QRP) and 100 W is only 13 dB (about 2 S units). The power disparity, as referenced to the 100 W standard) becomes quite large (23 dB or almost 4 S units) when the QRPer drops his power output to 500 milliwatts (mW). If we continue to reduce output to 500 microwatts (μW), the difference becomes a whopping 53 dB—about 9 S units! By now it should become quite apparent that hard-core QRP is not for those who are faint of heart. You have to *work* for QRPp contacts.

How does one become a milli- or microwatter? Simple: Attenuate the power output of your QRP rig into the milliwatt or microwatt range. Because CW is the preferred mode for ultra-low-power communication, this is not a difficult task. Most QRP transceivers have a drive control that will reduce the output power into the milliwatt range. From there the QRPer can use a step attenuator to reduce output into the microwatt range.

The easiest way to accomplish accurate power measurements is to terminate the transmitter into a dummy load and connect an oscilloscope across the load. Key the transmitter and note the value of the peak-to-peak voltage on the scope. Divide this number in half (to obtain peak voltage) and then multiply by 0.707 to obtain RMS voltage. The RMS voltage is then squared and divided by the resistance of the load (remember Ohm's law, $P = E^2/R$). The resultant figure is the average power output of the transmitter.

In order to reduce power into the microwatt region, the QRPer needs to establish an accurate RF output in the milliwatt range, and then feed the output of the transmitter into a step attenuator, such as the one shown on pages 26-40 and -41 of *The ARRL Handbook* (1995 edition). By watching the output of the oscilloscope, while switching in various combinations of attenuation

Paul, AA4XX, and his station assembled in the yard (so as to be near the antenna, thus reducing feedline losses) for the successful assault on the old miles-per-watt record.

(usually in 3, 6, 9, 10 and 20 dB steps), a very accurate measurement of RF output power down into the microwatt range can be obtained.

Prior planning is critical in microwatting on the lower HF bands. The way records are made or broken all depends on proper coordination between two stations. You need to set up a schedule to ensure that someone will be listening for your ultra-low-power signals. Band congestion, man-made and natural interference levels, and propagation conditions become obstacles that must be overcome by the ultra-low-power operator.

Chapter 5 in *Low Power Communications, Vol II, Advanced QRP Operating,*[3] chronicles the efforts of Bill Smith, WA6YPE; Bob Moody, K7IRK; and Bill Brown, WB8ELK, to establish a 10-meter world record in excess of 2 BILLION miles per watt.

It can be argued that microwatting on 10 meters is rather easy when band conditions are prime and when the ionosphere cooperates. Good propagation, uncrowded conditions, and low interference and noise levels work together to allow weak signals to stand out against the background noise quite easily. As the ultra-low-power communicator goes lower in frequency, the bands become noisier and more congested, and man-made and natural interference gets worse. Therefore, the hard-core QRPer must be ready for much tougher going on 40, 80 and 160 meters.

Without a doubt, the 40 meter amateur band is the best all-around QRP and QRPp band of the lower HF bands. At anytime—day or night—the low-power communicator can garner contacts on 40. The daylight hours are best for attempting microwatt communication. There are no foreign short-wave broadcast stations to contend with, and the skip zone is relatively short, so European SSB stations (which operate as low as 7035 kHz) are not a problem.

The Stateside QRP calling frequency on 40 meters is 7040 kHz. Move up the band at least 10 KHz to get away from any congestion around the QRP calling frequency. For the 1994 world record attempt on 40 meters, Fran Slavinski, KA3WTF, and Paul Stroud, AA4XX, elected to use 7050 kHz, which, after many days of careful listening, was found to be the least congested frequency in the CW portion of the band. For several days, Fran noted that there was a very solid north-south path between his location in Larksville, Pennsylvania, and Paul's, in Raleigh, North Carolina. This path (approximately 400 statute miles) peaked about local noon, but seemed to be stable as early as 10:30 AM EST (1530 UTC). Several successful contacts between KA3WTF and AA4XX were made, with Paul running first 10 mW, and then 900 μW.

This initial success started both hams wondering if they could make contact us-

ing 450 μW. During this time, they were notified by Chuck Adams, K5FO (awards manager for the QRP ARCI[4]) that the current official 40 meter record stood at 1,000,000 miles per watt. This meant that, in order to break the existing record, over their path, they would have to use less than 400 μW!

Paul and Fran accepted the challenge. December 26, 1994, was chosen as the day for the attempt. In an effort to minimize any feedline losses, Paul moved his entire station, including an Oak Hills Research "Classic" QRP 40/20-meter transceiver, storage battery, solar panel and charge controller, plus a 100 MHz oscilloscope, into his back yard, directly under his three-element 40-meter wire beam. AA4XX then performed a very careful power measurement, setting his power output at 221 μW.

At a prearranged time (1630 UTC) on 7050 KHz, AA4XX transmitted a series of **V**s and then started calling KA3WTF using 221 μW. Fran heard Paul's **V**s and answered him using 5 W output from a Ten-Tec Argonaut II into a Carolina Windom antenna 30 feet in the air. Paul acknowledged Fran's transmission and then immediately sent a signal report of 579 to Fran. Fran repeated the report he had received from AA4XX, and received confirmation on the numbers he'd copied. Then KA3WTF sent Paul a signal report of 229 to complete the exchange and qualify for a two-way contact. The record had been broken!

The path distance was computed using the exact longitude and latitude of Fran's location as determined by the Global Positioning System, and the published coordinates of Raleigh for Paul's location. It should be noted that Paul's actual location is 16 miles south of Raleigh, which gives the path calculations a conservative "fudge

factor" of an additional 16 miles.

Running these locations on W6EL's *MiniProp Plus* propagation software yielded a path distance of 424 miles. Taking this path distance and dividing it by the 221 μW Paul used to establish contact with Fran gives us the new 40-meter world record of over 1,900,000 miles per watt!

Microwatting, as demonstrated by these two QRPers, does not take a new transceiver or hundreds of dollars of additional hardware. If you are active on the HF bands, your current QRP rig should work just fine, with the addition of a step attenuator. One hint: remember to switch the attenuator out of the antenna path when you switch to receive mode. Failure to do so will result in receive signal levels being attenuated by whatever amount is dialed into the step attenuator.

The ability to communicate using micropower on the lower HF bands is more an exercise in planning and operator skill than luck. It's wits, not watts, that make the difference. One word of caution: the how-low-can-we-go syndrome is extremely infectious. Once you start milliwatting and microwatting, it becomes almost addictive. You, too, could turn down the RF power and join the ranks of the hard-core QRPers!

Notes
[1]Rich Arland, K7YHA, "What is QRP?", *QST*, Oct 1994, p 46-48.
[2]Chris Page, G4BUE, "QRPing With Milliwatts," *CQ*, Jun 1982, p 33-37.
[3]Rich Arland, K7YHA, *Low Power Communications, Vol II, Advanced QRP Operating* (Tiare Publications, PO Box 493, Lake Geneva, WI 53147).
[4]QRP Amateur Radio Club International (QRP ARCI), c/o Mike Bryce, 2225 Mayflower NW, Massillon, OH 44647 ($12 for new membership, $10 for renewal).

Fran, KA3WTF, and his neat and functional QRP shack; the other half of the new QRP record.

From QST, March 1996 p 47:

By Richard H. Arland, K7YHA

Low-Power Contesting

Some hams think you need a kilowatt and stacked monobanders to be a competitive HF contester—*wrong!*

A re you bored with ham radio? Are you just two contacts away from the DXCC Honor Roll with no DXpeditions in sight? Can you readily say, "Been there, done that," when another ham mentions DXing and contesting? Are you bummed out by the lack of good propagation at the bottom of sunspot Cycle 22?

Well, take heart! There is salvation. If you're *really* desperate for a challenge, try low-power contesting. Don't laugh; I'm serious! Contesting and QRP are *not* mutually exclusive. In recent years, low-power communication has become a major facet of the hobby. Better yet, most major contests provide a QRP category for those who choose to run 5 W or less. I should note here that, in contesting terms, "QRP" and "low power" are *not* interchangeable. Many contests have a "low-power" category for stations running not more than 100 or 150 W. As defined by most QRP clubs, *true* QRP is limited to 5 W output for CW or 10 W PEP output for SSB. That works out to a 13-dB difference between the low-power class and true QRP. (The ARRL defines QRP for HF contests as 5 W PEP output.—*Ed.*) QRP stations only compete against other QRP stations, which goes a long way toward leveling the playing field.

Put aside thoughts of kilowatts and huge monobanders. Raw RF power isn't everything. To be a successful QRP contester,

what you really need are outstanding operating skills, dedication and perseverance. As the late Howard Pyle, W7OE, often put it: "Power is no substitute for skill." Let's examine what the low-power communicator needs to be successful in the contesting arena, including which contests are best, plus some thoughts on contesting philosophy and radio hardware.

Why contest? Contests are a challenge for both high-power operators and QRPers. To the uninitiated, though, a contest weekend means the bands are trashed up by the ham radio equivalent of the schoolyard bullies. On its surface, ham radio contesting seems to prove little, except that whoever has the biggest signal wins. *Loud* is not necessarily *good*, however, if you don't have operating skills to match. Contests are full of operators who constantly transmit when they should be listening. These same operators consistently miss other stations' replies, fail to spot a rare station adjacent to their frequency, and transmit on top of others in an attempt to "hold the frequency."

Regularly entering contests in the QRP class improves your operating skills. Remember, you are giving up a power advantage, so you must rely on *wits*, not watts. Learning how to copy call signs and contest exchanges under extremely crowded band conditions expands your operating skills and increases your confidence. Wringing the maximum performance from your equipment enhances your technical abilities. Knowing how propagation affects the various bands and moving around to take full advantage of that information greatly increases your DXing skills. In short, you become a much better all-around operator, whether you are working a contest, DXing or handling emergency traffic for the local ARES group.

Which contests are best for the QRP operator? Most of the major contests are good, but a couple of operating events are regarded by some in the QRP fraternity as holy days of obligation. Among them are the ARRL Field Day and the QRP Amateur Radio Club International spring and fall QSO parties. Several regional clubs—like the Michigan QRP Club, the Northern Califor-

The undisputed "King of QRP Contesters," Randy Rand, AA2U, in his Denville, New Jersey, shack. Randy's 238,212 points in the 1994 ARRL 10-Meter Contest took first place as a QRP entry. It would have placed him fourth in the low-power (150 W) category and eighth in the high-power category.

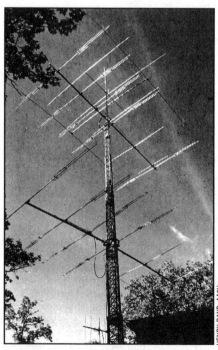

The AA2U antenna farm includes a 90-foot crank-up tower with two KT-34XAs at 38 and 90 feet, plus a two-element 40-meter Yagi and beams for 12, 17 and 30 meters. It also has an 80-meter full-wave loop.

Buck Switzer, N8CQA, of Marysville, Michigan, is a well-known QRP contester and president of the QRP Amateur Radio Club International.

QRP Contesting Tips

• Read the contest announcements thoroughly! Dumb as it sounds, it's nice to be on the air the same weekend as the contest. Also, know which stations you're supposed to be working and the correct contest exchange.

• Use the "search-and-pounce" (S&P) technique. Don't try to hold a frequency with only a few watts. You just don't have the raw RF power to do it. S&P gives you a chance to move around and grab QSOs and multipliers quickly. Tune across the bands and try working the loudest stations first (but don't waste time trying to break a pileup. Move on after a couple of tries). Then, go back and work the stations that aren't as loud (the so-called second-tier stations). Repeat the process for third-tier stations. This way, you'll thoroughly work each band.

• Initially, stay away from "kilowatt alley" (the bottom end of the bands). Instead, cruise the middle to high end of the bands where the QRM is less and your chances of being heard against the cacophony of signals are much better. Toward the end of the contest, slip down into the lower portions of the bands and grab the "big signals," who are, by then, desperate for contacts.

• Use a computer with a good contest logging program. These and others are available through ham radio dealers or through magazine ads in *National Contest Journal*[†] and other publications. The computer takes the work out of duping, and you obtain a real-time score. I guarantee that once you log with a computer, you will *never* go back to paper logs and dupe sheets.

• Antennas are the "great equalizer" in QRP. Therefore, erect the biggest and tallest antenna system you can. Do not skimp by using cheap or old coaxial-cable feed lines. New runs of RG-213 will ensure that as much of your power as possible makes it to the antenna.

• Regularly check other bands for surprise openings. A second receiver is very handy here. If 10 or 15 meters suddenly opens up, you stand a very good chance of picking up both extra QSOs and multipliers on bands where QRP power levels work very well.

• Do not use packet spots from the DX cluster. Under current contesting guidelines, doing so puts you in the "single-operator, assisted" category competing against high-power stations, *not* in the QRP category. (Besides, you'll be bucking heads with the crowd.)

• Sharpen your listening and tail-ending skills. Learn to read how the other operator is handling the pileup. Slide your call sign in at the appropriate time and, more often than not, you will get in the other operator's log on the first or second shot.

• Keep abreast of the latest developments in contesting by reading the major ham magazines, *National Contest Journal*, QRP club newsletters and books on contesting and QRP.[††]

• Approach QRP contesting as a challenge and a learning experience. Be open-minded and try new and different techniques during the contest. Keep those techniques that work, discard the rest and watch your operating skills improve.

[†]*National Contest Journal*, a bimonthly publication of the ARRL, is dedicated to all phases of contesting. It features a QRP contest column by Howie Cahn, WB2CPU. $12/year. ARRL, 225 Main St, Newington, CT 06111, 860-594-0250.

[††]K7YHA's QRP Library, Low Power Communications, Vols 1-3, are available directly from the author, Richard H. Arland, K7YHA, PO Box 1782, Shavertown, PA 18708, 717-822-7067; Ham Radio Contesting, by Robert Halprin, K1XA, is available from Tiare Publications, PO Box 493, Lake Geneva, WI 53147, 414-248-4845.

QRP Clubs

QRP Amateur Radio Club International, Mike Bryce, WB8VGE, 2225 Mayflower NW, Massilon, OH 44646. $12/year for new members, $10/year renewal. *QRP Quarterly* newsletter. Emphasis: home construction, operating news.

Michigan QRP Club, Buck Switzer, N8CQA, 654 Georgia, Marysville, MI 48040. $7/year for new member, $5/year renewal. *The Five Watter* quarterly newsletter. Emphasis: operating news, some home construction. Sponsors several QRP contests each year.

Northern California (NorCal) QRP Club, Jim Cates, WA6GER, 3241 Eastwood Rd, Sacramento, CA 95821. $10/year. *QRPp* quarterly newsletter. Emphasis: home construction, club projects, operating news. NorCal regularly sponsors club project kits for members at no profit to the club. Among their more notable offerings: the NorCal 40A (40-meter CW transceiver), the Sierra (multiband CW transceiver) and the Cascade (multiband SSB transceiver).

QRP Club of New England, Jim Fitton, W1FMR, PO Box 2226, Salem, NH 03079. $10/year for new members, $7/year renewal. *72* quarterly newsletter. Emphasis: homebrew, club projects, modifications, operating news. Current offering (through Small Wonder Labs): the NN1G 40-40, a 40-meter CW transceiver, as featured in the November 1995 *QST*.

---

nia QRP Club (NorCal) and the QRP Club of New England—also sponsor QRP contests and sprints (short-duration contests lasting 4 to 8 hours), which provide a real challenge and are loads of fun. QRP contests and QSO parties are great learning experiences because they pit you against other thoroughly QRP stations. Footing is much more equal in these contests, and they are designed to be an enjoyable experience.

Entering the ARRL DX Contest or the CQ World Wide DX Contest is a sure way to work new countries, if that's your primary goal. If you're trying to work 100 countries with QRP, either of these contests will provide prime hunting ground for new countries. After a few major contests, your country total should increase dramatically.

What kind of hardware do you need to enter QRP contesting? Basically, whatever you currently use on HF should work fine. For CW contesting, merely turn down the RF power output to 5 W. If SSB contesting is your forte, then you might have to modify

or trick the ALC circuitry to run SSB at low-power levels. Your rig's manufacturer has the details. [Sometimes just turning down the mike gain works, too.—*Ed.*]

Many within the QRP fraternity prefer the older Ten-Tec QRP rigs: the Argonaut 509 and 515 and the Argosy Model 525 and 525Ds. Although these sets use 15 to 20-year-old technology, they still have a lot to offer. This equates to better receiver performance. Adding optional crystal filters, switched-capacitance audio filters, a speech processor and Heil HC-4 microphone element can make these old workhorses into great little QRP contest machines at a fraction of the cost of an expensive, high-end radio.

Among the latest trends to hit the QRP scene are the club project transceivers by NorCal and the QRP Club of New England, marketed by Wilderness Radio and Small Wonder Labs, respectively.[1] While these tiny, kit-built radios cannot equal the performance of modern high-end transceivers,

they deliver outstanding performance for simple designs, and they are fun to build and equally fun to use, especially during Field Day and QRP-only contests.

Field Day 1995 found Fran Slavinski, KA3WTF, and me in a tent using a NorCal 40 transceiver. The little rig was cranked down to only 900 mW output and fed into a Radio Works BigSig 40-meter Loop. We managed 135 QSOs and had a *ball* running milliwatts in a major contest. If you, too, are ready to accept the challenge of working major contests using a fraction of the power that the "big guns" use, I encourage you to join us. You won't be bored, I promise.

[1]Wilderness Radio, PO Box 734, Los Altos, CA 94023-0734, 415-494-3806, markets both the NorCal-40A and Sierra CW transceivers. Small Wonder Labs, 80 East Robbins Ave, Newington, CT 06111, 860-667-3536, markets the NN1G 40-40 CW transceiver, available in 80, 40, 20, and 15-meter single-band versions.

Richard H. Arland, K7YHA, PO Box 1782, Shavertown, PA 18708, a dedicated QRP operator of many years' standing, has authored many articles and books on the fun of running low power and succeeding with it.

2. Construction Practices

Build it Yourself from *QST*, Parts 1-4
Bruce S. Hale, KB1MW/7
From *QST*, April-July 1992

Calculating the Power Limit of Circuits with Toroids
Zack Lau, KH6CP/1
From *QEX*, March 1995

6-Meter Transverter Design
Zack Lau, KH6CP/1
From *QEX*, September 1995

From QST, April-July 1992:

Build It Yourself from QST

Part 1—Thinking about starting to build some of your own gear?
Here's how to turn a *QST* project into reality.

By Bruce S. Hale, KB1MW/7
2238 168th Ave NE
Bellevue, WA 98008

So you've decided you'd like to build that project in the latest *QST*, but you don't know where to start? This series of articles can help. In it, I'll show you how to move a *QST* construction article off the printed page and into your ham shack.

As a sample project for the series, we'll build a 20-meter VXO-controlled QRP transmitter developed from Zack Lau's popular 18, 21 and 24-MHz transceiver design.[1] Fig 1 shows the circuit, and Zack describes its design and performance in the sidebar, "A 20-Meter VXO-Controlled Transmitter."

I'll take you through buying the parts, building the circuit using simple ground-plane construction or by installing its parts on a ready-made PC board, installing it in a box, testing it, and putting it on the air. Fig 2 shows the difference between ground-plane and PC-board construction, in case this sounds mysterious to you.

Although you can buy a ready-made circuit board for this project,[2] I haven't asked anyone to make up complete kits of parts for it. Ordering a kit doesn't take much effort or skill—and every project you'll want to build probably won't be available as a kit. I want you to get the feel of being your own purchasing manager. That means sniffing out parts sources and dealing with them in person, by mail and by telephone to get the parts you need. You won't be able to find all the parts at Radio Shack, so you'll have to order parts by mail. You'll also have to order from more than one mail-order company. (It's almost a corollary to Murphy's Law: No matter how wide a selection you find in one mail-order catalog, you'll always find at least one part you have to buy somewhere else!)

Building a Catalog Library

For starters, you'll need catalogs from part suppliers. Chapter 35 of the *ARRL Handbook* contains an excellent list of mail-order parts dealers. Some of these mail-order companies are listed in Table 1. If you have enough catalogs, you'll be able to find almost any part, so I suggest writing to all the companies in Table 1.

Be sure to check *QST* advertisements, too. The part suppliers represented there want to help you build what you read about in *QST*!

Putting Together a Parts List

While you're waiting for your catalogs, let's look at the parts list for the transmitter (see the Fig 1 caption). Hold it—we can't just photocopy this and send it off to a mail-order company with a note that says "please send me these parts." We need to convert the part-placement list into what I call a *part order list* that shows the type and quantity required of each part.

Resistors

We'll start with the resistors. First, check tolerance and power rating. If we needed resistors with different power ratings or tolerances, we'd group them by those parameters before grouping them by value. For this project, all the resistors are specified as ¼-watt, 5%-tolerance parts, so all we need to know is how many of each value to order. If all of the circuit's resistors are already grouped by value on the parts list, we can just count the number of each value. Each time you add parts to the order list, check them off the published parts list. Sometimes the parts list does not include common components like resistors and capacitors. If this is the case, make a copy of the schematic and check off the parts as you build your shopping list.

Capacitors

Next, check the capacitors. There will usually be a number of different capacitor types in an RF circuit, so group these by type first. Put all the common disc-ceramic caps in one column, the metal-film caps in another, and so on. Include any variable capacitors or trimmers. Then count the number of each and add them to the list.

Solid-State Parts: Transistors, Diodes, Integrated Circuits

Count the solid-state parts next. This includes diodes, transistors and integrated circuits (ICs). Make sure you check each part off the published list as you add it to the order list.

Coils and Cores

There are a number of coils (inductors) in our project, and each is wound on a toroidal core. Count the number and type of each toroid and add them to the list. The parts list also specifies the gauge of the wire for each coil. This is important—using a different size wire from that specified will give you a different inductance. Add all the different wire sizes to the parts list.

Connectors, Cases and Miscellaneous Stuff

When you're done with the coils and cores, there are a few miscellaneous parts—a switch, some connectors, a box, a piece of circuit board (or a ready-made PC board) and a crystal. You'll also need a heat sink for the final transistor, some heat-sink grease, some solid hookup wire (#22 or #24 insulated wire) and—maybe—a short piece of RG-174 coaxial cable to connect the transmitter to the antenna connector. I used one piece of hookup wire between the circuit's Antenna point and the center terminal of my **ANTENNA** connector. A second piece connects circuit common and chassis near the **ANTENNA**-connector shell. You can use a short piece of coax, shield grounded at both ends, for **ANTENNA**-jack connection in both versions.

Choosing connectors for the antenna, key and power supply is a controversial issue. Some people swear by SO-239 and PL-259 RF ("UHF") connectors, while others will use nothing but BNCs.[3] For my version of this transmitter, I used a BNC connector because it's easier to mount with simple hand tools than an SO-239. (SO-239s require 5/8-inch holes. BNCs need holes no larger than 3/8-inch, depending on whether you get flange- or single-hole mount versions.) I used a 1/8-inch phone jack for the **KEY** jack because my keyer uses a 1/8-inch plug, and I used two-pin polarized Radio Shack connectors (#274-222) for power connectors. You can use a different combination of jacks, but always use different connectors for the antenna, power supply and keyer, if possible. If you use a phono jack for both the antenna and power supply connectors, you'll eventually plug the power supply into the **ANTENNA** jack. In some projects, this may let the smoke out of some components by short-circuiting the supply. (Not in Zack's transmitter, though. Its output terminal has no dc connection to chassis.)

Once the Catalogs Arrive

Now that your catalogs have arrived, let's see who's got the parts we need. You'll be able to get the resistors just about anywhere, including (for common values) Radio Shack. But wait a minute: Most of these mail-order companies will only let you order a multiple of five resistors of one value, and you only need one of some of them. Does this seem like a waste of money? Well, I hope this isn't the only project you'll ever build, and you'll need parts for your next project. If you get more parts than you need now, you can use some of them in the next project. Keep the parts where you can find

them, and after you build a few projects you'll be able to reach into your *junk box* (containing all these good parts, not really junk) any time you see an interesting project. If you need fewer than five resistors of one value, order five and save the rest for your next project. They're cheap.

Ordinary disc-ceramic capacitors will be easy to find, but you can't use them everywhere in a circuit. Most disc-ceramic capacitors are rated at a tolerance of ±20%, and some are rated at +80% and −20%. This means that the actual value of the capacitor might be 80% more than the value

printed on it! Obviously, this won't do where the value is critical (in a timing, tuned or filter circuit, for example). If the project design specifies metal-film, silver-mica, or some other type of capacitor, *don't* substitute disc-ceramic or other capacitor types! Zack specified silver-mica caps for the filtering circuitry in our transmitter. They're widely available.

Solid-state parts and toroids can sometimes be hard to find, too. Most parts suppliers carry a good stock of digital logic ICs, but don't carry as many linear ICs or RF parts. A number of suppliers specialize in

---

Fig 1—Schematic diagram for the 20-meter VXO-controlled QRP transmitter. The inset shows how to connect jacks (J1, **KEY**; J2, **RECEIVER**; J3 (**ANTENNA**) and **POWER** binding posts (BP1 and BP2) to the circuit board. You can usually depend on the circuit common foil and mounting hardware to complete ground connections for dc circuits (**KEY, POWER**). Thorough authors will tell you when you shouldn't. For signal connections (**ANTENNA, RECEIVER**) though, use two wires (one for common, one for the *hot* [ungrounded] lead) or coaxial cable. The panel bushings of J1, J2 and J3 usually make sufficient contact with metal box walls to complete the chassis connection shown for them.

BP1, BP2—Plastic binding posts (Radio Shack #274-662) to serve as **POWER** terminals, red for + and black for − This is just a suggestion; you can use your choice of connector as necessary.

C1—0.082-μF ceramic or plastic-film capacitor. Even though this is an uncommon value, don't substitute a different value. This capacitor is important in determining the transmitter's keying characteristics.

C2—0.22-μF ceramic or plastic-film capacitor. Don't substitute a different value. This capacitor is important in determining the transmitter's keying characteristics.

C3—1.8- to 8.7-pF air variable. Johnson 160-104 used, but any panel-mountable air-dielectric variable with a maximum capacitance between 8 and 35 pF should work acceptably. If you're willing to forgo easy frequency adjustment, you can use a PC-board-mountable trimmer capacitor and mount it on the circuit board as shown in Fig 2. (Ceramic- and plastic-dielectric trimmers will also work, but may be a bit less frequency-stable than air-dielectric types.)

C4-C11—General-purpose disc or monolithic ceramic capacitors, values from 0.01 to 0.1-μF suitable. Don't use plastic-film types (Mylar, metallized polyester, etc) here. Such capacitors generally don't work as well as ceramic-dielectric types in radio circuits.

C12—120 pF, silver mica.
C13, C14—390 pF, silver mica.
C15—180 pF, silver mica.
C16—22 pF, silver mica.
D1-D3, D5, D6—1N914, 1N4148 or 1N4152 silicon switching diode.
D4—33-V, 0.5-W Zener diode (1N5257).
J1-J3—**ANTENNA, RECEIVER** and **KEY** connectors of your choice (see text).

L1, L3—15 turns #22 enameled wire on T-37-6 toroid core (0.8 μH).
L2—15 turns #28 enameled wire on T-37-6 toroid core (0.9 μH).
L4—35 turns #30 enameled wire on T-30-2 toroid core (5.9 μH).
Q1, Q2—2N3906 bipolar transistor.
Q3—2N918, MPS918, 2N5179 or MPS5179 bipolar transistor.
Q4—2N2222 or 2N2222A bipolar transistor. Metal- and plastic-cased versions (PN2222, MPS2222) are suitable.
Q5—2N5109 bipolar transistor.
Q6—2N3553 bipolar transistor, with added heat sink. The Fig 2B version uses a Thermalloy 2215B heat sink, but other types are suitable (see text).
R1—22 kΩ. This and all of the other resistors are 5%-tolerance, 1/4-watt carbon-film or carbon-composition units.
R2—100 kΩ.
R3—10 kΩ.
R4, R6—1 kΩ.
R5—270 Ω.
R7, R10—4.7 kΩ.
R8, R13, R14—100 Ω.
R9—47 Ω.
R11—15 kΩ.
R12—470 Ω.
R15—2.2 kΩ.
R16—4.7 Ω.
RFC1—Toroidal RF choke. Use 20 turns of #26 enameled wire on FT-37-67 ferrite toroid (7.7 μH). 6 turns on FT-37-43 should also work.
S1—Normally open, momentary push button (Radio Shack #275-1547 suitable).
T1—Broadband transformer, 5:1 turns ratio. 20 turns of #26 or 28 enameled wire on an FT-37-43 ferrite toroid (primary). Secondary has 4 turns of #24 or 26 enameled wire over primary winding.
T2—Broadband transformer, 3:1 turns ratio. 9 turns of #26 or 28 enameled wire on an FT-37-43 ferrite toroid (primary). Secondary has 3 turns of #24 or 26 enameled wire over primary winding.
Y1—Fundamental crystal, HC-25/U or equivalent holder (International FM-2), parallel resonant, 20-pF load capacitance, room temperature calibration. Specify a frequency 4 kHz lower than the spot frequency (or bottom edge of the frequency range) you want to cover. (Example: For 14060 kHz, the 20-meter QRP calling frequency, specify 14056.000 kHz.) You'll probably be able to hit your spot frequency by adjusting C3, **FREQUENCY**. Frequency swings of 7 to 12 kHz, beginning at 3 or 4 kHz lower than the frequency marked on the crystal holder, are in the ballpark for this circuit.

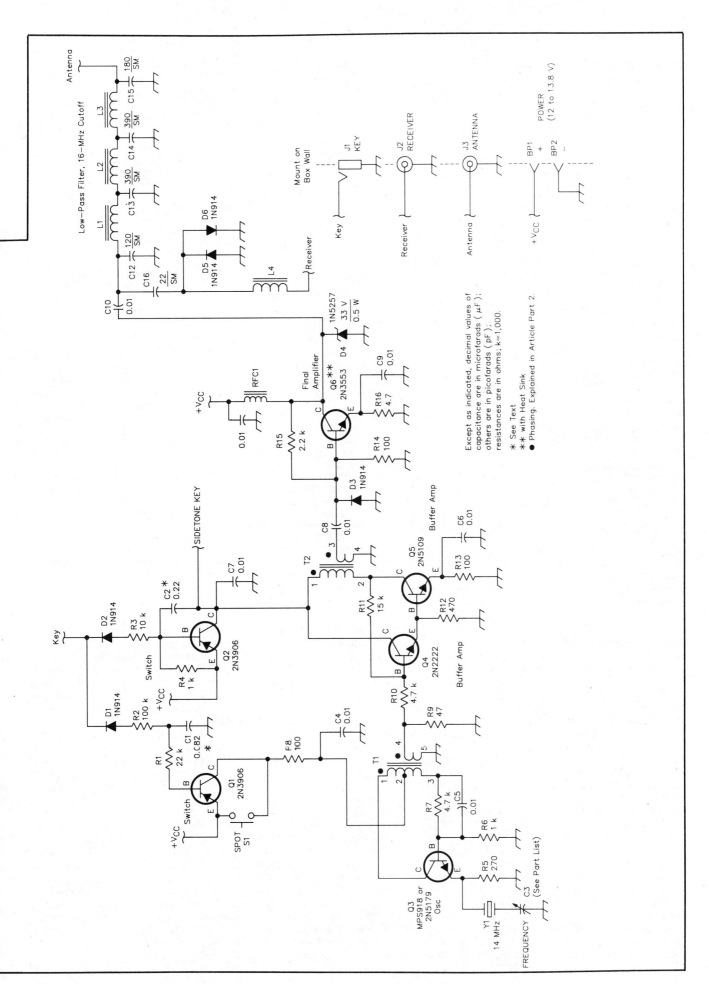

Table 1
Parts Suppliers

All Electronics Corp
PO Box 567
Van Nuys, CA 91408
information/customer service
tel 818-904-0524, fax 818-781-2653
order tel 800-826-5432

Digi-Key Corp
701 Brooks Ave S
PO Box 677
Thief River Falls, MN 56701-0677
tel 800-344-4539, fax 218-681-3380

Easy Tech
2917 Bayview Dr
Fremont, CA 94538
tel 800-582-4044, fax 800-582-1255

International Crystal Manufacturing Co
701 W Sheridan
PO Box 26330
Oklahoma City, OK 73126-0330
fax 800-322-9426

JAN Crystals
2341 Crystal Dr
PO Box 06017
Fort Myers, FL 33906-6017
tel 800-526-9825, fax 813-936-3750

Oak Hills Research
20879 Madison St
Big Rapids, MI 49307
(enclose 50 cents for catalog)
tel 616-796-0920

Ocean State Electronics
PO Box 1458
Westerly, RI 02891
tel 401-596-3080, fax 401-596-3590
order tel 800-866-6626

Because *QST* space is limited, this list is necessarily incomplete. See *QST* advertisements and the 1992 *ARRL Handbook*'s ARRL Parts Suppliers List (Table 42, Chapter 35) for additional suppliers.

Table 2
Transmitter Part Order List

Resistors

Quantity	Value
1	4.7 Ω
1	47 Ω
3	100 Ω
1	270 Ω
1	470 Ω
2	1 kΩ
1	2.2 kΩ
2	4.7 kΩ
1	10 kΩ
1	15 kΩ
1	22 kΩ
1	100 kΩ

Capacitors

Quantity	Value	Type
1	0.082	µF ceramic
1	0.22	µF ceramic
9	0.01	µF ceramic
1	120 pF	silver mica
1	180 pF	silver mica
2	390 pF	silver mica
1	1.8- to 8.7-pF air-dielectric, panel-mountable variable (Johnson 160-104)	

Solid-State Devices

Quantity	Part	(Possible Replacement)
5	1N914	diode (1N4148, 1N4152)
1	1N5257	Zener diode (1N4752)
2	2N3906	transistor (2N2905, 2N2907)
1	2N2222	transistor (2N2222A, PN2222)
1	2N5109	transistor
1	2N5179	transistor (MPS918, PN5179)
1	2N3553	transistor

Toroidal Cores/Inductors

Quantity	Part
2	FT-37-43 ferrite core
1	FT-37-67 ferrite core
3	T-37-6 iron-powder core
1	T-30-2 iron-powder core
¼ pound	#22 enameled magnet wire
¼ pound	#26 enameled magnet wire
¼ pound	#28 enameled magnet wire
¼ pound	#30 enameled magnet wire

(#22, #26 and #30 are currently available at Radio Shack; order #28 from Ocean State)

Miscellaneous (see text for details)

Quantity	Part
1	normally open push button
1	project box or other enclosure
1	PC board (optional; see text)
1	antenna connector
1	key jack
1	power connector
1	heat sink
1	small tube of heat-sink grease
1	knob for 1/8-inch shaft
1	20-meter fundamental crystal, 20-pF parallel load capacitance, FM-2 holder (International Crystal part number 434173). For JAN Crystals, specify frequency, HC-25/U holder, 50 ppm tolerance, parallel resonance, 20-pF load capacitance, non-oven.
1	FM-2 or HC-25/U crystal socket (International Crystal part number 035006; JAN Crystals CE-25)
10	feet RG-174 coaxial cable (optional; see text)

22- or 24-gauge insulated solid hookup wire

RF parts, however, and our list includes some of them. All of the solid-state parts (and the variable capacitor) in our project are available from Ocean State Electronics.

Although you'll probably be able to order exactly the right number of each capacitor and transistor for this project, consider buying a few extras for your junk box. It's always good to have a few extra parts on hand—you may break a lead on a part when you're assembling the project, or damage a solid-state component with too much soldering heat or by wiring it in backwards. If you don't have extras, you'll have to order another part. Even if you don't need the extras for this project, they'll always come in handy, and you'll be encouraged to build another project!

Pick up an extra toroid or two as well—Zack used common types that you'll see in other shortwave transmitting and receiving projects.

We need several different sizes of enameled copper wire for the coils. Sometimes called *magnet wire* because of its use in electric-motor windings, it's usually sold by the pound, with a minimum order of ¼ pound. A quarter pound of each size will be more than enough for many RF projects, so we'll have plenty left over for the junk box. You may find a supplier who will sell wire by the foot, but you'll probably pay extra for this convenience. Radio Shack has a magnet-wire package containing three of the sizes we need, and Ocean State Electronics carries all of them. All Electronics has the hookup wire and 10-foot lengths of RG-174 coax.

I ordered my crystal from International Crystal Manufacturing. JAN Crystals is another good source. (Some part dealers list crystals in their catalogs, but I recommend going right to the source.) A variety of crystal holder styles are available that differ in pin spacing and how the can pieces are bonded together. Hams have long known them by their military nomenclature (designators that start with *HC* and end with */U*). The crystal holder we want is generically known by hams as *HC-25/U*. Its pins are 0.040 inch in diameter, 0.25 inch long and

spaced 0.192 inch center to center. International Crystals classes HC-25/U-sized holders as *FM-2*. (How the two holder pieces are sealed—solder, cold weld or resistance weld—determines the holder's actual HC designator. For our purposes, this doesn't matter. If you order from International, just specify *FM-2*.) The HC-25/U holder plugs in, so you'll also need to buy a socket to hold it. Crystal manufacturers usually sell sockets in addition to crystals. Table 2 lists particulars for crystals and sockets from International and JAN.

I recommend plug-in crystals because you can easily use them in other projects. You may prefer to solder your crystal in, though. You can order crystals in an HC-25-sized *wire-lead* holder known generically as the HC-18/U. HC-18/U holders solder in and don't fit HC-25/U sockets. If you're after maximum miniaturization, International's solder-in FM-5 holder is the way to go: it's less than 5/16 inch across. You'll see an FM-5 crystal in my transmitter in Part 2 of this series.

A 20-Meter VXO-Controlled Transmitter

The QRP Three-Bander* can be modified for single-band operation at 20 meters by substituting a different receiver-input transformer† and modifying the transmitter. Because the Three-Bander's NE602-based receiver performs marginally under the strong-signal conditions common on this busy band, I decided to develop only a 20-meter *transmitter* from the Three-Bander design and use a separate receiver. The 20-meter transmitter's output circuit is a bit more rugged than the original Three-Bander's MRF237 final.

The main text's Fig 1 shows the circuit. The 20-meter transmitter's VXO and buffer amplifier are almost identical to the Three-Bander's, the major change being the use of a 14-MHz crystal. (By the way, if you're looking for the ultimate in miniaturization, you might consider using FM-5 cased crystals [International Crystal Manufacturing Co order number #434193]. Note, however, that I found the frequency swing available with FM-5 crystals to be about 1 kHz less than that achievable with standard HC-25/U-cased [International FM-2] crystals—14048.5 to 14055.9 kHz with a crystal cut for 14045.00 kHz [parallel resonant, 20-pF load capacitance].) The VXO exhibits some voltage sensitivity: I measured a 50-Hz shift when varying the supply voltage from 11.0 to 13.8—not enough to warrant building in a voltage regulator, in my opinion.

Compared to the original Three-Bander, the final amplifier (Q6 and its associated circuitry) is a bit more complex. I added a bypassed 4.7-Ω emitter resistor (R16) for thermal stability (one MRF237 I tried without an emitter resistor went into thermal runaway). Q6's base clipping diode, D3, is optional, but I recommend including it because it seems to lower Q6's drive requirement about 1 dB. D4, a 33-V Zener diode, protects Q6 when its output (circuitry to the right of C10) is shorted to ground. Short-circuiting the low-pass filter capacitors (C12-C15) in succession caused no apparent damage to Q6, so the circuit seems pretty rugged. (Q6 may oscillate under some conditions of very high SWR, however; so the circuit's stability could be further improved.)

The low-pass filter (L1-L3, C12-C15) may raise a few eyebrows. Yes, all three inductors have the same number of turns, but L2 uses thinner wire (#28) than that used in L1 and L3 (#22), causing L2's inductance (0.9 μH) to be higher than that of L1 and L3 (0.8 μH). (Wind these inductors according to Fig 70B in the 1992 *ARRL Handbook*—with a single layer covering most of the core.) Measured at the RECEIVER point (L4's free end), the filter's insertion loss is only 1 dB throughout the 20-m CW band.†† I measured the worst-case transmit feedthrough to the RECEIVER jack point as −6 dBm (0.25 mW). (Some authors suggest that the RECEIVER tap should be on the ANTENNA jack end of the low-pass filter, but this makes the odd harmonics [3, 5, etc] stronger.)

As to performance: The Fig 2B transmitter's second harmonic is 57 dB below the fundamental carrier; higher-order harmonics are at least 64 dB down. Connecting a receiver to the RECEIVER jack decreases the second harmonic slightly (to −60 dBc) but lowers the circuit's higher-order-harmonic suppression to 50 dB at the third harmonic, 54 dB at the fifth and 60 dB at the seventh. These numbers meet current FCC requirements for signal purity, assuming that your harmonics cause no harmful interference.

As for transmitter output power, you can expect about 1 W with an 11-V supply and 1.8 W at 13.8 V. The transmitter's frequency should be stable. With decent heat sinking at Q6, so should the transmitter's power output. If your transmitter's output power rises when you hold the key down for a long stretch, you're not witnessing miraculous transmitter self-improvement—that's the onset of thermal runaway! If this happens with your transmitter, improve Q6's heat sinking and/or don't hold the key down for so long.—*Zack Lau, KH6CP/1, ARRL Lab Engineer*

*Z. Lau, "The QRP Three-Bander," *QST*, Oct 1989, pp 25-30. See also Feedback, *QST*, Jan 1992, pages 55 and 91. *QRP Classics*, available from The ARRL Bookshelf as #3169, includes the QRP Three-Bander article, but went to press before the Feedback was published in *QST*.

†For 20-meter reception, replace the original Three-Bander's T1 with a transformer wound as follows: Primary, 25 turns of #24 enameled wire on a T-50-6 toroidal, powdered-iron core, ≈80° spacing between winding start and finish; secondary, 2 turns of #24 enameled wire over the RF-ground end of the primary. Use a 14-MHz crystal at Y1 (in the receiver local oscillator).

††Builders who've experienced receive-sensitivity problems in attempting to move the QRP Three-Bander's filter to 20 meters may not have been accurately measuring their filter coils' inductance. Too much inductance can produce a filter that cuts off received signals!

Now's the time to decide whether you're going to build your project ground-plane or with a ready-made PC board. If you need a PC-board, FAR Circuits has them. (It's 5 × 2 inches in size.) If you're going to give ground-plane a go, buy a good-sized piece of single-sided copper-clad board—at least 3 × 5 inches. Get *glass-epoxy* board if you can. *Phenolic* board is distinctly inferior because it's brittle and deteriorates rapidly with soldering heat. You can use either single-sided or double-sided board, and Ocean State has a good selection of sizes. Radio Shack sells a 4-1/2- × 6-3/8-inch piece of double-sided board; I cut this with a hacksaw to 4-1/2 × 2-1/2 inches.

We'll also need a box for the transmitter. This is often overlooked in parts lists for most projects, because different builders like different enclosures. Zack likes die-cast aluminum boxes. They are easy to work with, provide excellent shielding, and can probably protect your project against a pet panda. They're a bit expensive, however. Radio Shack sells two-piece aluminum boxes that are a bit more difficult to work with, but they're cheaper. Boxes of both types, and many more, are available from many mail-order companies as well.

Make sure there's room in the box for the variable capacitor and connectors as well as your ground-plane or PC board. Some people like to cram projects in the smallest possible box, but miniaturization can be extremely frustrating if you're not good at it. (I'm not, but Zack is a master.) I used a Radio Shack P-Box measuring 5-1/4 × 3 × 2-1/8 inches (part #270-238) for both the PC-board and ground-plane versions of the transmitter.

The variable capacitor specified has a 3/16-inch shaft, and it's hard to find a knob that will fit this shaft. You can use a 1/4-inch-shaft knob by building the shaft up to 1/4 inch using plastic or metal shim stock. Another approach is to find knobs to fit 1/8-inch shafts and carefully drill the hole out to 3/16. It's best to do this with a drill press, but you can do it with a hand drill and a vise if you're careful. I don't even have a vise—I did it with a hand drill and held the knob in a pair of pliers. I used a KNB-65 knob from All Electronics, but a KNB-181 might work better. (Get at least one of each; they're cheap and you might need a backup if you make a mistake.)

Several heat sinks in the Ocean State catalog will work in our transmitter (anything that fits a TO-5 or TO-39 transistor will be fine). Ocean State's #HS-05 works well, and it's cheap. You'll need a small tube of heat-sink compound. (You apply a *thin* film of heat-sink compound to the transistor body where it contacts the heat sink. The compound, also known generically as *silicone grease*, greatly improves heat transfer from the transistor to the sink.) You don't need much, so the smallest tube will be plenty for several projects. Both Ocean State and Ra-

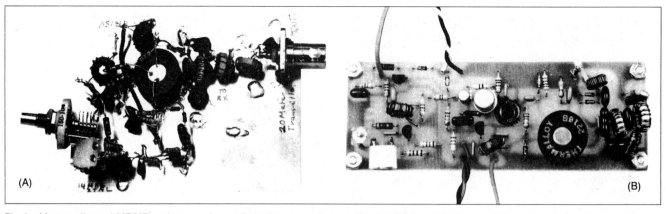

Fig 2—Most audio and MF/HF projects work equally well in ground-plane (A) and PC-board (B) forms. (Where there's a difference, ground-plane construction usually has the edge because of improved grounding.) Most published projects stem from ground-plane prototypes (see Fig 7 in Chapter 35 of the 1992 *ARRL Handbook*, for instance). Hams experienced in ground-plane (sometimes called *dead-bug* or *ugly*) construction can often build a ground-plane prototype faster than its PC-board equivalent! Part 2 of this series describes how to build a 20-meter transmitter using ground-plane techniques. If you prefer to use the PC board available as per Note 2, you'll learn how to install parts on it in Part 3 of this series.

dio Shack have heat-sink grease, and in this case Radio Shack's price is slightly cheaper.

For this project, then, we can buy everything but the crystal and a few of the capacitors from Ocean State Electronics, we can buy the crystal from International or JAN, and we can buy the capacitors from All Electronics. You'll also have to make a trip to Radio Shack for the box, PC board, and screws and nuts to put it all together.

Redistributing the Parts to Reach Minimum Order

Remember I said there would almost always be a few items you can't get from one company? All Electronics has a $10 minimum order, and the capacitors are much less than this, so we need to redistribute the order. If we get the resistors and some of the transistors from All Electronics, we can bring the order up to $10. All Electronics has a minimum purchase of 10 resistors of one value, but they're still cheap. Zack used common values in the transmitter, so you'll be able to use the extra resistors in your next project. Even if you can get something you need from Radio Shack, consider adding it to a mail order if it helps you meet a minimum-order requirement.

Why did I pick these suppliers? Ocean State was easy—they have almost all the parts. I picked All Electronics because they had good prices on the rest of the components, a reasonable selection and low shipping charges. Some companies put out beautiful catalogs, but their minimum order is $25 or they charge $5 for shipping if you place a small order. I've ordered from All Electronics before, and I know they're pretty quick. You can get the parts from other companies, of course. You'll find out which companies you like to deal with and which ones often *back-order* parts or take forever to send anything.

Back-ordering is what many suppliers automatically do if they're out of stock on something you've ordered. They fill your order as fully as they can, ship it to you, and tell you on the invoice when you can

expect to receive the out-of-stock parts. Sometimes the delay can be a month or longer! That's back-ordering, and it can be terrifically frustrating because it ties up your money and your project. If the order form includes a box you can check to indicate that you don't want back orders, *check it*. If the order form doesn't give you this vote, write it in in big red letters: *PLEASE DO NOT BACK-ORDER OUT-OF-STOCK PARTS.*

If you're in a huge hurry, most companies will accept telephone credit-card orders. If you order by phone, you can also check at order time to be sure that none of the parts will be back-ordered. Be aware, though, that phone credit-card orders may compromise your credit-card security. So, I don't routinely place credit-card orders by phone.

If you're in a bit less of a hurry but still want your parts quickly, you should pay for your order with a bank check or money order. If you pay with a personal check, some companies will hold your order until your check clears their bank, and this can take up to ten days. Even if you pay with a check, you can still call the company to check on parts availability, but most companies don't like it if you use their 800 order number just for this.

When I've filled out the order forms from the catalogs and the bank checks are ready to go, I like to make a photocopy of the order form and the check before I send it off. I've only had an order lost in the mail once, but it was good to have the photocopy so I could reconstruct the order and send it off again. This also tells you when you ordered the parts, so you know when to start looking for the UPS truck.

Summary, Part 1

For now, get busy with your parts orders. In the next article, we'll look into construction techniques. We'll build the transmitter using ground-plane construction on a piece of copper-clad circuit board. We'll also consider building a power supply if you don't already have one. (Radio Shack carries the

parts for this, by the way!) In article three, we'll build a transmitter using a PC board, and think about adding a sidetone oscillator. In the last article of the series, we'll put the transmitter in the box and put it on the air. You really *can* build good radio gear yourself—stay tuned!

Notes

[1]Z. Lau, "The QRP Three-Bander," *QST*, Oct 1989, pp 25-30. See also Feedback, *QST*, Jan 1992, pages 55 and 91.

[2]PC boards are available from FAR Circuits, 18N640 Field Ct, Dundee, IL 60118; price, $4 plus $1.50 shipping and handling. Check or money order only; credit cards are not accepted.

PC-board templates and part overlays for the 20-meter VXO-controlled transmitter featured here are available free of charge from the ARRL Technical Department Secretary. With your request for the HALE 20-M TRANSMITTER PC BOARD TEMPLATE PACKAGE, send a #10 self-addressed envelope with one First-Class stamp.

[3]D. Newkirk, "Connectors for (Almost) All Occasions," *Part 1*, *QST*, Apr 1991, pp 35-38; *Part 2*, *QST*, May 1991, pp 34-40.

Build It Yourself from *QST*

Part 2: Now that you've gotten the parts, here's how to build your project using ground-plane construction.

By Bruce S. Hale, KB1MW/7

2238 168th Ave NE
Bellevue WA 98008

In Part 1, we ordered the parts for the 20-meter version of Zack Lau's QRP transmitter.[3] This transmitter is a great first project—you can build it even if you've never used a soldering iron. You should have a nice pile of parts by now, and this month we're going to put them together using a construction technique called *ground-plane construction*. If you've decided to build your 20-meter transmitter using the FAR Circuits board,[4] I suggest sticking with us this month, because I'll cover transistor pinouts and other component information you'll need in completing your PC-board transmitter.

Ground-Plane Construction Overview

Ground-plane, sometimes called *ugly* construction, is simple: You build the circuit on an unetched piece of copper-clad circuit board. Wherever a component connects to ground, you solder it to the copper board. Ungrounded connections between components are made point to point.

Once you learn how to build with a ground-plane board, you can grab a piece of circuit board and start building any time you see an interesting circuit. It's easy to trace and modify a ground-plane-built circuit. Ham designers generally also find that building on a large copper ground plane makes most MF/HF circuits more stable than building them on a PC board—at least until the PC-board version goes through several iterations to cure circuit instabilities!

Building a ground-plane board is fun, and I think it's more rewarding than simply stuffing and soldering a PC board. Ground-plane construction is something like model building, connecting parts using solder almost—but not exactly—like glue. Because you build the circuit directly from the schematic, ground-plane construction can help you get familiar with a circuit and how it works much better than etched-PC-board construction can.

Ground-plane construction is very flexible because you can build subsections of a large circuit as small ground-plane modules and string them together into a larger design. The prototype of Dave Newkirk's 10/18 receiver (Fig 7 in Chapter 30 of the 1992 *ARRL Handbook*) is a good example of this design technique. I've used an audio amplifier from one receiver design and combined it with a VFO circuit and mixer from two other designs, all built on individual ground-plane boards. Once I had the audio amp and VFO working, I modified the mixer board until I was satisfied. This is a great way to learn about electronics!

Don't be bashful about how your ground-plane projects look. Your transmitter probably won't look as slick as an etched-PC-board circuit or factory-produced rig. It'll probably look more like Part 1's Fig 2A! Part of the philosophy behind ground-plane construction is that you don't have to build "pretty" to build radio gear that's first-rate in ruggedness and performance. The important part is how well your circuit works—don't worry about how it looks. Remember, ground-plane and etched-PC-board versions of a circuit that give the same electronic performance both "look" the same *on the air*. Building is supposed to be *fun*.

Tools

Soldering is the foundation of ground-plane construction, so you'll need a soldering iron. It needs to be hot enough to do the job, and small and lightweight enough for agility and comfort. A 100-watt soldering gun, for instance, is overkill, but any iron in the 15- to 45-watt range should work. (A temperature-controlled iron is also okay. These cost more than they're worth for occasional projects, though.) I used a 30-watt soldering iron from Radio Shack (part #64-2067) to build this transmitter. Get an iron with (or that can be equipped with) a small conical or chisel-shaped tip. If this is your first time with a soldering iron, see the "Soldering Basics" sidebar for how to get started in soldering.

You'll also need a pair of needle-nose pliers to bend component leads, and a pair of diagonal cutters to clip the leads. Wire strippers are handy, but you can strip wire with a knife if you're careful. You can also use the knife to scrape off magnet-wire insulation. I use my Swiss Army knife. A package of "clip leads" (short wires with alligator clips on both ends, Radio Shack #278-1156) will come in handy when you start testing the board, especially if you get impatient and want to test your transmitter before you put it in the box. (After completing a project, I usually end up making at least my first contact with the circuit board buried under an amazing pile of clip leads.)

Laying Out the Circuit

Because you wire your circuit instead of following an etched circuit pattern, you can build it however you like. Here are a few guidelines that will help your transmitter work well:

• Avoid laying out circuits that filter or amplify so their outputs end up near their inputs. With our transmitter, this means that the antenna connection should be made on the opposite side of the board from the VXO components. It also means that the buffer amplifier's output shouldn't double back to be near its input, or near the VXO. If a stage's output is too near a previous stage's input, the output signal can *feed back* into the input and cause problems. Building a filter's output too near its input may allow signals to leak around the filter.

• Keep component leads as short as practical. I didn't say "as short as *possible*"—just keep lead length in mind. You'll have to clip component leads shorter than their untrimmed lengths—that's what the diagonal cutters are for. Don't clip them off 1/16 inch from the component body, but don't leave them 1-1/2 inches long, either.

• Remember that metal transistor cases conduct, and that a transistor's metal case is usually connected to one of its leads (most commonly, in bipolar junction transistors, the collector). Because of this, it's a good idea to keep the case away from other components. Also, don't let the case touch the ground plane unless you're sure the case can

Soldering Basics

You can build the 20-meter VXO transmitter using ground-plane construction even if you've never used a soldering iron before. You don't need an expensive iron—I used a 30-watt Radio Shack iron (64-2067, $4.79 in the 1992 catalog). Don't try to use a soldering gun, though; you'll melt components. Here are a few more tips:

Keep everything *clean*. When you let the iron sit between making solder joints, the old solder vaporizes and leaves impurities on the iron tip. These appear as black gummy junk on the tip. You don't want this in your next solder joint, so keep a damp sponge near the iron and use it to wipe off the tip just before you apply it to a solder joint. You can keep the sponge in an empty sardine can or any other container that will keep the water off your workbench. The Radio Shack soldering iron holder (part #64-2078) combines a stand for the hot iron with a sponge for cleaning the tip. You'll see soldering-iron holders like this in other catalogs as well.

Clean the component leads, too. If a component's leads look dull and slightly corroded, scrape or steel-wool the leads bright before you solder them into the circuit. Resistor leads are prime candidates—they can sometimes be almost black from oxidation, and the oxide on the leads will prevent solder from making a good electrical connection. (Keep the steel wool away from your circuit board—you don't want pieces of steel wool to fall into the circuit and cause short circuits.)

Heat the solder joint, not the solder. Apply the iron to one side of the connection, let the connection heat for a second, and then apply the solder to the other side of the joint (see Fig A). Don't try to melt the solder and let it drip onto the connection; it's not glue. Good soldering actually forms *alloys* at the interface between ground-plane copper and solder, and solder and component lead metal. (This is why copper soldering tips slowly dissolve away over weeks of soldering. They actually contribute a little copper to every joint they solder!)

When you solder a lead to the ground-plane circuit board, press the lead between the iron tip and the board. Wait a second or two for the board to heat up, and then flow the solder between the iron tip and the board. Make sure you heat the component lead *and* the circuit board, or the solder's surface tension will keep it lying on top of the board in a big glob.

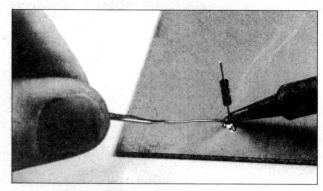

Fig A—Apply the soldering iron to the connection, wait a second or two for the joint to heat up, and then apply the solder from the other side. (*All photos, except Fig 7, by Kirk Kleinschmidt, NTØZ*)

Don't use acid-core solder; that's for plumbing. Use only *rosin-core* (sometimes called *electronics*) solder. I like to use thin (0.032-inch-diameter) solder. Thin solder makes it easier to use just enough solder for each connection. Thicker solder sometimes melts all over everything and overloads joints.

If you're unsure of your soldering skills, make tighter mechanical connections between components. That way, you won't be relying on the solder to make a mechanical bond as well as an electrical connection. Once you get a little practice, you can use the "side-by-side lead" techniques described in the article.

Don't get discouraged if your first soldering efforts look like they were done by a gorilla with a blowtorch. Like any skill, soldering takes practice. You'll get better at it as you build more projects. (That's a not-too-subtle hint to *keep building!*)—KB1MW

For more about soldering, see B. Bergeron, "Making Soldering Safer," *QST*, Mar 1991, pp 28-30. Also see G. Myers, "More on Making Soldering Safer," Technical Correspondence, *QST*, Aug 1991, p 42, and Chapter 24 of the 1992 *ARRL Handbook*.

---

be grounded. (More later on how to ensure this.) This also applies to metal heat sinks in direct contact with metal transistor cases.

Getting Started

Before you start soldering, make sure your piece of circuit board will fit in the box you're going to use. It's much easier to cut the circuit board and drill its mounting holes *before* you build the circuit on it. (This sounds obvious, and it is if you think of it before you start building, but many builders, including me, have forgotten this more than once!) If you bought the circuit board and minibox from Radio Shack, cut your ground-plane board with a hacksaw to 4½ × 2½ inches. Lightly buff the copper with a piece of extra-fine steel wool. This removes any oxidation, which can make it hard to solder to the board.

QST schematics are usually drawn to begin at the left with input or oscillator circuitry and proceed toward output or antenna at the right. Thus, the easiest way to build a ground-plane circuit from *QST*

articles is to lay out and build the circuit from left to right as it's shown on the schematic. (As you gain more building experience, you'll find it easy to lay out a circuit no matter how its schematic is drawn.) With our 20-meter VXO transmitter, this means we start building with the VXO (Q3 and associated components).

Fig 3—Cut and bend both leads of the first resistor, and then solder one lead to the ground plane.

Where to start building *in* the VXO circuit is the next decision. Because we're building ground-plane, we'll start with a *grounded* component because it supports other components above the ground-plane board.

R5—Q3's 270-Ω emitter resistor—is a good place to start. Clip its leads about ¼ inch from each end of the resistor body. Bend both ends at a 90° angle from the resistor body, and solder one end to the ground plane, about ½ inch from the board's lower left corner. This point determines where the rest of the circuit will be on the circuit board. Solder the resistor so it stands up on end, as shown in Fig 3. Use the tip of the iron to hold the lead down on the circuit board, wait a second or two for the board to heat up, and then flow the solder between the tip of the iron and the board. Put down the solder and hold the resistor *steady* by its free end. Pull the soldering iron off the joint and keep holding the resistor steady until the solder solidifies. (Movement in the solder joint during cooling can cause a poorly conductive, *cold-soldered* joint that may lead to circuit failure.) Congratulations: You've taken your first step in ground-plane construction!

Alternatively: Apply enough solder to the board to make a small (¼-inch diameter), slightly domed circle where you want the grounded component to be soldered to the board. Tin the component lead to be grounded (coat it with just enough hot solder to make it shiny). Press the tinned lead down atop the solder circle. Touch the solder iron tip against the lead and the circle to melt the solder in both. Pull the soldering iron away and hold the component *steady* by its free end until the solder solidifies.

If you come to a spot where a grounded component would simplify construction but there's no grounded component at that point in the circuit, you have two choices: You can add *terminal strips* as necessary. These are insulating strips bearing rows of solder lugs; the foot of one or two lugs in a strip can be screwed or soldered to the ground plane to hold the strip in place. Radio Shack carries five-lug strips (#274-688); and other suppliers carry them in wider variety.

A Power Supply for the Transmitter

The transmitter needs a source of 12 to 13.8 volts at around 250 milliamps. You can use batteries, but a regulated, ac-operated 12-V power supply is a handy accessory, especially if you plan to build any other simple transmitters or receivers. Radio Shack and other suppliers carry small 12- or 13.8-V regulated supplies capable of providing 2 to 6 amps or so; these generally cost in the $30 to $50 range. If you need only 1 ampere or less, building your own supply can save you money *and* provide building experience. Such a power supply is very simple, so it's a great first project and good soldering practice.

The circuit (Fig A) uses a 7812 three-terminal regulator; you'll find it and all the other parts at Radio Shack for around $30. This power supply can provide about an ampere of regulated 12-V dc. I used ground-plane construction techniques, as discussed in the article. Use a small amount of heatsink grease on the back of the regulator. No insulator is needed between the regulator case and box top.—*KB1MW*

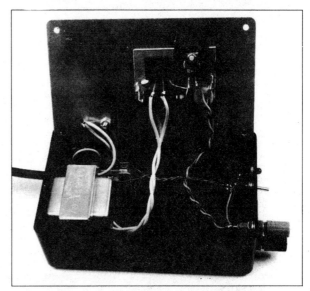

Fig B—Power-supply construction. Be sure to wire the fuseholder in series with the line cord's *black* (hot or live) wire. Connect the cordset's *green* (ground) wire to the power transformer's metal case, the box's aluminum cover, and the regulator circuit's negative wire. This circuit uses an electrolytic capacitor (C1), which is polarized. Be sure to connect C1's + and − leads correctly.

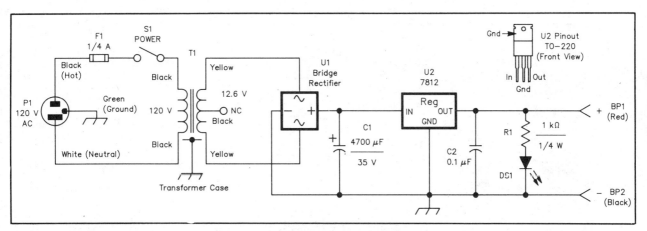

Fig A—All of the power-supply parts are available at Radio Shack. Wall-socket power is dangerous, so wire your supply carefully. Don't work on the power supply wiring while the supply is plugged into the wall—unplug the supply first. If in doubt, have your wiring checked by an experienced equipment builder before plugging in the supply. All the part numbers listed are Radio Shack; other suppliers carry suitable equivalents.

BP1, BP2—Nylon binding posts (274-662).
C1—4700-μF, 35-V electrolytic (272-1022).
C2—0.1-μF, 50-V disc ceramic (272-135).
DS1—Jumbo red LED (276-041).
F1—¼-A, 250-V fuse (270-1270) in chassis-mount holder (270-739).
P1—Three-wire ac cordset (278-1258).
R1—1-kΩ, ¼-W resistor (271-1321).

S1—Subminiature SPST toggle switch (275-612).
T1—Transformer: 120 V ac input, 12.6 V (center-tapped), 1.2 A output (273-1352).
U1—50-PIV, 4-A bridge rectifier (276-1146).
U2—7812 voltage-regulator IC (276-1771).
Miscellaneous—TO-220 heat sink (276-1363); 6¼ × 3¾ × 2 inch project box (270-627).

Fig 4—A terminal strip can anchor floating components or wire ends where no grounded circuit component exists to do the job. High-value resistors can also be used to do this.

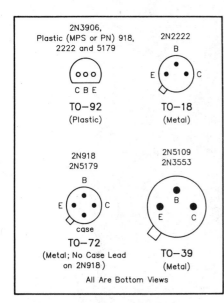

Fig 5—Pinout for the transistors used in the 20-meter VXO transmitter. The electronics industry identifies transistor cases with standardized designators that begin with *TO* (for *transistor outline*).

Fig 6—The first lead of each component must make a firm mechanical connection. Bend the emitter lead of Q3 and crimp it over the resistor lead before you solder it. Notice that the case lead of this 2N5179 is clipped off at the transistor. In the 20-meter VXO transmitter, this lead can be clipped or connected to ground—it doesn't matter. The plastic version of the 2N5179 has no case lead. When a device comes in different cases, thorough authors will tell you whether or not case type makes a difference. Some transistors first released only in metal-cased form are now available in plastic cases.

Fig 4 shows how I used a miniature five-lug strip to anchor **SPOT** switch and keying connections to my transmitter board. Or you can add a grounded component that has little or no effect on the circuit. High-value resistors—470 kΩ and higher for circuits operating at and below 28 V—will work for this because (in most cases) they'll draw so little current that the circuit will operate as if they aren't there.

Junction Points

Grounded components run from the circuit down to the ground plane, and other two-lead components (such as capacitors and resistors) run from one circuit point to the next. Components with more leads (transistors and transformers) determine "junction points" where several components come together. Work from one junction point to the next.

I like to orient transistors so that it's easy to remember which lead is which. Most transistor base diagrams show the leads from the bottom (Fig 5), so it's easiest to mount transistors bottom up. It's also easier to solder the rest of the components to the transistor when it's got its leads sticking up in the air—otherwise you have to try to work underneath the transistor to connect the other components.

The first transistor lead soldered to a grounded component must be crimped to the component lead to support the transistor. Use the needle-nose pliers to make a small hook in the transistor lead and pinch it over the resistor lead. Once you've got a good mechanical connection, you can solder the components. Fig 6 shows the emitter of Q3 soldered to R5.

When you've got the transistor supported by a grounded component, the remaining connections can be made without such tight mechanical work. Fig 7 shows the base lead of Q3 brought over the top of the transistor and aligned with one lead of R6. This connection can be soldered as is.

What we're trying to do is establish a good mechanical connection on at least one lead of each component. Once the component is supported by the soldered mechanical connection, other connections to the same component can be made just with solder.

Winding Coils

Once we've got most of the junction components mounted at Q3, we move over to the next junction, T1. This coil has five leads, so it must be mounted carefully so that all of its connections point in the right direction. T1's primary winding has 20 turns. When you wind toroids, remember that just sticking the wire through the core counts as "one turn." Wrapping the wire around the core and passing it back through the core is two turns. You can count the number of turns by counting the number of times the wire passes through the center of the coil. When you get to the 13th turn, twist

Fig 7—Once a component is firmly supported, you can make further connections without crimping. Just solder the leads as they lie side by side. This 2N5179 has its case lead grounded.

the wire together about 1/8 inch from the core to make a tap point, as shown in Fig 8. Use a knife to scrape the insulation off the wire before you solder it into the circuit. Wind the secondary over the primary winding, *in the same rotational direction.*

The dots on the schematic show you how the windings are oriented, or phased, relative to each other. Concerning T1 in Fig 1, the dots tell you to connect the start of the primary to the collector of Q3 and the start of the secondary to the junction of R9 and R10. Fig 8 details the windings of T1 and T2.

Moving On

Use R9 to support T1, and then use R10 to determine where you put the base of Q4. Solder the base connection, and then use R12 for support and connect the base of Q5.

We're still working with the transistors upside-down, but notice that the Q5's collector is connected to the transistor's metal

---

A Note on Multifilar Transformers

Some projects (not this one, though) use toroidal transformers containing *multifilar*—"many wired"—windings that consist of two or more wires wound together. (*Bifilar* windings use two wires, *trifilar* windings use three.) The most practical way to wind such transformers is to twist their wires together (at a pitch of 5 to 10 twists per inch) and wind all of the wires at once. Paint the wires before winding to tell which is which, or make continuity checks with an ohmmeter to sort out which winding start goes with which end. Wire multifilar transformers into your circuit carefully to ensure that each winding is connected to the proper points in the proper phase.—*WJ1Z*

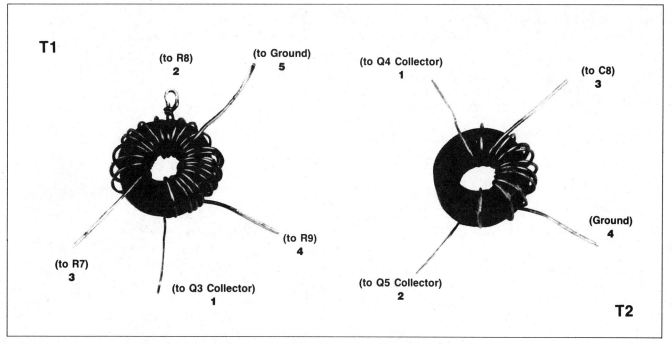

Fig 8—The dots on the schematic show how the coil windings are phased. Twist the wire a few times to form the tap on T1. As is true of the coil ends, you'll need to scrape the insulation off the twisted wires so you can solder to them.

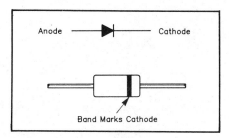

Fig 9—The line on the diode case marks the cathode. The arrowhead in the diode schematic symbol points to the cathode.

Fig 10—Here's my completed ground-plane transmitter, mounted in a minibox. If you're in a hurry to get your 20-meter transmitter on the air, you don't even need a box—this circuit doesn't need a lot of shielding with most antennas. Fig 2A (in Part 1) shows Zack Lau's prototype—he soldered both the BNC ANTENNA connector and VXO FREQUENCY capacitor to the circuit board, and connected the power supply and key with clip leads. (You can also use a short length of RG-174 coax to attach the ANTENNA connector, and connect the KEY and POWER jacks with short wires.) When I first completed *my* transmitter board, I had it working on my bench next to a ground-plane version of Zack's receiver under a mess of clip leads. You can use the transmitter like this, but eventually you'll probably want to put it in a box.

case. If we let the case touch the ground plane, we'll connect the collector to ground. This will cause excessive power supply current to flow through Q2 and T2, possibly destroying Q2, when we key the transmitter. Put a piece of electrical tape on the circuit board to insulate Q5 from the board. You'll have to do this for Q6 as well (and Q4, if you use a metal-cased 2N2222 there). Q6 also needs a heat sink. Put a *little* heat-sink grease on the outside of the transistor case before you slide the heat sink onto the transistor. (I haven't yet found a way to use heat sink grease without getting it all over my fingers.)

When you install the circuit's diodes, use Fig 9 for a guide—the line on a diode's case marks its cathode. Diodes won't work properly if you put them in backwards.

Work from one transistor to the next, and you'll be done before you know it. Check your wiring carefully. One way to do this is to use a photocopy of the schematic and mark each lead on the schematic with a red X when you've verified that it's connected

to the right spot in your circuit. Fig 10 shows my completed ground-plane transmitter board.

Summary, Part 2

In this article, I've described ground-plane construction, an increasingly popular building technique that's useful for prototyping and completed ham projects alike. You've got a project waiting to be powered up and tested if you built the ground-plane version. How about checking and rechecking your

wiring a few more times?

PC-board builders, I'll be talking to you next month. (Ground-plane builders, you're invited, too, because we'll also look next month at ground-planing a sidetone oscillator.) Once everyone has a complete transmitter board, we'll put the boards into boxes, test them, and get them on the air.

Notes
[3]B. Hale, "Build it Yourself from *QST*," Part 1, *QST*, Apr 1992, pp 31-36.
[4]See Note 2.

Build It Yourself from *QST*

Part 3: Many hams prefer to go from schematic to finished product with the help of ready-made circuit boards. Here's how to stuff, solder and snip your way to success in PC-board construction.

By Bruce S. Hale, KB1MW/7
2238 168th Ave NE
Bellevue, WA 98008

I n Part 1 of this series, we ordered the parts for Zack (KH6CP) Lau's 20-meter QRP transmitter.[5] Last month, in Part 2, we built the transmitter using ground-plane construction.[6] This month, we're going to build the transmitter with the printed-circuit (PC) board from FAR Circuits.[7]

If you haven't read last month's article yet, do so soon. Much of what I said there applies to PC-board construction as well. You'll need the same tools: needle-nose pliers, diagonal cutters, pocket knife, wire strippers, clip leads and soldering iron. I used the same 30-watt soldering iron from Radio Shack (#64-2067) to build the PC-board transmitter. If you've never used a soldering iron before, you should read last month's soldering sidebar before you start.

Getting Started

Here's the short description of PC-board construction: Stick the components in the right board holes, solder the leads, and cut off the extra lead length. The board's *part-placement diagram* (Fig 11) shows where the components go. Getting the components in the right holes is called *stuffing* the circuit board, and there are a number of ways to do it.

Inserting and soldering one component at a time takes too long. Some people like to put the components in all at once, and then turn the board over and solder all the leads. If you bend the leads a bit after you push them through the board, the components aren't supposed to fall out when you turn the board over, but this never works for me. (Half of them fall out anyway, and the rest fall halfway out so they look stupid when I solder them). Another approach is to put in all the components of one type

(resistors, for example) and *then* turn the board over for soldering. When *I* try this, some of the components still fall out—and the remaining leads are so close together that they're difficult to solder.

I like to use a variation on this last approach. I put in *some* components of one type (like the first five resistors) and then solder these in. Then I put in the next five and solder them, and so on. I start with the shortest components (the diodes and resistors). If you start with tall components (like the capacitors), the board will rest on the top of the capacitors when you turn it over, and the resistors can fall out before you solder them (or slip part way down so they're not flat against the board). There are usually more resistors than anything else, too—if you install the resistors first

you don't have to balance the board on the capacitors when you install the resistors. You can also use adhesive tape to temporarily hold difficult components in place while you solder.

Make sure your PC board and component leads are *clean*. The copper on the PC board is tinned, so it shouldn't be corroded, but it can't hurt to clean the solder side of the board with rubbing alcohol. If any of your components' leads look corroded (they'll look dark instead of bright and shiny), use a piece of extra-fine steel wool to brighten the leads before you put them

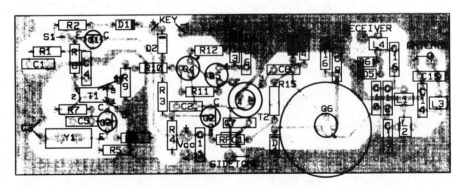

Fig 11—This diagram shows where to install parts on the QRP-transmitter board. It also shows *how* to install certain parts by depicting transistor flats, tabs and/or pinouts; diode and capacitor polarities; transformer wire numbers; and terminal names. This is a *single-sided* board because it has copper on only one side. Unless specifically instructed to do otherwise, mount components on the *foilless* side of single-sided boards. [*Note:* The Q1 emitter and collector (E and C) should be transposed from the way they appear on this diagram.]

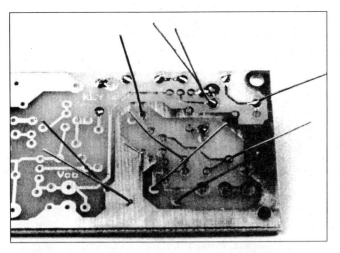

Fig 12—After you stick the component leads through the circuit board, bend them at an angle to keep the components from falling out when you turn the board over. *(photos by Kirk Kleinschmidt, NT0Z)*

Fig 13—Apply the soldering iron to one side of a component lead and the PC-board pad, heat the lead and the solder pad, and then flow the solder in from the other side.

in the circuit board.

Fig 12 shows the back of a PC board with several diodes and resistors installed. Some of the components are already soldered and clipped. Bend the leads at a slight angle; apply the soldering iron to one side of the lead, and flow the solder in from the other side (Fig 13). Make sure you heat the pad on the circuit board, but don't heat it for too long—the pad can lift off the board if it gets too hot. Soldering takes practice—you need enough heat to melt the solder and vaporize the flux in the solder's core, but too much heat will lift the pads or damage components. Once you've got a nice solder connection, clip the lead flush with the solder (using diagonal cutters, as shown in the title photo). You can install several components, solder the leads, and then clip the leads all at once. Then move on to the next bunch of components.

Special Concerns

Make sure you have the components in

the right holes before you solder them. You'll almost never see a component mounted at an angle on a PC board (there are no angle-mounted components on the transmitter board) so make sure all your components are parallel or perpendicular to the edge of the board.

The diodes *must* be oriented as shown on the placement diagram—the line on the diagram shows where the line on the diode should be placed. Otherwise, the circuit won't work properly.

You should have no trouble getting the resistors in the mounting holes. The capacitors may be more difficult—Zack used small monolithic ceramic capacitors, and FAR Circuits designed the board for Zack's capacitors. The capacitors I used are a bit larger, and their leads are too far apart to

just stick into the holes on the board. If your capacitors are too large, you may have to bend their leads as shown in Fig 14.

When you get to the transistors, pay attention to the part-placement diagram. The diagram shows how plastic transistors' flats and metal transistors' tabs should be oriented. Remember that the tab marks the emitter of the metal transistors. There are only three holes for the VXO transistor; a plastic '5179 has three leads, but the metal 2N5179 has four—one of the leads is connected to the case, and it does not have to be connected in the transmitter circuit. You can clip this lead off near the transistor body, then align the other three leads so the tab is pointing away from the coil, as shown in Fig 15. Make sure the metal transistor cases don't touch any other components (be extra careful with Q4 and Q5—they must not touch each other).

Fig 8 and its supporting text (in Part 2 of this series) explain how to wind the coils. Make sure you scrape the insulation from the wires before you solder the coils in place.

Don't forget to use heat-sink grease on

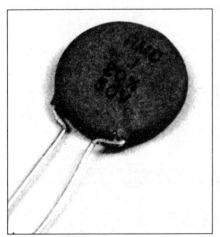

Fig 14—If your capacitors are too large, you may have to bend their leads to make them fit the circuit board.

Fig 15—If you use a metal 2N5179 transistor, cut off its case lead and orient the transistor tab as shown. This photo also shows how T1 should be mounted on the board.

Fig 16—You can use leftover resistor leads to solder the socket to the PC board.

Build a Sidetone Oscillator

A sidetone oscillator is a useful transmitter accessory. The sidetone oscillator from Zack's three-band QRP transceiver (Fig A)* uses a simple op-amp circuit—it's easy to build. If you've built your transmitter using ground-plane techniques, there may be room on the transmitter board for the sidetone circuit. If there isn't room, or if you're using the PC board, you can build the sidetone oscillator on a separate piece of circuit board.

Because an IC has so many pins and determines where other components will be located, it should be soldered in place first. It's best to find at least two pins of an IC that can be soldered to the ground plane so the IC won't move when you solder the rest of the components.

The sidetone's 741 op amp has its V– connection on pin 4 and pin 8 is not connected, so we can solder both of those pins to ground. (I always solder ICs right-side up in a ground-plane circuit because pin diagrams always show the IC from the top. If I solder ICs in upside down, I get confused.)

Once the 741 is soldered to the ground plane, connecting the rest of the components is easy. Fig B shows the parts layout for the sidetone oscillator. Make a good mechanical connection to one end of each component—the grounded components should be soldered to the ground plane first and then to the IC. You'll find more construction tips in Part 2 of this series.—*KB1MW*

*See Note 1, Part 1 (Apr 1992 *QST*, p 36).

Fig A—A sidetone oscillator for the 20-meter transmitter. Radio Shack carries all of its parts, as do most of the general component suppliers listed in Table 1 of Part 1 (April 1992 *QST*, page 34).

C17, C18—0.01-µF, disc-ceramic capacitor (RS 272-131).
R17, R21—100-kΩ, ¼-W, carbon-film resistor (271-1347).
R18, R19—47-kΩ, ¼-W, carbon-film resistor (271-1342).
R20—10-kΩ PC-mount trimmer potentiometer (271-282).
J4—Coaxial jack (phono suitable) for routing the sidetone signal to receiver circuitry.
U1—741 operational-amplifier IC (276-007).
Miscellaneous—PC-board scrap for ground-plane construction, wire for connecting the oscillator to the transmitter circuitry and J4.

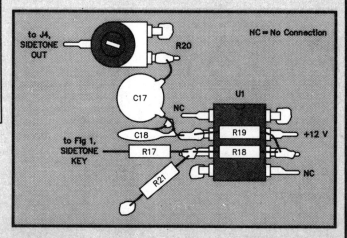

Fig B—The sidetone schematic turned into hardware. Even if you build your transmitter using a ready-made PC board, how about ground-planing a sidetone oscillator? Once you try it, you may want to build your *next* project using ground-plane construction!

the outside of Q6. Put a small amount of grease on the transistor, slip the heat sink over the case, and then wipe the grease off your fingers.

If you're using the FM-5 crystal (with wire leads), you can solder it directly to the board. If you're using the HC-16 crystal and a socket, you can solder leftover component leads to the socket and use them to solder the socket to the PC board, as shown in Fig 16.

That's All There Is

That's the long description of PC-board construction. Start with the smallest components (the resistors and diodes) and work through the transistors and capacitors and finish with the coils. Fig 17 shows the completed PC board. Here's a final checklist:

• The only holes left on the board should be the connections for +12 V, ground, key, sidetone key, antenna and receiver. If you have extra holes, something is missing! Check the part-placement diagram again.

• Do the diodes point the right way?

• Do the tabs on the metal transistors line up as shown on the part-placement diagram?

• Are the flat sides of the plastic transistors lined up as shown on the diagram?

• Are the metal transistors touching each other, or anything else?

• Are there any *solder bridges* between adjacent circuit-board traces? Solder bridges (Fig 18) occur when solder spans a copperless board area to connect traces or pads that aren't supposed to be connect-

Fig 17—The completed circuit board. Use this as a guide when you check your board.

Fig 18—A slip of the iron, or applying too much solder, sometimes creates a *solder bridge* between circuit traces not intended to be connected. Remelting the bridge usually clears it. A toothpick may be useful in clearing stubborn shorts.

ed. Inspect the board's foil side carefully. Solder's silvery glints can hide bridges and poorly soldered connections, so breathe on the board to dull the highlights. If you find a bridge, remelt it and the adjacent trace or traces to allow solder's surface tension to absorb it.

If everything checks out, you're done. Next month, we'll put your board in a box and get it on the air!

Notes

[5]B. Hale, "Build It Yourself from *QST*," *Part 1*, *QST*, Apr 1992, pp 31-36.
[6]B. Hale, "Build It Yourself from *QST*," *Part 2*, *QST*, May 1992, pp 35-39.
[7]See Note 2 (Apr 1992 *QST*, p 36).

Build it Yourself from *QST*

Part 4: Here's how to take the final steps—mounting your completed project in the enclosure of your choice, testing it and putting it on the air.

By Bruce S. Hale, KB1MW/7

2238 168th Ave NE
Bellevue, WA 98008

This is the last article in a series on turning a *QST* project into radio gear you can use on the air. In Parts 1 through 3,[8] I described how to figure out what parts you need and how to order them, and how to get started in ground-plane and PC-board construction. A VXO-controlled, 20-meter QRP transmitter (see Part 1) serves as our example project. This month we're going to put that transmitter in a box and get it on the air.

Parts of this article are specific to the Radio Shack metal box (#270-239) we bought in Part 1, but most of the article applies to whatever box you've chosen for your transmitter. Believe me, you can put this transmitter in almost anything—I've built projects in some pretty strange enclosures, like glass jars and cookie tins. You can even use it with no box at all, but it's more convenient if you have a front and back panel to mount jacks and controls.

Tools

I chose the Radio Shack aluminum box because aluminum is easy to work with hand tools. See Fig 20. You'll need 1/8-inch, 3/16-inch and 1/4-inch drill bits; you'll also need larger drills or a hand reamer to make holes for the RF connectors. I got my hand reamer at a local hardware store; Easy Tech and Ocean State Electronics (see Table 1 in Part 1) carry them. If you can't find a hand reamer, you can use a nibbling tool (Radio Shack #64-823) to make large holes, but it's hard to make round holes with a nibbler. A small hand file is useful for removing the sharp edges from drilled holes.

You'll also need some #4-40 machine screws and nuts, and a screwdriver to fit the screws. A package of assorted #4-40 screws from Radio Shack (#64-3011) and a package of #4-40 nuts (#64-3018) will be plenty. Although they're not essential, installing toothed lock washers under every nut can help hold hardware in place. Digi-Key and Ocean State Electronics (see Table 1, Part 1), among other mail-order

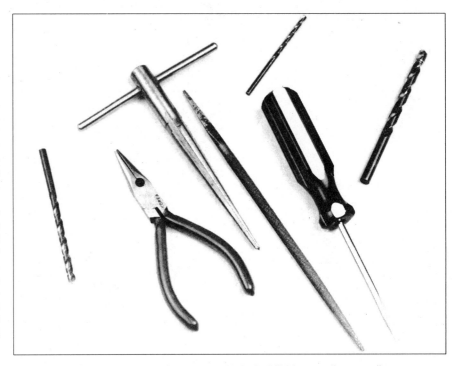

Fig 20—You'll need 1/8-inch, 3/16-inch and 1/4-inch drill bits, needle-nose pliers, a screwdriver, a small round file and a hand reamer.

suppliers, carry them. Many home-improvement centers carry all of this hardware, tools, and then some.

Panel Layout

The dc power leads, **ANTENNA** connector and **RX OUT** jack are mounted on the back panel. (So is the **SIDETONE OUT** jack if you added the sidetone oscillator described last month.) The **SPOT** switch, **KEY** jack and **FREQUENCY** capacitor are mounted on the front panel. It's best to orient the circuit board so the connections to the panel are as short as possible—this is one reason I put the **KEY** jack on the front panel, but I also think it's more convenient there. You can mount the **KEY** jack on the back panel if you like—it's your project!

Marking, Center-Punching and Drilling

Once you know where everything goes, you can mark the panels for the holes. Be sure to locate connectors far enough from

the box edges to allow for their outer dimensions. Fig 21 shows how I laid out the panels. I used the part of the box with the bent-over flanges as the top of the box.

If you want to make sure you don't scratch the box as you drill the holes, temporarily cover the entire box with masking tape. I usually don't bother.

Measure carefully and mark the center of each hole with a permanent marker (something that won't rub off as you work with the box). It's a good idea to center-punch the holes so the drill won't wander away from the marked hole as you drill. You can do this with a special center-punch tool, but I just use a large (8- or 10-penny) nail. Use a block of wood to support the panel from behind and center the nail or punch on the mark where you'll be drilling, as shown in Fig 22. Strike the punch with a hammer—one or two light taps should be enough to make a small indentation in the metal. Punch all the holes the same way.

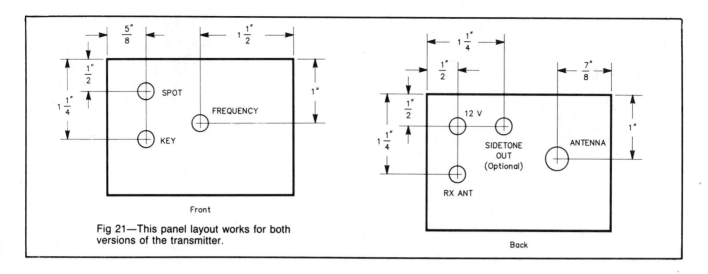

Fig 21—This panel layout works for both versions of the transmitter.

Drill all the holes with the 1/8-inch drill first. Leave the wood block behind the panel, wear eye protection and hold the box firmly—the drill bit can grab as it goes through the panel. I've had boxes fly out of my hands and spin around when the drill grabbed; this is not fun. Once you've drilled all the holes with the 1/8-inch bit, switch to the 1/4-inch bit and redrill the holes. *Don't* try to drill 1/4-inch holes without predrilling pilot holes with the smaller bit! Doing so will almost guarantee that the bit will walk away from the center mark and grab as it goes through the panel.

The 1/4-inch holes will be large enough for everything but the **RX OUT** phono jack, the **SPOT** push button and your **ANTENNA** connector. If you're using a BNC connector and you've got the right-sized drill bits, just drill out the 1/4-inch holes using the larger bit. Be extra careful when you use the larger bits—they're even more prone to grabbing the panel as they pass through.

If you don't have the right-sized bits, or you're using an SO-239 antenna connector, you'll need to use the reamer, the file or the nibbling tool for the larger holes. You can use your file to make the holes slightly larger, but it will be a lot of work to make large holes with a file. Using the nibbler will take some practice, and it's appropriately named. You must "nibble" small pieces from the edge of the hole until it's large enough, and then round the hole with a file. It's a pain in the neck—you're better off trying to find the right-sized drill bits!

Once you've got all the holes drilled, use a file or large drill bit to remove the burrs (sharp pieces of metal) from the edges of the holes. Then mark the screw holes for the RF connectors. You can mount the **ANTENNA** connector (BNC or SO-239) with its flange either inside or outside the box. (I like to mount them with the flange outside the box.) Two screws in opposite corners are enough—you don't need to use all four holes in the connector. Place the connector in the hole and use a pen to mark the mounting hole locations, then punch

and drill them with the 1/8-inch bit. You may need to drill the mounting holes in BNC flanges with the 1/8-inch drill bit—the holes in many BNCs' flanges are tapped for #3 screws.

I like to use phono connectors with flanges. Phono connectors that mount with a single nut around the connector bushing may work loose unless you use lock washers that usually don't come with them (1/4-inch internal-tooth lock washers, available at home improvement centers, are just right for Radio Shack's #274-346 phono connectors). Mount flanged connectors outside the box, making certain that their center conductors do not touch the edges of their panel holes.

If you're using a ground-plane transmitter board, it's time to drill mounting holes in it if you haven't already done so. Drill two 1/8-inch holes in opposite corners of the board. (The PC board already has mounting holes drilled in its corners.) Two holes are enough to mount a ground-plane

Fig 22—Use a center punch or an 8- or 10-penny nail to make a small indentation at the center of each hole so the drill bit won't walk away from where you want to drill.

board, but use all four for the PC board. Center the board in the bottom of the box and mark and center punch the holes. Then drill the holes with the 1/8-inch bit, and deburr them with the file.

Painting and Labeling

When all the holes are drilled, you can paint the box and label the controls. I usually don't bother with this either—the paint usually flakes off or scratches so it looks worse than bare aluminum. If I can't remember what the controls do, I mark them with a permanent felt-tip marker. It may not look professional, but I don't care.

Mounting the Board

Mount the board in the box *before* you mount all the connectors and switches, and wire the PC board before you mount it in the box. (You can wire the ground-plane board after you've mounted it in the box—another advantage of ground-plane over PC-board construction.) Cut two 12-inch lengths of hookup wire (it's most convenient to use two different colored wires if you have them), strip one end of each and solder them to the + and − **12 V** connections. You don't need shielded wire for the **ANTENNA** and **RX OUT** connections in this project—the connectors are close enough to the board that hookup wire works fine. Cut 6-inch lengths of solid hookup wire, strip one end of each and solder them to the **SPOT** switch, **KEY**, **RX OUT**, **ANTENNA** and **FREQUENCY** capacitor locations on the board. There's no PC-board hole for the connection to the ground side of the **SPOT** switch (it's connected to + 12 V) so I carefully soldered a wire to the bottom of the board on the trace near the emitter of Q1.

The circuit board's mounting screws will electrically connect it to the aluminum box. Unless an author tells you otherwise, you can depend on this connection for the ground returns of circuits and jacks that carry only dc (in this project, the **KEY** jack and 12-V power). It's *not* a good idea to expect circuit-board mounting hardware to

Fig 23—Connect the wire from the crystal to the side of the tuning capacitor that is not grounded to the chassis.

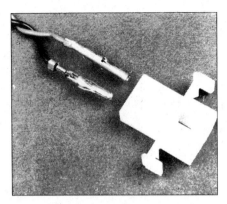

Fig 24—Assembling Radio Shack #274-222 power connectors. Crimp and solder a male connector pin to one power lead, and solder a female pin to the other lead. Push the pins into the plastic shell from the back.

handle ground returns for ac circuits (audio and RF) because this can cause unwanted coupling and feedback. This applies to the transmitter's **RX OUT** and **ANTENNA** jacks, and the ground return for the **FREQUENCY** capacitor. Using coax for the **RX OUT** and **ANTENNA** jacks avoids this problem because you can (and should) ground the coax braid at both ends of each run. If you don't use coax to connect the **RX OUT** and **ANTENNA** jacks to your board, solder a 6-inch piece of wire to circuit-board ground adjacent to where these jacks' ungrounded (*hot*) wires leave the board. (Some PC-board designs include ground-foil holes for this—the FAR Circuits board for our 20-meter transmitter does.) Also do this for **SIDETONE OUT** if you added the sidetone oscillator.

You must use spacers between the back of the PC board and the box so the traces on the board do not touch the aluminum box. You can buy spacers, but I just used two extra #4-40 nuts on each screw. Poke the screws though the holes from the outside, thread two nuts onto the screws and tighten them down. Then place the PC board over the screws and add another nut on top of the PC board. The ground-plane board does not require spacers, so you only need one nut per screw.

If you built the sidetone oscillator, and you built it in a corner of your ground-plane board, you've already mounted it! If you built the sidetone on a scrap of ground-plane board, you can mount it to the chassis with a single screw and nut. Or you can solder a heavy wire or two between its foil and the copper foil of the main transmitter board. It's low-mass, so it won't shake loose and go anywhere.

Wiring The Panels

Once you've got the board mounted in the box, attach the jacks and switches. Mount all the components in the appropriate holes. Nut drivers work best for tightening the nuts on the **SPOT** switch (and **FREQUENCY** capacitor, if you used one that mounts with a single nut over its shaft bushing), but if you don't have a nut driver you can use needle-nose pliers or a small adjustable wrench.

Strip and solder the wires to the **SPOT** switch and **KEY** jack; cut the wires if they're too long. Connect the wire from the crystal to the ungrounded terminal of the **FREQUENCY** capacitor (Fig 23). If you panel-mounted your **FREQUENCY** capacitor, give it a ground wire even if its mounting bushing grounds its rotor (moving plates). If your **FREQUENCY** capacitor's mounting hardware grounds neither its rotor nor its stator (stationary plates), you have a choice of which to ground. Ground the rotor. Solder hot and ground wires to the connectors on the back panel and run the dc wires through the hole in the back panel.

You can twist together the dc wires, and wires to the **RX OUT**, **ANTENNA** and **SIDETONE OUT** jacks (if you didn't use coax), to make things neater. I wrapped the dc wires with electrical tape to hold them firmly in the hole in the box. If you used

Radio Shack #274-222 power connectors, strip the ends of the wires, solder a male connector pin to one wire and a female connector pin to the other wire and push the pins into the plastic connector shell (see Fig 24). Solder the other half of the polarized power connector to another pair of wires and connect them to your power supply. Make sure the positive side of the power supply connects to the + connection on the circuit board.

If your **FREQUENCY** capacitor has a 3/16-inch-diameter shaft, remove the set-screw from one of the knobs you bought. Hold the knob firmly with pliers or a vise, and drill the 1/8-inch shaft hole out with the 3/16-inch drill bit. Don't drill all the way through the knob! It's not easy to drill the knob straight without a drill press, but you can do it if you're careful. (This is why I told you to buy more than one knob—if you make a mistake you can try again.) Once you get the hole drilled, replace the set-screw, slip the knob over the capacitor shaft and tighten the set-screw.

Testing the Transmitter

Once everything's connected, the inside of your transmitter box should look some-

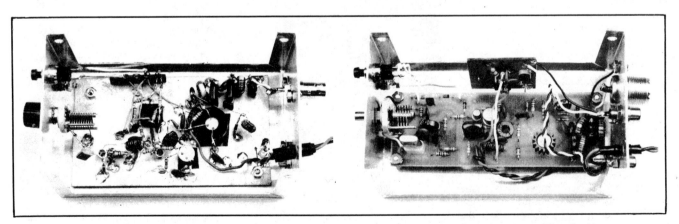

Fig 25—Inside the completed transmitters. The PC-board transmitter (right) also includes the sidetone oscillator described in Part 3.

thing like one of the two examples in Fig 25. Now you're ready to test the transmitter. You'll need a dummy antenna—a 47-ohm, 2-watt resistor works great, or you can wire a pair of Radio Shack 100-ohm, 1-watt metal-oxide resistors (271-152) in parallel. Don't use wire-wound resistors for your dummy antenna—they have too much inductance and may cause your transmitter to do unexpected things.

Plug in the dummy antenna, connect the power supply (through a multimeter, if you have one, set for measuring current) and switch it on. If you've got an oscilloscope, connect it to the dummy antenna with the probe center conductor on the center of the antenna connector. If you don't have an oscilloscope, put the dummy antenna near the **ANTENNA** jack of your receiver and tune the receiver near the transmitter's crystal frequency.

When you press the **SPOT** switch, the transmitter should draw about 12 milliamps, and you should see RF on your oscilloscope or hear the transmitter in your receiver. You may have to tune the receiver slightly to find the transmitter—switch in the receiver's widest IF filter. When you key the transmitter, it should draw about 260 milliamps, and you should see more RF on your oscilloscope (or hear a louder signal in your receiver).

If nothing happens when you press the **SPOT** switch, it's likely that the transmitter oscillator isn't working. Check all the connections in that area of the circuit. If you can't find any bad connections, try replacing the VXO transistor (Q3). If the oscillator works, but the transmitter doesn't draw more current when you key it, the problem is in a later stage. Again, check all your connections. Look for cold solder joints on the PC board—remelt any connections that look suspicious. Replace transistors only as a last resort—the problem is usually somewhere else.

If you built the sidetone oscillator and your receiver has a sidetone input, connect a cable between the transmitter's **SIDETONE OUT** jack, J4, and the receiver's sidetone input. Set R20, **SIDETONE LEVEL**, to the center of its range. Key the transmitter and adjust **SIDETONE LEVEL** for the volume you want.

On the Air

Once you've got the transmitter working into a dummy antenna, you can connect your outside antenna to the transmitter and connect a short cable from the transmitter's **RX OUT** jack to your receiver. Now you're ready to get on the air.

If you're new to low-power operating, see *The ARRL Operating Manual*[9] for an introduction to QRP. QRP isn't like operating with a high-powered station. If you're extremely lucky, there will be a loud station calling CQ on your crystal frequency when you turn on your receiver. More likely, you won't hear anyone, or you'll hear stations in a QSO. This is fine—just wait until they finish the QSO, and then call the louder of the two stations. (If the louder station closes down [signs with CL], call the other station.)

If I don't hear anyone at all, I use the "wait and pounce" technique. I spot the transmitter on the receiver, and then leave the receiver on while I do something else in the shack (I usually work on another project!). Sooner or later, someone will find the quiet frequency and start calling CQ, and I'm right there to answer them. If they don't hear my return call, someone else usually does, and then I call one of them after they end their QSO. As an absolute last resort, I call CQ. But I'd much rather let someone else do the work!

Contests are great for QRP operating, especially after the initial few hours and people are getting desperate for new blood. You'll find their ears have developed quite well, even for weak QRP signals!

Summary

If you're like me, once you've got the building bug, you won't let your soldering iron stay cold for long. Warming it up the very first time is the hardest part! In this four-part series, I've shown how you can build your own radio gear from published *QST* articles. I hope you've enjoyed building the transmitter we used for our example project, and I know you'll enjoy using it on the air. Now, the next time you think about adding another *QST* project to your station, you'll know where to start.

Notes
[8]B. Hale, "Build It Yourself from *QST*," *Part 1*, *QST*, Apr 1992, pp 31-36; *Part 2*, *QST*, May 1992, pp 35-39; *Part 3*, *QST*, Jun 1992, pp 42-45.
[9]J. Bauer, "Less is More...Or Enjoying QRP," S. Ford, ed, *The ARRL Operating Manual*, 4th ed (Newington: ARRL, 1991), pp 3-16 and 3-17. Available from the ARRL Bookshelf as #1086.

From QEX, *March 1995, p 24:*

RF

By Zack Lau, KH6CP/1

Calculating the Power Limit of Circuits with Toroids

A notable black hole in RF design is the calculation of how much power toroidal inductors can handle. The reason is pretty obvious—just look at books like Grover's *Inductance Calculations* to see how difficult it is to solve the "easy" cases, without the complications of real RF circuits such as skin and proximity effects.[1] On the other hand, even a rough approximation is better than nothing, especially for those without practical experience on which to base a guess, uh, estimate.

The approach is as follows. First, measure the Q of each inductor at the operating frequency. Next, using the measured Q values, analyze the circuit and calculate the current through each inductor as a function of the input power. (Computer modeling is useful, but not essential. Matrix algebra will handle the most commonly used networks.) This will let you calculate the power lost by the inductor. Finally, relate the power loss to a surface temperature rise. That's what we want to know: how much power makes the inductors too hot?

225 Main Street
Newington, CT 06111
email: zlau@arrl.org

Actually, you can get acceptable results by guessing the Q. If you think the Q will be low, guess 100. If you think it will be high, guess 300. This works well for the type-2 and type-6 iron-powder materials used at HF. (If you are thinking about using type-1 material at 160 meters, don't—use type-2 material instead. Apparently, the core loss of type-1 material offsets the decrease in copper loss, so the only advantage is the fewer turns required.) Another source of Q values is the charts in the Amidon booklet, *Iron-Powder and Ferrite Coil Forms.*[2] Of course, the preferred method is to measure the Q at the frequency of operation. The charts show that the Q will be optimum at a particular frequency and degrade as you move away. A set of equations for calculating this would make an excellent *QEX* article by someone who wants a challenge!

If you are fortunate enough to have a Q meter, you can just set the frequency and make the measurement. But you can also measure Q with simple equipment. Just measure the bandwidth and insertion loss of a filter and use this to calculate the Q of the components involved. If you want simplicity, you can use very light coupling so that the measured Q approaches the inductor Q. You can ignore the loss of the capacitors to make the math easier, although this isn't

necessary if you are using a computer modeling program such as *ARRL Radio Designer* (*ARD*). In any case, ignoring the capacitor loss will add a safety factor by making the Q of the inductor appear slightly worse than it actually is.

Finally, for those of you who need some information right now, you might use the measurements I've listed in Table 1. I took this data over a number of years using a Hewlett-Packard 4342A Q meter. Unlike the equipment we use here in the ARRL Lab for product-review testing, the Q meter isn't calibrated on a regular basis. Still, the numbers should be reasonably useful.

If you wonder about the particular coil selection of Table 1, keep in mind that the goal was usually to quickly optimize Q given some constraints—it is hardly the measurement of random coils. Hopefully, more people will be willing to share their measured data with the amateur community to improve the quality of homebrew designs.

Example 1

The circuit in Fig 1 is a 3-element π network that transforms 50 Ω to 84.5 Ω at 14.1 MHz. My simplified analysis of the network by hand indicates that I_L is $V_1/42.8$ Ω. With a simple ladder or π network, the math is straightforward—it isn't necessary to resort to matrix algebra to get the loop currents. If you have a computer program such as *ARD*, you can model the inductor as an ideal inductor in series with a resistor. The power lost across the resistor is the power loss. It can be surprisingly high if you have a lot of circulating current. Keep in mind that *ARD* applies the voltage though the source resistance. Thus, if you set the source to 1 V (RMS), you are applying 5 mW to a matched circuit, not the 20 mW to the 50-Ω circuit one might expect.

Calculating the resistive loss in the circuit of Fig 1 gives:

$$R_S = 2\pi f L_1 / Q$$
$$= 62.9\,\Omega / 236$$
$$= 0.266\,\Omega$$

The power lost in this resistive component is:

$$P_{loss} = R_S I_L^2$$
$$= 0.266\,\Omega(V_1 / 42.8\,\Omega)^2$$

How much does the toroid heat up?

According to the Micrometals catalog, the temperature rise of a toroidal inductor is:

$$\Delta T = \left[\frac{\text{power loss (mW)}}{\text{surface area (cm}^2)}\right]^{0.833}$$

where ΔT is in °C.[3] Since it takes 2 hours for the core to stabilize at this temperature, this is quite conservative for most amateur applications. Normal amateur duty cycles will allow you to double or triple the allowable power loss.

The surface area is easily found in the reference data: the surface area of a T-50 core is 6.86 cm[2]. If a 25 °C temperature rise is acceptable:

$$P_{loss} = (\text{surface area})(\Delta T)^{1.2}$$
$$= 6.86(25)^{1.2}$$
$$= 326\,\text{mW}$$

Thus, we now have a loss value from which calculate the allowable power input:

$$0.266\,\Omega(V_1 / 42.8\,\Omega)^2 = 326\,\text{mW}$$
$$V_1 / 42.8 = \sqrt{0.326 / 0.266}$$
$$V_1 = 47.4\,\text{V}$$

By comparison, *ARD* reports 0.00307 V across the inductor resistor when 0.496 V is across C1. Thus, P_{in} is 45.3 W according to the computer

model. I think this is reasonably close.

Example 2

A tuned two-pole band-pass filter is usually designed for a narrow bandwidth. As a result, it isn't unusual to have a loss of 2 dB, or 37%. If the capacitor losses aren't a factor, 18.5% of the power is lost in each inductor. Thus, this circuit will only handle 1.8 W, using the same 25 °C temperature-rise criterion. Note that instead of going through all the work of calculating the actual current in the inductor, we have instead used the loss of the circuit. This is often easier to measure and calculate.

It can be argued that this isn't exactly correct—that for high-loss filters the loss in each inductor will be slightly different. Perhaps. But I'll point out that trying to get precision results is quite apt to result in answers that are entirely wrong because of mistakes made in the overly complicated analysis. For most of us, rough numbers that are easily calculated make more sense. After all, in real life each component will be slightly different.

How reasonable is the 25 °C temperature rise criterion? On a warm summer day, you might end up with a temperature of 55 °C, which is pretty warm to the touch. (Of course, smart RF experimenters know better than to touch circuits with lots of RF applied— RF burns do hurt!)

Another consideration is temperature stability. Type-6 iron-powder is one of the better materials, with a temperature coefficient of 35 ppm/°C. Thus, the inductance will only change by 880 ppm, or 0.088%. On the other

hand, suppose your inductors were made out of type-67 ferrite, with a temperature coefficient of 0.13%/°C. A 25 °C rise would result in a variation of 3.2%, which can be quite noticeable if there is a large impedance transformation or if the circuit bandwidth is narrow. Also, magnetic materials have a Curie temperature at which they cease to be ferromagnetic. This is as low as 130 °C for type-43 ferrite material and as high as 500 °C for type-67 material. Micrometals, a company that makes iron-powder toroids, recommends that the toroids only be used between –55° and 125 °C, as "continued operation above 125 °C will generally result in a permanent decrease in both inductance and Q."[3]

Finally, you might wonder why I didn't mention any flux-density calculations. Since flux density is inversely proportional to frequency, saturating an inductor at 10 MHz is 1000 times as difficult as it is at 10 kHz. Thus, while it is a concern when designing switching power supplies, it is rarely a problem at RF.

An Inexpensive Dish Source

You can buy RCA DSS 18-inch dish parts from MCM Electronics, 650 Congress Park Drive, Centerville, OH 45459, tel: 1-800-543-4330, fax: 1-513-434-6959. (See p 209 of MCM's Catalog 34.) These 18-inch offset-feed dishes are inexpensive—one version of the steel reflecting surface is only $13.15, while an apparently reinforced version goes for $22. The mounting bracket is another $14.85. These are new replacement parts, so getting large quantities for club projects shouldn't be a problem. The offset-feed requirement complicates feed positioning slightly, as there are two positioning variables to deal with instead of one. But once someone comes up with a duplicable feed design, these dishes promise to be a low-cost route onto the microwave bands.

Notes

[1]Grover, F. W., *Inductance Calculations*, Dover Publications, ISBN 0-87664-557-0.
[2]Amidon Associates, PO Box 956, Torrance, CA 90508. Tel: 310-763-5770; fax: 310-763-2250.
[3]*RF Applications, Micrometals Iron Powder Cores*, Catalog 3 Issue D. Micrometals, Inc, 1190 N. Hawk Circle, Anaheim, CA 92807. Tel: 1-800-356-5977.

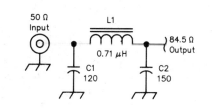

Fig 1—Schematic diagram of a 50 to 84.5-Ω π network at 14.1 MHz. L1—12 turns #22 enameled wire on a T-50-6 iron-powder toroid core. (0.71 μH, Q=236 at 14.1 MHz.)

Table 1—Measured Toroidal Inductor Q Values

In the following list, the Q of some coils was measured at several frequencies. These measurements are grouped together, with only one of the values showing a measured inductance. The tracking code allows me to go back and check my notebook—everyone has at least one notebook, right?

L (uH)	Q, f (MHz), turns, wire gauge, core, tracking code	L (uH)	Q, f (MHz), turns, wire gauge, core, tracking code
0.0885	64.5, 25.2, 10t, #24, T-25-0, 3p2	0.495	223, 14.1, 10t, #22, T-50-6, 2p7
0.0931	114, 25.2, 5t, #24, T-16-6, 3p3		223, 18.1
0.0949	111, 25.2, 5t, #26, T-16-6, 3p2		216, 21.2
0.0975	116, 25.2, 4t, #24, T-37-6, 1p108		200, 25.2
0.104	95, 25.2, 6t, #24, T-30-12, 3p78		182, 28.5
0.1079	73, 25.2, 12t, #24, T-25-0, 3p2		
0.111	130, 25.2, 5t, #24, T-37-10, 1p129	0.58	188, 25.2, 12t, #24, T-37-6, 3p70
0.124	134, 25.2, 4t, #24, T-50-6, 1p108		
0.127	114, 25.2, 6t, #28, T-16-6, 3p2	0.59	209, 25.9, 11t, #20, T-50-6, 1p118
0.129	140, 25.2, 5t, #24, T-37-6, 1p108		188, 28.5
0.139	102, 25.2, 5t, #24, T-25-2, 1p136		
0.140	90, 25.2, 7t, #26, T-20-2, 1p136		270, 18.1
0.158	107, 25.2, 7t, #26, T-20-6, 3p79		256, 21.2
0.158	126, 25.2, 6t, #24, T-37-10, 1p129		235, 24.5
0.17	99.9, 25.2, 6t, #24, T-25-2, 1p136	0.62	231, 25.2, 9t, #20, T-68-6, 1p118
0.173	95, 25.2, 7t, #26, T-20-2, 1p136		208, 28.5
0.180	136, 25.2, 5t, #24, T-50-6, 1p108		
0.215	125, 25.2, 8t, #26, T-20-6, 3p79	0.63	183, 25.2, 12t, #24, T-30-6, 1p150
0.215	152, 25.2, 6t, #24, T-37-2, 2p62	0.65	190, 25.2, 12t, #24, T-20-6, 1p150
0.219	154, 25.2, 8t, #26, T-30-10, 2p58	0.66	180, 25.2, 12t, #26, T-30-6, 2p45
0.220	146, 25.2, 6t, #24, T-50-6, 1p108	0.67	185, 25.2, 13t, #24, T-37-6, 3p70
0.221	143, 25.2, 8t, #24, T-25-6, 2p47	0.67	192, 25.2, 14t, #22, T-37-6, 2p39
0.23	170, 25.2, 6t, #22, T-44-6, 3p61		
0.234	124, 25.2, 8t, #24, T-37-10, 2p62		237, 10.1
0.234	177, 25.2, 7t, #24, T-30-6, 1p149		246, 14.1
0.247	139, 25.2, 8t, #24, T-37-19, 1p129		242, 18.0
0.258	178, 25.2, 7t, #24, T-30-6, 2p62		232, 21.0
0.269	167, 25.2, 8t, #24, T-37-6, 2p62	0.69	210, 25.2, 11t, #20, T-50-6, 50% coverage, 1p118
0.27	177, 25.2, 7t, #22, T-50-6, 3p69		189, 28.5, see 0.59
0.275	143, 25.2, 9t, #24, T-25-6, 2p47		
0.276	147, 25.2, 9t, #24, T-25-6, 2p51	0.71	132, 25.2, 11t, #24, T-37-2
0.285	104, 25.2, 10t, #26, T-20-2, 1p136		
0.30	167, 25.2, 10t, #26, T-30-10, 2p58	0.71	227, 10.1, 12t, #22, T-50-6, 2p7
0.303	164, 25.2, 9t, #24, T-37-6, 2p62		236, 14.1
0.31	172, 25.2, 7t, #22, T-50-6, 3p68		232, 18.1
0.325	170, 25.2, 8t, #24, T-30-6		222, 21.1
0.332	105, 25.2, 11t, #26, T-20-2, 1p136		201, 24.9
0.342	115, 25.2, 9t, #26, T-25-2		200, 25.2
0.36	142, 25.2, 9t, #28, T-25-6		178, 28.5
0.36	172, 25.2, 11t, #24, T-37-10, 1p129		
0.362	106, 25.2, 9t, #26, T-25-2	0.72	183, 25.2, 15t, #22, T-37-6, 2p39
0.362	122, 25.2, 9t+1/2, inch, lead, #26, T-25-2		182, 10.1
0.37	183, 25.2, 8t, #22, T-50-6, 3p68		188, 14.0
0.38	163, 25.2, 10t, #24, T-37-6, 2p62		188, 18.0
0.40	169, 25.2, 9t, #26, T-30-6, 3p79		186, 21.0
0.42	116, 25.2, 10t, #26, T-25-2		
0.43	146, 25.2, 12t, #26, T-25-6, 2p39,	0.72	195, 25.2, 13t, #24, T-30-6, 1p150
0.44	166, 25.2, 11t, #24, T-37-6, 2p62,	0.73	179, 25.2, 13t, #24, T-30-6, 1p150
0.45	146, 25.2, 13t, #28, T-20-6, 1p150	0.74	181, 25.2, 13t, #24, T-30-6, 1p150
0.47	172, 25.2, 9t, #20, T-44-6		
0.47	189, 25.2, 9t, #20, T-44-6		182, 10.1
0.489	186, 25.2, 10t, #24, T-30-6, 2p48		188, 14.0
0.49	174, 25.2, 11t, #24, T-37-10, 1p129, close wound		188, 18.0
0.49	146, 25.2, 12t, #26, T-25-6, 2p39		186, 21.0
0.49	151, 25.2, 14t, #28, T-16-6		179, 24.5

L (uH)	Q, f (MHz), turns, wire gauge, core, tracking code
0.74	177, 25.2, 14t, #20, T-50-10, 1p118
	172, 28.5
0.75	195, 25.2, 13t, #24, T-30-6, 1p150
0.75	194, 25.2, 13t, #24, T-30-6
0.75	188, 25.2, 12t, #22, T-50-6
0.76	185, 25.2, 13t, #24, T-30-6
0.76	192, 25.2, 12t, #20, T-44-6
0.78	163, 25.2, 14t, #28, T-37-6, 1p149
0.79	147, 25.2, 18t, #30, T-20-6, 1p150
0.79	149, 25.2, 18t, #30, T-20-6, 1p150
0.79	122, 25.2, 12t, #24, T-37-2
0.79	194, 25.2, 12t, #22, T-50-6, 3p68
0.80	148, 25.2, 18t, #30, T-20-6, 1p150
0.80	113, 25.2, 13t, #24, T-37-2, 1p135
0.81	120, 7.9, 13t, #24, T-37-2, 1p135
0.82	148, 25.2, 18t, #30, T-20-6, 1p150
	220, 10.1
	234, 14.1
	228, 21.0
	212, 24.9
0.83	211, 25.2, 15t, #24, T-37-6, 1p131
	196, 28.0
0.83	188, 25.2, 14, t, #24, T-30-6, 1p150
0.853	166, 7.9, 11t, #22, T-50-2, 3p68
0.86	162, 7.9, 13t+lead, #24, T-37-2
0.878	243, 7.9, 13t, #20, T-50-6, 1p118
	255, 10.1
	260, 14.1
	237, 21.0
0.88	210, 25.9
	188, 28.5
	233, 7.1, 0.869, 286, 7.9
	294, 10.1
	286, 14.1
	266, 18.1
	246, 21.0
	218, 24.5
0.88	212, 25.2, 12t, #16, T-68-6, 1p118
	186, 28.5
0.91	166, 25.2, 15t, #28, T-37-6, 1p149
0.918	202, 7.9, 12t, #22, T-44-2, 3p89
0.93	130, 25.2, 13t, #24, T-37-2
0.93	191, 7.9, 12t, #22, T-50-2, 2p65
0.931	145, 7.9, 18t, #30, T-20-2, 2p4
	150, 10
	148, 14
	138, 18
	128, 21
0.932	232, 7.9, 14t, #22, T-50-6, 2p7
	240, 10.1

L (uH)	Q, f (MHz), turns, wire gauge, core, tracking code
	245, 14.1
	236, 18.1
	223, 21.2
	198, 24.9
	174, 28.5
	290, 10.1
	294, 14.1
	280, 18.1
	236, 24.5
0.94	232, 25.9, 12t, #20, T-68-6, 1p118
	206, 28.5
0.95,	172, 7.9, 14t, #24, T-37-2
0.965	183, 7.9, 12t, #22, T-44-2, 3p89
0.97	168, 7.9, 12t, #22, T-50-2, 3p68
0.98	166, 25.2, 16t, #28, T-37-6, 1p149
0.99	167, 7.9, 16t, #26, T-25-2, 2p4
	168, 10.1
	160, 14
	144, 18
	132, 21
1.03	214, 7.9, 17t, #24, T-37-6, 1p131
	228, 10.1
	241, 14.0
	232, 21.0
	214, 24.9
	197, 28.0
1.038	213, 7.9, 16t, #24, T-30-6, 1p149
1.05	169, 7.9, 17t, #26, T-30-2, 2p4
	173, 10
	168, 14
	167, 7.3
1.06	270, 7.9, 15t, #20, T-50-6, 2p12
	283, 10.1
	283, 14.2
	268, 18.1
	250, 21.0
1.065	173, 7.9, 13t, #22, T-50-2, 3p68
1.105	182, 7.9, 15t, #24, T-37-2
1.12	255, 7.9, 15t, #20, T-50-6, 1p118
	265, 10.1
	270, 14.1
	242, 21.1
	210, 24.5
	182, 28.5
1.13	180, 7.9, 15t, #24, T-37-2
1.165	238, 7.9, 16t, #22, T-50-6, 2p13
	249, 14.2
	237, 18.1
	224, 21

L (uH)	Q, f (MHz), turns, wire gauge, core, tracking code
	293, 7.0
	300, 10.1
	285, 14.1
	255, 18.1
	228, 21.2
1.2	194, 25.2, 14t, #20, T-68-7, 1p118
	167, 28.5
1.22	215, 7.9, 19t, #24, T-37-6
	157, 28.0
1.22	225, 7.9, 19t, #24, T-37-6, 2p12
	190, 24.9
	170, 28.0
1.22	215, 7.9, 14t, #22, T-50-2, 2p65
1.23	215, 7.9, 19t, #24, T-37-6, 2p12
	187, 24.9
	168, 28.0
1.23	188, 7.9, 16t, #24, T-37-2
	226, 7.1
1.23	233, 7.9, 16t, #22, T-50-6, 2p12
	241, 10.1
	240, 14.2
	226, 18.1
1.255	238, 7.9, 16t, #22, T-50-6, 2p7
	231, 7.1
	247, 10.1
	248, 14.2
	234, 18.1
	217, 21.2
	191, 24.9
	215, 7.1
1.26	224, 7.9, 19t, #24, T-37-6, 1p131
	237, 10.1
	248, 14.0
	215, 24.9
	196, 28.0
1.28	176, 7.9, 16t, #24, T-37-2, evenly spaced
1.28	241, 7.1, 16t, #22, T-50-6, 2p11
	247, 7.9
	256, 10.1
	255, 14.2
	242, 18.1
	225, 21.2
1.3	260, 14, 17t, #22, T-50-6, 2p12
1.32	250, 14, 17t, #22, T-50-6, 2p12
1.33	237, 7.1, 16t, #22, T-44-6, 2p7
	243, 7.9
	248, 10.1
	241, 14.1

L (uH)	Q, f (MHz), turns, wire gauge, core, tracking code
	222, 18.1
	202, 21.2
	322, 7.1
1.34	332, 7.9, 15t, #20, T-68-6, 1p118
	342, 10.1
	335, 14.1
	309, 18
	280, 21.2
1.36	177, 7.9, 17t, #24, T-37-2
1.36	282, 14, 15t, #22, T-68-6, 3p99
	278, 7.9
1.39	218, 7.9, 15t, #22, T-44-2, 3p89
1.39	185, 7.9, 15t, #22, T-44-2, 2p65
1.4	253, 7.9, 17t, #22, T-50-6
1.43	246, 7.1, 17t, #22, T-50-6, 2p11
	252, 7.9
	259, 10.1
	256, 14.2
	230, 18.1
	222, 21.2
1.43	225, 7.9, 15t, #22, T-50-2, 2p65
1.44	182, 7.9, 17t, #26, T-30-2
1.44	192, 7.9, 17t, #24, T-37-2
1.44	225, 7.9, 21t, #24, T-37-6, 2p12
	183, 24.9
	164, 28.0
1.45	228, 7.9, 21t, #24, T-37-6
	238, 10.1
	238, 14.2
	226, 18.1
	209, 21.2
	184, 24.9
	163, 28.0
1.57	180, 7.9, 19t, #22, T-50-2, 1p102
	168, 10.1
	144, 14.0
1.58	190, 7.9, 18t, #24, T-37-2
	230, 7
1.67	237, 7.9, 22t, #24, T-37-7, 1p101
	248, 10
	237, 14
	213, 18
1.69	240, 7.9, 18t, #20, T-50-2
1.75	217, 25.9, 21t, #26, T-30-6, 2p53
1.78	181, 7.9, 20t, #, 24, T-37-2,
1.79	170, 7.9, 19t, #24, T-44-2

L (uH)	Q, f (MHz), turns, wire gauge, core, tracking code
1.8	231, 7.9, 17t, #22, T-50-2, 2p65
	335, 7.1
1.82	342, 7.9, 18t, #20, T-68-6, 1p117
	348, 10.1
	330, 14.1
	260, 21.2
1.86	167, 7.9, 22t, #30, T-25-2, 2p4
	164, 7.1
	168, 10.1
	162, 14.0
	147, 18.0
	134, 21.0
2.0	172, 7.9, 23t, #30, T-25-2, 2p4
	168, 7.1
	172, 10.1
	163, 14.0
	147, 18.0
	134, 21.0
	335, 7.1
2.04	335, 7.9, 19t, #18, T-68-7, 1p129
	325, 10.1
	278, 14.2
	236, 18.1
2.1	225, 7.9, 19t, #24, T-44-2
2.12	286, 7.9, 12t, #18, T-130-2
2.15	280, 7.9, 13t, #18, T-130-2
	229, 7.0
2.2	227, 7.9, 19t, #22, T-50-2, 1p127
	219, 10.1
2.25	231, 7.9, 19t, #22, T-50-2, 2p65
2.34	287, 7.9, 13t, #18, T-130-2
2.4	220, 7.9, 25t, #28, T-30-6, T-30-6, 1p149
2.44	168, 7.9, 22t+1", #28, T-30-2, 3p81
2.44	223, 7.9, 20t, #24, T-44-2
	268, 7.1
2.47	271, 7.9, 24t, #22, T-50-6, 2p12
	269, 10.1
2.52	262, 7.1, 24t, #22, T-50-6, 2p11
	263, 7.9
	260, 10.1
	233, 14.2
2.62	227, 7.9, 21t, #24, T-44-2
2.63	168, 7.9, 23t, #28, T-30-2, 3p81
2.63	191, 7.9, 22t, #22, T-50-2, 2p66
	330, 5.0
	335, 5.0
	345, 7.0
2.7	343, 7.9, 11t, #20, bifilar, T-68-6, 1p79

L (uH)	Q, f (MHz), turns, wire gauge, core, tracking code
	332, 10
	330, 10.5
	275, 14
	221, 18
2.72	222, 7.9, 30t, #26, T-37-6, 2p54
2.82	172, 7.9, 24t, #28, T-30-2, 3p81
2.82	212, 7.9, 25t, #26, T-37-2, 3p55
	281, 7.1
2.85	282, 7.9, 26t, #22, T-50-6
	282, 10.1
	268, 7.1
2.86	267, 7.9, 26t, #22, T-50-6, 2p13
	257, 10.1
2.9	272, 7.1, 26t, #22, T-50-6, 2p11
	273, 7.9
	267, 10.2
	233, 14.2
2.91	225, 7.9, 23t, #22, T-50-2, 1p127
3.0	232, 7.9, 26t, #22, T-50-2, 1p127
3.07	239, 7.9, 24t, #22, T-50-2, 2p65
3.08	222, 7.9, 24t, #22, T-50-2, 2p65
3.1	228, 7.1, 24t, #22, T-50-2, 2p11
	224, 7.9
	209, 10.1
	175, 14.2
3.13	195, 7.9, 26t, #26, T-37-2
	247, 7.1
3.19	242, 7.9, 24t, #22, T-50-2, 1p127
	225, 10.0
	300, 7
3.25	300, 7.9, 26t, #20, T-80-6, 1p78, see 3.4, bifilar
	290, 10
	290, 10.5
	260, 14
3.27	192, 7.9, 28t, #26, T-37-2, 1p136
	239, 7
3.29	254, 7.9, 31t, #26, T-37-7, 1p101
	248, 10
	237, 14
	213, 18
3.35	202, 7.9, 27t, #26, T-37-2
3.36	182, 7.9, 28t, #26, T-37-2, 1p136
	291, 5.0
	299, 5.2
	309, 5.4
	315, 6
	320, 7

$$\frac{L_1}{L_2} \cong \frac{N_1^2}{N_2^2}$$

$$N_2^2 = \frac{N_1^2 L_2}{L_1}$$

L (uH)	Q, f (MHz), turns, wire gauge, core, tracking code	L (uH)	Q, f (MHz), turns, wire gauge, core, tracking code
3.4	320, 7.9, 13t, bifilar, #20, T-80-6, 1p78	6.4	206, 7.9, 35t, #24, T-50-2, 2p38, see 5.9 & 6.7
	310, 10		461, 3.4
	309, 10.5		462, 3.5
	280, 13		465, 3.8
	265, 14		468, 4.0
3.5	233, 4.0, 25t, #22, T-50-2, 2p11	6.4	388, 7.9, 17t, #16, T-200A-6
	231, 7.1	6.7	219, 7.9, 35t, #24, broken, T-50-2, epoxied, 2p38, see 5.9 & 6.4
	226, 7.9	7.0	197, 7.9, 35t, #28, T-44-2, 3p2
	209, 10.1	7.2	263, 7.9, 21t+lead, #18, T-225-2
	172, 14.2	7.3	172, 9, 40t, #28, T-37-2, 3p83
3.6	183, 7.9, 28t, #28, T-30-2		223, 3.5
3.6	204, 7.9, 26t, #24, T-44-2, 2p47		258, 5.4
3.7	210, 7.9, 26t, #24, T-44-2, 2p47	7.3	254, 7.9, 40t, #28, T-50-7, tap at 10t, 2p39, see 8.2
3.75	210, 7.9, 26t, #25, T-44-2, 3p2	7.4	265, 7.9, 22t+lead, #18, T-225-2
3.9	202, 7.9, 26t, #24, T-44-2		415, 3.5
4.2	216, 7.9, 27t, #24, T-44-2		415, 3.6
4.2	204, 7.9, 27t, #24, T-44-2		415, 4.0
5.2	263, 7.9, 19t, #18, T-225-2		352, 7.1
5.4	350, 7.9, 26t, #18, T-94-6, 2p2	7.5	323, 7.9, 31t, #18, T-94-6, 1p126
5.4	273, 7.9, 19t, #18, T-225-2	8.0	201, 7.9, 38t, #28, T-44-6, 3p2
5.5	195, 7.9, 34t, #30, T-30-2	8.0	258, 7.9, 23t, #18, T-225-2
	335, 5		202, 3.5
5.6	330, 7.9, 33t, #22, T-68-6, 1p98		228, 5.4
5.8	271, 7.9, 20t, #18, T-225-2		238, 7.0
5.81	197, 7.9, 35t, #30, T-30-2	8.2	237, 7.9, 40t, #28, T-50-7, tap at 10t, 2p39, see 7.3
5.9	224, 7.9, 35t, #24, T-50-2, 2p38, see 6.7 & 6.4		232, 10.1
	232, 3.5		411, 3.5
	243, 3.6		411, 3.6
	244, 3.8		410, 3.8
	245, 4.0		408, 4.0
	183, 10.0	9.5	282, 7.9, 27t, #16, T-200-6, 2p66
	183, 14.1		212, 7.1
	184, 18.0	9.5	200, 7.9, 42t, #26, T-50-2, 1p131
	182, 21.0		170, 10.1
6.0	176, 25.9, 12t, #20, T-50-10, 1p118	9.8	192, 7.9, 43t, #26, T-50-2, 1p131
	171, 28.5	10.5	195, 7.9, 44t, #26, T-50-2, 1p131
6.1	217, 7.9, 34t, #24, T-50-2, 2p13,	11.35	166, 2.52, 52t, #30, T-37-2, 2p4
	236, 3.5		174, 7.05
	237, 3.6	11.9	166, 7.9, 52t, #30, T-37-2, 2p4
	238, 4.0	12.0	203, 2.52, 53t, T-50-6
6.25	212, 7.9, 34t, #24, T-50-2, 2p13,	12.1	195, 2.52, 53t, T-50-6, w/crossover, in, winding
6.3	213, 7.9, 34t, #24, T-50-2, 3p9	12.9	181, 2.52, 48t, #28, T-50-2, 3p52
	152, 12.4		

From QEX, September 1995. p 24:

RF

By Zack Lau, KH6CP/1

6-Meter Transverter Design

This month I present a design for a 6-meter transverter. You might say that this design is meant for illustrative purposes only—I expect anyone who builds a project like this to customize it to their needs. All the building blocks shown in Fig 1 feature 50-Ω input and output impedances. You can pick the parts of this design you think are best and integrate them into your own design. I don't intend to develop a set of boards for this project. If you are looking for something of that sort, check out Ten-Tec's popular kit with its 14-MHz IF.

The question every nonengineer asks about the Ten-Tec kit is, "why 14 MHz?" Very simply, it makes it

225 Main Street
Newington, CT 06111
email: zlau@arrl.org

practical to market an inexpensive kit that someone can put together and have a reasonable chance of meeting FCC spectral-purity requirements. A 28-MHz IF is a bit of a challenge—the second harmonic of the IF falls just outside the band where it can interfere with broadcast TV. Not that a 28-MHz IF can't be done, particularly if you narrow up the band-pass filters to cover just the first 1 MHz of the band. But the good layout and shielding needed are impractical if you want the project to be inexpensive.

One of the reasons hams like the idea of a 28-MHz IF is the availability of low-cost 10-meter SSB/CW radios. While such radios work—sort of—as an IF, you'll notice markedly better performance with a better radio. Unlike in satellite operation, where the bird limits the dynamic range of the signals you hear, the range of received VHF signals can be from extremely loud to extremely weak—at the same time. A prime example of this occurs with multihop E-skip. Single-hop signals are often ridiculously loud, while stations requiring multiple hops or scatter paths will often be right at the noise floor. It's not just dynamic range that counts, either; filtering also makes a difference. Expensive HF transceivers often have filters at two or more IFs. This gets around the problem of signals leaking past the filters, since you can typically add the rejection obtained at each frequency. As a lot of people have discovered the hard way, putting two 50-dB filters in series at one frequency rarely adds up to 100 dB of rejection.

Fig 1 shows the block diagram of the transverter. I chose a 144 to 148-MHz IF since I normally carry several 2-meter radios when I operate QRP portable. Turns out that this also works well in terms of spurious transmitter products. Since the QRP power limit is 10-W PEP, this was my design-goal power output. As for receiver performance, according to Ray Rector, WA4NJP, a 3-dB NF is adequate for 6-meter EME due to the high amount of sky noise.[1] He shows a plot that indicates minimum noise levels to be around 4000 kelvins. On the other hand, if you have a really bad location that looks into hills in every direction, it's certainly possible to have a much lower background noise temperature, possibly approaching the temperature of the ground. Of course, real locations often have man-made noise, so I doubt that anyone ever sees anything below 500 kelvins. I decided that the measured 2.9-dB NF and 10-dB insertion gain of this transverter is adequate for use with a sensitive 2-meter IF radio.

Fig 2 shows the T/R relay and the output low-pass filter, a straightforward design.

6-meter band-pass filters are used in the receive converter, the transmit converter and the common circuitry. Since these filters affect both the transverter performance and its ease of adjustment, some thought is required in selecting an appropriate design. Unlike in narrowband microwave applications, there is a distinct advantage to using more than two resonators in a 50 to 54-MHz band-pass filter. Not only are the filter skirts steeper, but you can make the passband flatter. In other words, as you add filter elements you can make the filter closer to the ideal rectangular filter. Such a filter has a flat response across the passband and infinite rejection everywhere else. There is also a distinct disadvantage: multiresonator filters can be difficult to adjust. Most people use a sweep network, which is ideally a tracking generator and a spectrum analyzer. It's also possible to use a sweep generator and a log detector, although spurious signals and responses are more of a problem with this technique. I've provided two band-pass filter designs (Figs 3 and 4). You can use either design for any of the BPF blocks of Fig 1. There are tradeoffs, though.

A software simulator, such as *ARRL Radio Designer*, is convenient for modeling real filters. You can also get more details by studying Anatol I. Zverev's *Handbook of Filter Synthesis*. (This classic, published by Wiley, will set you back over $100.) In these designs, I assumed Qs of 80 for the inductors

and 300 for the capacitors. Fig 3 shows the 3-pole filter design that resulted from the design process. (An interesting exercise is to compare two- and three-pole filters—the three-pole filter is markedly better.)

The three-pole filter is, of course, more difficult to adjust than a two-pole design. So, why not just cascade a pair of two-pole filters? I did just that, using the filter circuit shown in Fig 4. One of the cascaded filters is in the circuitry common to both transmit and

receive, while the separate transmit and receive chains each have a BPF within them. For transmit, this has the advantage of lowering the amount of broadband transmitted noise as the second filter is placed after several amplifier stages. The disadvantage is that cascading filters makes their nonideal passband responses even worse. True, you could cleverly design and tune up the cascaded filters as a unit to avoid this problem, but I don't think this is a realistic approach, par-

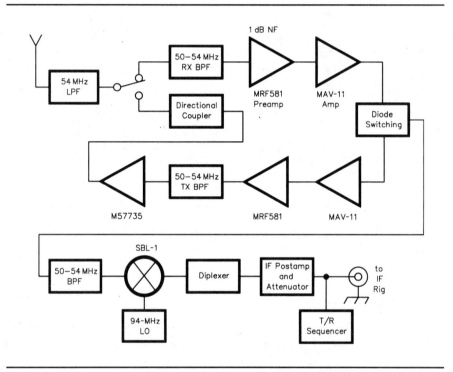

Fig 1—Block diagram of the transverter.

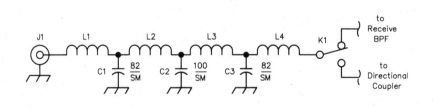

Fig 2—54-MHz low-pass filter and T/R relay. The filter has a 62-MHz –3dB cut off and 0.2 dB of insertion loss.

J1—UG-58 Type-N panel jack.
K1— Omron G5Y-1-DC12 relay (Digi-Key part Z24-ND).
L1, L4—90 nH, 5 turns no. 20 closewound, 0.19-inch inside diameter.

L2, L3—0.22 µH. 10 turns no. 20 closewound, 0.19-inch inside diameter.

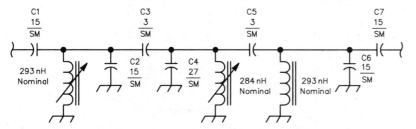

Measured filter response relative to 1.2-dB insertion loss

Response (dB)	Frequency (MHz)
-0.4	50.0, 54.0
-1	49.4, 54.6
-3	48.8, 55.4
-10	47.6, 57.6
-20	46.0, 61.8
-30	43.8, 69.6
-40	41.2

Fig 3—A 3-pole band-pass filter design.
L1, L2, L3—0.3-µH adjustable inductors with a Q of 80. Toko America, Inc. type MC120 with case, part No. E526HNA-100301 (Digi-Key part TK-2708-ND).

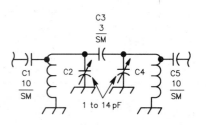

Fig 4—The low-loss, 2-pole band-pass filter.
C2, C4—1 to 14-pF Johanson piston trimmer capacitors.
L1, L2—8.5 turns no. 14 wire, space wound, 0.90-inch length. Tap ½ turn from top. Center-to-center spacing between coils is 1.0 inches. Coils are wound in the opposite sense from each other. Substitution is *not* recommended.

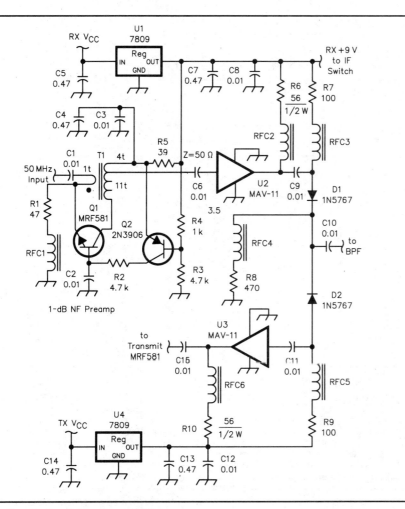

Fig 5—Small-signal 6-meter amplifiers.
D1, D2—1N5767 PIN diodes. Exact type not critical.
Q1—MRF581 low-noise transistor.
RFC1-6—10 turns no. 28 enam on FT-23-43 toroid core.

T1—15-turn primary on FT-37-67 toroid, with core material selected for low loss. Tap 11 turns from collector. 1-turn secondary. Use no. 28 enam. wire for both windings. *Phasing is critical for stable operation.*

ticularly if your reason for avoiding three-pole filters in the first place is the difficulty of tuning them up! The filter of Fig 4 is very low-loss, about 0.3 or 0.4 dB, but rather costly to construct, both in time and materials. It is quite similar to a 1.1-MHz-wide design I published previously.[2] Of course, if you have the appropriate test equipment, go ahead and use the 3-pole design.

I built the needed three filters using the design of Fig 4 and chose the best of them to put in front of the receiver preamplifier. At least for me, this made cascading filters a practical approach. This results in good immunity to interference from other transmitters. It would work even better at rejecting TV transmitter interference if the filter was just 1-MHz wide, but then it couldn't cover the entire 6-meter band. Of course, to maintain the low loss it's necessary to use even lower loss components. I'd consider a helical filter based on the design procedure in chapter 16 of the *ARRL Handbook*.[3] When tuning one of these up, it helps to understand the filter concepts discussed by Hayward.[4]

The preamplifier of Fig 5 is an optimized Norton design. This lossless feedback amplifier has been around a long time—so long that the patent has run out. Using type-67 ferrite to construct a low-loss transformer gives measured noise figures just under 1 dB with a gain of 10.5 dB. However, I found the output intercept at low bias current (under 10 mA) to be only +20 dBm. I was able to raise the output intercept to +31 dBm, while sacrificing 0.06 dB of noise figure, by raising the bias current to 16 mA. A variable resistor in series with R5 can be used as a bias-current adjustment. The use of an MRF 581 device also helps, as it performs a bit better than the MRF 586. (The latter device is no longer listed in the new Motorola data book—they are phasing out devices in that package.) Due to the low permeability (40) of type-67 material, the preamp isn't as broadband as one might expect. It will cover the 6-meter band just fine, but the noise figure degrades at 30 and 60 MHz.

There are several potential problems with this design. First, it is easy to convert into an oscillator. Switching the sense of the one-turn loop is enough to make it oscillate. Insufficient bypassing of the power supply also may result in oscillation. And the input-to-output isolation is poor. Thus, cascading a pair of these is ill-advised. On the other hand, you do get a very good output intercept and noise figure without any tweaking on expensive test equipment. I decided that using an MAV-11 as the second stage was an acceptable compromise, though someone building a high-performance system would use something more exotic. An MAV-11 typically has a 3.5-dB NF and 12 dB of gain at low frequencies.

Improved Local Oscillator Design

A complaint I've heard about the 222-MHz no-tune design I published in the July 1993 *QEX* is that there aren't enough tuning adjustments! People want to be able to tweak that crystal to a precise frequency. In the design shown in Fig 6, I was able to move the frequency upward with the following procedure. First, adjust L1 for parallel resonance with the holder capacitance. This can be done with a sweep setup that looks at the insertion loss of the device under test. At resonance, the shunting effect of the stray reactance is minimized, resulting in maximum attenuation. Next, try different capacitors for C4. The higher the capacitance, the lower the frequency. A piston trimmer isn't needed for C1, but it's an easy way to adjust the circuit inside a shielded box. It also serves as a rugged tie point for ground-plane construction.

I originally planned to use a Mini-Circuits TAK-1H high-level mixer in this design (Fig 6) but had difficulty getting the expected input intercept when integrating the system. I did get the expected performance from an SBL-1 mixer. A low-pass filter between the LO and mixer is needed for adequate transmit spectral purity. Otherwise the second harmonic of the local oscillator would mix with the RF signal and generate a large spurious signal around 44 MHz. Adding the filter dropped the spur from −11 to −38 dB, relative to the desired signal. Unfortunately, the SBL-1 is the weak link of the transverter since its input intercept is around +15 dBm while the output intercept of the MAV-11 is +30 dBm. I didn't worry too much about that since the weak link of the *system* is the 2-meter IF radio. It's difficult to find even HF transceivers with low noise figures and input intercepts in excess of +20 dBm, never mind getting it out of a 2-meter multimode radio.

The post-mixer IF amplifier of Fig 7 is another MAV-11, which is switched out of the path during transmit.

T/R switching

T/R switching is done with switch-

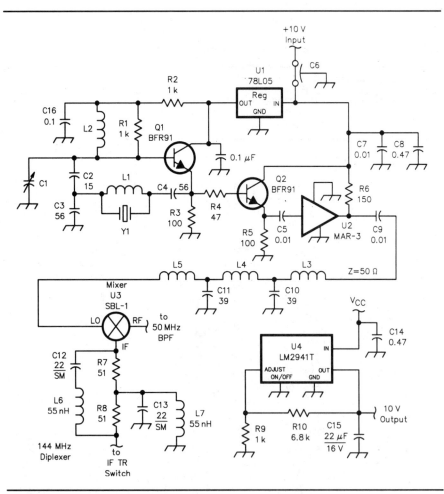

Fig 6—The mixer and 94-MHz local oscillator.

C1—Johanson 5459 1 to 14-pF piston trimmer. (See text.)
C4—Select for desired frequency. (See text.)
C6—Feedthrough capacitor. Value not critical. 100 pF to 0.01 µF works fine.
C15—22-µF tantalum capacitor, 16 V. *Absolutely required* for stable regulator operation. May be replaced with 100-µF electrolytic.
L1—Approximately 15 turns no. 28 enam on T-25-6 core. Inductance resonates with holder capacitance of crystal. (See text.)
L2—0.13 µH, 9 turns no. 28 close wound. Length is 0.14 inches. 0.10-inch inside diameter.

L3, L5—57 nH, 4 turns no. 26 enam space wound so that length is 0.25 inches. 0.19-inch inside diameter.
L4—0.12 µH, 7 turns no. 26 enam close wound. Length is 0.375 inches. 0.19-inch inside diameter.
L6, L7—55 nH, 5 turns no. 24 enam close wound. 0.125-inch inside diameter.
U4—LM2941T low-dropout regulator.
Y1—94-MHz, 5th-overtone crystal. International Crystal Manufacturing 473390.

ing diodes, PIN diodes and a relay. The switching diodes are used in the transmit signal path. While PIN diodes do offer a bit better performance than switching diodes, who needs high performance in a lossy transmit path where the idea is to dump excessive transmit power? The Omron RF relay is used for the high-power switching and seems to work well at the 10-W level, particularly if you use a sequencer, like the one by Chip Angle, N6CA, on page 22.57 of the 1995 *ARRL Handbook*. (Sequencer boards are available from FAR Circuits.[5]) I added a few switching transistors so that the sequencer switches the +12-V supplies. (See Fig 8.)

I modified my IF radios so they put a +5 to +12-V signal on the antenna line during transmit. The sequencer senses this voltage and switches the voltages appropriately. For the input attenuator, 1- and 2-W metal-oxide resistors work just fine at 144 MHz, so it isn't necessary to track down carbon composition resistors. The latter do make a better overload indicator, though. (You can smell 'em.) The attenuator and switching circuitry of Fig 7 is needed because the radios put out 2 W of RF. Much of this circuit can be omitted if a milliwatt-level IF radio is available. I use red LEDs to indicate transmit and green LEDs to indicate receive as a matter of personal preference.

The M57735 power module (Fig 9) is the easiest way to generate 10 W on this band. Tests show that only +15 dBm of input is needed to get 10 W out. This input level is easily provided with the +20-dBm MRF 581 design published in the March 1994 issue of *QEX*. Normally, people mount the power module directly to a heat sink. Instead, I mounted the module to a

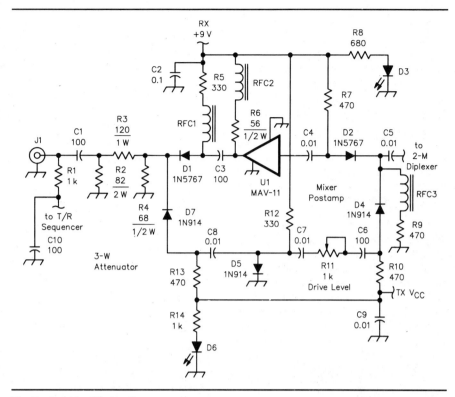

Fig 7—2-meter IF circuitry.
D1, D2—1N5767 PIN diode. Exact type not important.
D3—Green LED.
D6—Red LED.
J1—UG-290A/U BNC Jack.
RFC1-3—10 turns no. 28 enam on FT-23-43 toroid core.

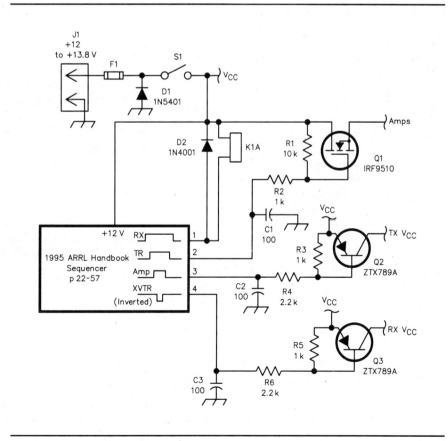

Fig 8—Sequencer circuitry.
F1—5-A fuse used in prototype. 3-A fuse may be more appropriate.
J1—Panel-mounted ARRL recommended 12-V power connector (MOLEX 1545), as specified on page 22.6 of the *ARRL Handbook*. Female housing with male pins; + line is indexed (Radio Shack part RS 274-222).
K1A— Omron G5Y-1-DC12 relay (Digi-Key part Z24-ND).
Q1—IRF9510 P-channel HEXFET.
Q2, Q3—3-A plastic cased PNP transistor (very high current) (Digi-Key part ZTX-789A-ND).
S1—25-A, 12-V dc power switch (Radio Shack part RS 275-708).

$2 \times 3 \times \frac{1}{4}$-inch piece of 6061-T6 aluminum bar stock and attached the metal block to a heat sink. This is similar to the approach that I've seen used in some microwave power amplifiers. The sheet stock is much easier to machine than most heat sink extrusions, yet thick enough to not bend easily.

SWR Coupler

This circuit board design has an unusually high directivity for a microstrip design using $\frac{1}{16}$-inch FR-4 circuit board. Two samples showed directivities of 26 and 31 dB. I've talked with several people who found it exceedingly difficult to come up with a similar design and gave up. I found it necessary to optimize the design by hand with the assistance of *Microwave Harmonica*, an expensive simulation program sold by Compact Software. This is the big brother to *ARRL Radio Designer* that has the sophisticated microstrip models that engineers spend big money to get. (Don't bother asking about a 2-meter design—I'm still working on it.)

The coupler shown in Fig 10 is quite simple—it's just two 135-mil-wide microstrips with a spacing of 20 mils, along with some right-angle transitions to get signals in and out of the coupler. The length of the closely coupled lines is 3000 mils. The expected dielectric thickness is 56 mils—this is perhaps the most variable aspect of working with glass epoxy board. A significantly different thickness will upset the impedance of the lines. The dielectric constant is 4.8. I wouldn't worry about this too much, unless you use a different type of board material. I got better directivity by drilling holes through the board and directly connecting the center conductors of small coax to the traces and the shields to the ground plane than by trying to make end-launch BNC connections.

The insertion loss of the coupler is too low to measure easily, perhaps 0.05 dB. For best accuracy, it may be worthwhile to place another low-pass filter between the transmit amplifier and the coupler since the coupler will respond to harmonics. Omitting the filter between the coupler and the antenna will increase the likelihood of interference to the SWR measurement from other transmitters as the broadband diode detector has little selectivity.

A single coupler can measure both forward and reverse power. People have encountered problems with

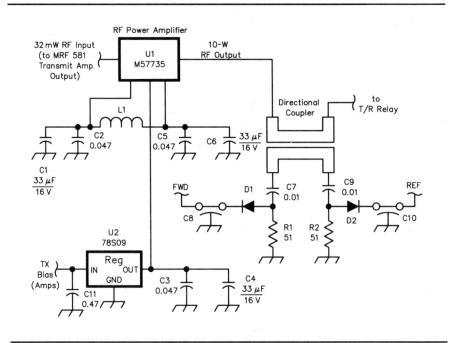

Fig 9—The 10-W power amplifier and directional coupler.
C8, C10—100 pF to 0.01 µF feedthrough capacitors.
D1, D2—Detector diodes. 1N34As may work best, though Shottky types will also work.
L1—7 turns no. 22 enam closewound. 0.19-inch inside diameter. Exact inductance shouldn't be critical.
U1—Mitsubishi M57735 RF power module.
U2—78S09 9-V regulator.

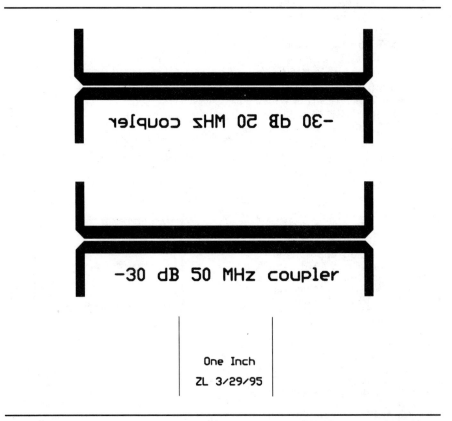

Fig 10—Etching pattern for a directional coupler on $\frac{1}{16}$-inch FR-4 circuit board.

detector diodes generating dc bias, upsetting the reverse-power measurement, leading them to use dual couplers. Instead, I used dc blocking capacitors. The coupling is –30 dB. Thus, 10 W through the detector, assuming 50-Ω terminations, results in 10 mW of forward power and 10 µW of unwanted reflected power. Ideally, there would be no reflected power. Chapter 22 of the 1995 *ARRL Handbook* has a good low-power wattmeter circuit that could take advantage of the high directivity of this coupler. I was able to buy new 50 µA meters—which are getting rare—from Ocean State Electronics.[6]

For the most part, the components used in these circuits are pretty easily found from Ocean State, your local Radio Shack or Digi-Key.[7]

If you'd like copies of the proceedings papers mentioned here, contact the ARRL Technical Department Secretary at ARRL HQ. Copies are $3 per article.

Notes

[1]Rector, R., WA4NJP, "6 Meter EME," *Proceedings of the Central States VHF Society*, 1988, ARRL.

[2]Lau, Z., KH6CP, "A Collection of VHF Filters," *Proceedings of the 20th Eastern VHF/UHF Conference*, 1994, ARRL.

[3]Schetgen, R., KU7G, ed, *The ARRL Handbook for Radio Amateurs*, Newington: 1995, ARRL.

[4]Hayward, W., W7ZOI, "The Double-Tuned Circuit: An Experimenter's Tutorial," *QST*, Dec 1991, pp 29-34.

[5]FAR Circuits, 18N640 Field Ct, Dundee, IL 60118-9269, fax/voice-mail: 708-836-9148.

[6]Ocean State Electronics, PO Box 1458, 6 Industrial Drive, Westerly, RI 02891, tel: 401-596-3080, 800-866-6626.

[7]Digi-Key Corporation, 701 Brooks Ave South, PO Box 677, Thief River Falls, MN 56701-0677, tel: 800-344-4539, fax: 218-681-3380.

☐☐

3. Transceivers/Transmitters

A Single-Board Superhet QRP Transceiver for 40 or 30 Meters
Dave Benson, NN1G
From *QST,* November 1994

Revisiting the 40-40
Mitchell Lee, KB6FPW and Dennis Monticelli, AE6C

Modifications and Improvements to the HW-9
S. W. McLellan, ND3P
From *QEX*, October 1990

A Small High Performance CW Transceiver
Rick Campbell, KK7B
From *QST,* November 1995

Single-Conversion Microwave SSB/CW Transceivers
Rick Campbell, KK7B
From *QST,* May 1993

A Multimode Phasing Exciter for 1 to 500 MHz
Rick Campbell, KK7B
From *QST,* April 1993

Build a One-Watt Transmitter in a Kodak Film Box
Robert S. Capon, WA3ULH
From *QST,* October 1994

Birth of a 7-MHz Transceiver
Zack Lau, KH6CP/1
From *QEX*, March 1993

From QST, November 1994, p 37:

A Single-Board Superhet QRP Transceiver for 40 or 30 Meters

Superhet performance in a small, inexpensive package— just the thing for traveling or low-profile operating.

By Dave Benson, NN1G
80 E Robbins Ave
Newington, CT 06111

I suspect it's been a while since most of us have truly understood what goes on behind the front panel of our transceivers. Perhaps the dazzling array of features at our disposal mutes the recognition of elegant simplicity as a design philosphy. With all this convenience at hand, why would anyone wish to build his own gear? Because there's a certain satisfaction to being able to say "I did it myself." You can't get that satisfaction in a box!

This article describes the "40-40," a single-board superhet transceiver project designed with ease of construction in mind. This design was initially developed under the auspices of the New England QRP (NE-QRP) club for use as a club project (see the sidebar for details). Far from being a "one-of-a-kind" special, nearly 200 of these transceivers have been built to date! Members of the Boston Amateur Radio Club have also built about a dozen of these transceivers.

NE-QRP emphasizes homebrewing to encourage member participation. We recognize that this isn't everyone's cup of tea, though, and sought easily reproduceable designs. We insisted that the product be as simple as possible (consistent with good performance), be modestly priced, and offer the builder a high probability of success. This project's nickname is symbolic of its original band coverage (40 meters) and cost to members ($40).

With these goals in mind, the club settled on a "bare-bones" superhet transceiver board. When you get right down to it, a workable superhet design needn't be more complex than a good direct-conversion (D-C) transceiver. This approach pays off in relative freedom from received QRM and a stable transmitted signal. We did cut several corners to hold cost and complexity to a minimum:

• We deleted the receiver's intermediate-frequency (IF) amplifier to save cur-

Figure 1—Mounted in an enclosure, the 30 and 40-meter transceivers make handy portable rigs.

rent drain and shave the parts count. As a result, standby (quiet-signal) current for this transceiver is only 21 mA! This approach has been described by DeMaw previously[1] and reflects our club's interest in solar/battery operation. Consequently, this design is intended for headphone use only. It provides more-than-adequate audio levels with a good set of low-impedance phones.

• We left out RIT (receiver incremental tuning) for much the same reason. The result of this minimalist philosophy is a radio with only two controls: gain and tuning! The design lends itself to adding RIT as an outboard option.

The design efforts resulted in a single printed-circuit board measuring only 2.8 × 4 inches lending itself readily to packaging in any of a number of commercial enclosures (Figure 1). Packaged as a complete

board kit, the offering included the PC-board, all on-board parts and wire for toroid winding, and a comprehensive instruction manual.[2] Builders provided the enclosure, assembly labor, and controls and connectors. These last items are all available from Radio Shack, so rounding up the necessary parts to complete the project needn't be an exercise in frustration! Let's take the 25-cent tour through the design:

So How's It Work?

Refer to Figure 1 for the following discussion. Although this text describes the 40-meter version, the 30-meter version is identical except for the choice of IF (8.0 MHz) and local oscillator (2.1 MHz). The receiver RF input is applied to U1 through T1, C1, and C2, which provide a bandpass filter tuned to the band in use. This circuitry attenuates out-of-band sig-

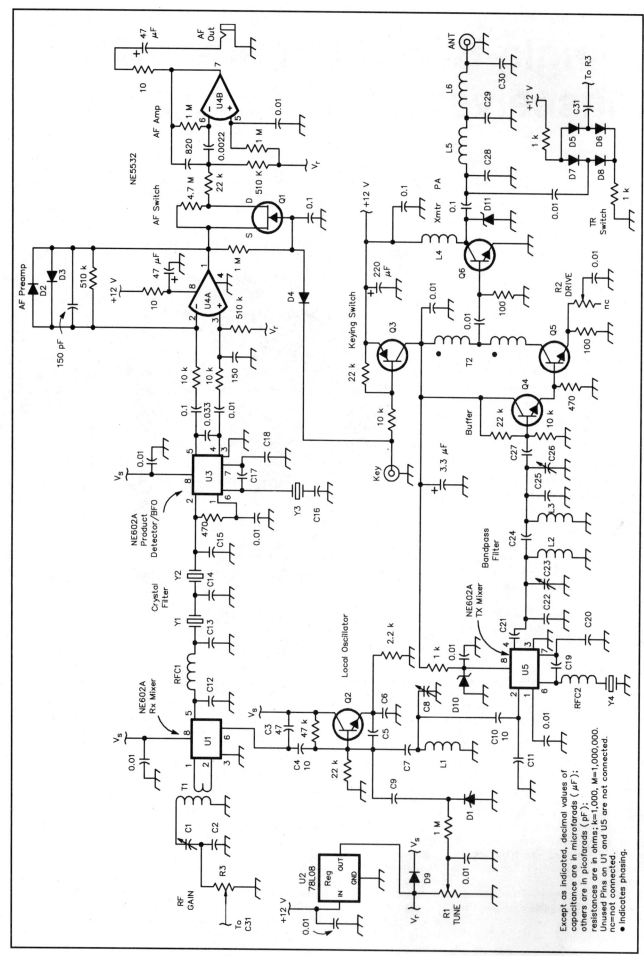

Figure 2—Schematic diagram of the transceivers. Table 1 is the parts list. See the text for additional details. Etched circuit boards and kits of board-mounted parts are available. See Note 2.

Except as indicated, decimal values of capacitance are in microfarads (μF); others are in picofarads (pF); resistances are in ohms; k=1,000, M=1,000,000. Unused Pins on U1 and U5 are not connected. nc=not connected.
● Indicates phasing.

Anatomy Of A Club Homebrew Project

A well-organized project can attract new members to your club, and entice old members to return to meetings. Here are some suggestions to help other clubs repeat the success of the 40-40:

• Identify Your Goals

Your organization probably has a central theme, whether it be Public Service, DXing or any of the many specialties that draw us together. By focusing on your needs and interests, your group can identify that perfect building project to serve as a focal point for boosting club camaraderie.

• Choose Wisely

A review of the literature will turn up candidate kit projects suited to your group's needs. The project's complexity, of course, hinges on the skill level of the membership and the availability of technical guidance. For the club lucky enough to boast an experienced builder, you might even consider "rolling your own." This will be especially true of the specialty groups (eg, ATV, VHF) who may be more construction-oriented to begin with.

• Seek the Guru

If you're going to develop your own project, you need a "Guru"! This doesn't imply a doctorate in engineering with a labful of gear, but your candidate should have a track record of successful homebrew work. This person understands the pitfalls inherent in designing an item that can be duplicated, not just once, but dozens of times! These folks aren't as rare as you might think—you might be surprised at the depth of experience among your club's ranks!

• The Project Leader

It's imperative to establish a key player to "pull it together." Unless your guru enjoys bringing an idea to production, this is a function distinct from the technical role. The project leader establishes and maintains a schedule, orders and receives parts, and enlists the aid of other necessary helpers.

A few words about scheduling: Much as we all dislike deadlines, once you've advertised a schedule for getting a project on the street, stick with it! The project leader needs to identify milestones early-on for such elements as completing tests, ordering parts and lining up help. Remember that Murphy doesn't take vacations, so allow extra time for parts orders to arrive!

• "Beta" Testing

Whether the project is a commercial kit or your own handiwork, you want to be assured that the kit goes together smoothly. You need to discover schematic errors or parts kitting shortages *before* your entire group warms up their soldering irons! You need one or more volunteers who build up the project solely from the furnished kit materials and instructions. If you have a "Guru," leave him out of this! He knows too much, and you're better off having people more representative of the average club member. This assures that the designer didn't overlook anything or leave crucial information out of the document package.

• The "Parts Team"

If you're purchasing a kit, this step is easy—send money to your chosen supplier and he sends you pre-packaged kits in return. You may expect the occasional missing, defective, or "I plugged it in backwards" parts problems to occur. If you're ordering in quantity, consider buying a spare from which to cannibalize parts. This avoids the inevitable delays involved in calling the supplier and waiting for replacements to arrive.

If it's your club's own brainchild, though, you've got a little more work ahead! The project leader needs several volunteers who can bag parts, reproduce and staple instruction sheets, etc. Once all the parts are in hand, the "kitting party" becomes part work and part social occasion. If your club is far-flung geographically, you may be able to find several willing members within reasonable driving distance to serve this function.

Allocate at least a half-day, preferably on a weekend, to get all the kitting done in one session. One suggestion: You don't want to be kitting parts while you're fatigued, so avoid late evenings. It takes a surprising amount of concentration to count out parts from their containers (we used cereal bowls). Interruptions should also be kept to a minimum—take the phone off the hook and turn off the H-Ts!

• Spreading the Word

Be sure to keep the membership apprised of the project's status. This helps maintain a high level of interest and anticipation in the outcome, and if snags arise, you may get additional help by keeping people informed. Your club's newsletter is the ideal vehicle for disseminating this information. The project leader should be working closely with the newsletter's editor to get the message across and to assure sufficient publicity. One other tip—when you're ready to release the project to the membership, make sure the point of contact for handling orders, collecting checks, etc is clearly identified. This should be one person, not a committee. Nothing beats confusion as a source of unnecessary work!

• Elmers

Every club has Elmers—experienced people willing to share their time and expertise with others. Make use of them! Provide your members with names of a couple of experienced hams who can answer questions and suggest troubleshooting tips if necessary. There's nothing like a "mentor" when you need assistance!

• Follow-Up

Put that new project to work! This step is critical to maintaining member interest and to ensure that the new gizmo doesn't sit unused on the back of the workbench! If appropriate to the project, your club might sponsor an operating event featuring the completed items. A "troubleshooting session" is also a good idea for local organizations. This lends members the impetus to give their work the "smoke test." And finally, follow up your club's results by publishing summaries in your newsletter. Don't forget to keep your ARRL Section Manager informed, so that your club's good name shares its rightful spot in the limelight!

---

nals to minimize the risk of overloading U1. U1 converts the RF input to the IF of 4.000 MHz and provides about 13 dB of gain. The L network (C12 and RFC1) following the mixer matches that stage's output impedance to the crystal filter's design value.

The crystal filter itself uses only two crystals instead of the usual four. This works well because of the choice of a low intermediate frequency. (The 8-MHz IF used for the 30-meter version is somewhat broader, but the result is still usable.) Loss through the filter is less than 2 dB, and with the component values shown, the –6 dB bandwidth is about 500 Hz. Despite the filter's low parts count, performance is adequate when combined with the AF section's selectivity. The unwanted sideband image is down about 45 dB at the audio chain's 800-Hz peak response frequency.

The filter output is terminated in a 470-Ω resistor at the input to U3, the product-detector stage. U3 converts the 4.0-MHz IF signal to audio and contributes another 13 dB of gain. BFO crystal Y3 has been selected to match the IF filter frequency, so there's no BFO frequency trimming needed. The 0.033-μF capacitor across pins 4 and 5 of U3 provides the first measure of audio low-pass filtering.

The two sections of U4 each provide roughly 30 dB of amplification. The first section is configured as a differential amplifier to make use of U3's differential output, and rolls off the audio response

Table 1

Parts List For The Transceivers

Designation (See Figure 2)	40-Meter Version	30-Meter Version
C1, C23, C26	8 to 70-pF, 6-mm trimmer	8 to 70 pF, 6-mm trimmer
C2	220 pF	150 pF
C3	47 pF	47 pF
C4	10 pF	10 pF
C5 to C7	0.0022 μF, 5% Polystyrene, radial lead	0.0047 μF, 5%, Polystyrene, radial lead
C8	2 to 27 pF (Digi-Key SG3004)	2 to 27 pF (Digi-Key SG3004)
C9	68 pF	150 pF
C10	10 pF	10 pF
C11	220 pF	220 pF
C12	47 pF	22 pF
C13	150 pF, 5%	270 pF, 5%
C14	150 pF, 5%	270 pF, 5%
C15	150 pF, 5%	270 pF, 5%
C16	68 pF	none (replace with jumper)
C17	47 pF	68 pF
C18	47 pF	150 pF, 5%
C19	47 pF	47 pF
C20	150 pF	220 pF
C21	10 pF	10 pF
C22	150 pF, 5%	150 pF, 5%
C24	5 pF	5 pF
C25	150 pF, 5%	150 pF, 5%
C27	47 pF	47 pF
C28	470 pF	330 pF
C29	0.001 μF	680 pF
C30	470 pF	330 pF
C31	68 pF	47 pF
L1	3.65 μH (27 t #22 on T-50-2 toroid)	3.65 μH (27 t #22 on T-50-2 toroid)
L2, L3	2.5 μH (25 t #26 on T-37-2 toroid)	1.2 μH (20 t #26 on T-37-6 toroid)
L4	10 μH (5 t #22 on FT-37-43 toroid)	7 μH (4 t #22 on FT-37-43 toroid)
L5,L6	1.0 μH (16 t on T-37-2 toroid)	0.68 μH (15 t #26 on T-37-6 toroid)
RFC1	22-μH epoxy RF choke	10-μH epoxy RF choke
RFC2	22-μH epoxy RF ckoke	4.7-μH epoxy RF choke
T1	Primary 16 t #26; secondary 4 t on FT-37-61 toroid	Primary, 11 t #26; secondary 6 t on FT-37-61 toroid
Y1 to Y4	4.000 MHz (see text)	8.000 MHz (see text)

(Remaining parts are identical for both bands)

D1	MV1662 Varicap diode
D2 to D9	1N4148 or 1N914
D10	7.5-V Zener, 0.5 W, 5% (1N5236 or equiv.)
D11	33-V Zener, 0.5 W, 5% (1N5257 or equiv.)
R1	100-kΩ linear-taper pot
R2	200-Ω Cermet trimmer pot (Digi-Key 36C22)
R3	5-kΩ linear-taper pot
Q1	2N5486 (2N5485 or MPF102 substitutes)
Q2, Q4, Q5	2N2222A metal
Q3	2N3906 or equivalent PNP GP Switch
Q6	2N3553 (MRF-237 substitute)
T2	4 bifilar turns on FT-37-43 toroid (use 3-inch piece of two-conductor ribbon cable)
U1, U3, U5	NE602A(N) Signetics mixer/oscillator IC
U2	78L08 voltage regulator IC
U4	NE5532

Notes

Small-value capacitors are 10% tolerance ceramic disc, unless otherwise noted.
Decoupling capacitors are ±20% ceramic or monolithic types.
Electrolytic capacitors are minimum 16 V dc.
All resistors are 1/4-W, 5% tolerance.

---

above 1.5 kHz. Diodes D2 and D3 limit the audio swing during transmitter key-down to reasonable values. Without these diodes, this stage saturates and upsets the operation of the FET switch section that follows.

The AF mute function is the familiar series-FET switch popularized by W7EL.[3] Despite its relative simplicity, it's hard to beat this circuit for click-free audio switch-ing. In the key-up condition the FET is zero-biased and acts like a resistance of several hundred ohms. In the key-down condition the FET is in cutoff (because the gate is now 7 to 8 V below the source) and acts like an open-circuit, preventing audio from getting to U4B, the audio final stage. The 4.7-MΩ resistor across the FET serves to "leak" a sample of the received signal

during key-down, and thus provides a built-in sidetone.

The audio final stage is configured as a bandpass filter centered at 800 Hz. The high gain of the two NE5532 stages allows a design with no IF amplifier stage. The audio output level is adequate to drive head-phones, but it won't cut the mustard for loud-speaker applications. The AF-output stage is internally overcurrent limited on loud signals, to provide ready-made ear protection. (In this respect, it accomplishes what you'd want an AGC for anyway.) If you're interested in saving a few milliamperes on receive, either TL072 or an MC1458 may be substituted, although at reduced maximum AF output levels. Use good quality low-impedance headphones for best results. Walkman headphones are fine, but remember—you get what you pay for. The $3 cheap imitations are distinctly inferior!

Diodes D5 through D8 and associated components provide full break-in (QSK), to eliminate the annoyance of a switching relay. This "bridge" circuit presents a low resistance to small signals (in the receive mode), yet limits the receiver input voltage swing during key-down to several volts peak-to-peak.

The local oscillator uses the familiar Colpitts configuration. Polystyrene capacitors aren't the usual candidate of choice when used alone in a VFO design, but I used them here because they're compact and available in 5%-tolerance values. The resulting temperature stability is more than adequate at 3 MHz. Coverage is about 40 kHz on 40 meters and 25 to 30 kHz on 30 meters. Both transceivers cover the parts of the subbands most used by QRPers, and allow use of a single-turn tuning pot. If you want broader frequency coverage, the value of C9 may be increased. Use NP0 or silver-mica capacitors if you experiment with this circuit. The design uses a varicap tuning diode for tuning. While a smooth ball-bearing tuning capacitor and vernier reduction drive are the preferred approach, that choice drives up the cost and mechanical complexity of a transceiver considerably.

The transmitter portion of this design consists of mixer/oscillator U5, driver stages Q4 and Q5, and the power amplifier (PA) stage, Q6. The output power is about 1.5 W and a drive control (R2) at the emitter of Q5 sets the output level. The L-C components between U5 and Q4 form a bandpass filter that serves to filter the relatively complex waveform at U5's output into a clean sine wave.

Performance Summary

Testing conducted in the ARRL Lab confirmed that this design met FCC requirements for transmitter spectral purity. All harmonics were down more than 34 dB from the carrier for the 40-meter version and 32 dB for the 30-meter version. Spurious outputs were down at least 35 dB. While additional filtering would improve the characteristics, these values meet present FCC requirements. Transmitted-waveform rise and fall times are 1 to 2 milliseconds. The receiver performance was also evaluated. The two-tone dynamic range (90 dB) and blocking dynamic range (115 dB) are fine for a receiver of this simplicity.

Construction

Table 1 lists parts for both versions of the transceiver. A few tips on constructing this project are in order. Although a printed-circuit board is available, there's nothing to prevent you from duplicating this design using "dead-bug" or "ugly" construction. Remember to keep all leads and connections short and direct if you're employing this approach.

Soldering

Use a small (25-W) iron (such as a Radio Shack 64-2070) and keep the tip clean. Use a moistened sponge or paper towel to clean the tip periodically as you work. Apply only as much heat as is needed to get a good joint. The use of a high-wattage soldering gun is not recommended, as it will tend to lift traces off the board.

Unsoldering

Sooner or later, you're going to need to remove a part installed in the wrong location, or perhaps pull a part for troubleshooting purposes. There's an easy way: get yourself a roll of desoldering braid (Radio Shack 64-2090B). Lay the end of the braid down on the joint to be cleaned and press the soldering iron tip over the braid. Within a second or so, you'll see the braid begin to wick up solder from the joint. Remove the braid and reapply a new section as needed until the joint is clean. This is good stuff—with care, it's possible to remove ICs from the board without damaging them.

Checking Your Work

Get into the habit of checking your work each time you put down the soldering iron. It's much easier and ultimately less frustrating to find solder bridges sooner rather than later.

If you're rolling your own version of this transceiver from scratch, select the crystals (Y1 through Y4) for identical frequency characteristics. The design makes uses of readily available microprocessor crystals to keep the cost low. A batch of 8 to 10 of these should yield four crystals that oscillate within 50 to 100 Hz of each other, and the most closely grouped crystals are the ones you want! A "what-have-you" test oscillator may be kluged up on a scrap of circuit-board material. Its characteristics are noncritical, as you're interested in frequency consistency rather than absolute accuracy. A frequency counter or main-station receiver is used to perform this grading "by the numbers" or "by ear," respectively. Incidentally, the choice of 4.000 MHz as the 40-meter IF yields a strong "birdy" at 7.000 MHz. If your plans include

the use of the extreme low end of the band, 4.032-MHz crystals are a better choice.

Alignment

Alignment of this little rig is a piece of cake. For test equipment, you'll need a main-station rig and SWR meter or wattmeter. Here's how:

Receiver

• Double-check your power supply polarity *before* you apply power!

• Apply dc power and connect a pair of headphones to the receiver AF output.

• Set tuning pot R1 to full counterclockwise (0 V on R1's center terminal). Using your main-station rig (at minimum power into a dummy load, please!), transmit a string of dots at the frequency you desire for the low end of your band coverage. Adjust trimmer cap C8 until you hear your main-station rig's transmitted signal. You may need to remove a turn from L1 to get the tuning range up into the 40-meter band. If the band coverage is too high in frequency, squeeze the turns on L1 together to reduce the operating frequency.

• Connect a matched antenna. Using a *nonmetallic* tuning tool, peak C1 for maximum signal (or noise). If you don't have one of these tools, you can make one from a narrow strip of PC board material with the tip filed down to fit the slot in the tuning cap. The use of an insulated tool is important because body capacity will make adjustment difficult otherwise. Once this step is complete, background noise will be noticeably higher with an antenna connected than without.

Transmitter

• Set drive adjustment pot R2 to its full counterclockwise position.

• Add a clip lead to the case (collector) of Q5 to serve as a short antenna. (Leave the other end of the clip lead unconnected.) Ground the "key" input and tune in your transmitted signal on your "big rig" receiver. Adjust trimmers C23 and C26 for maximum indicated signal on your receiver's S-meter. The capacitors will be somewhat interactive, so alternate between the two as you tune for maximum output.

Remove the clip lead. Connect the RF output to a wattmeter. If you lack this luxury, you can use your SWR meter in the **FORWARD** position, connected to a dummy load. Adjust R2 as needed for 1.5 W keydown power into a dummy load or the test circuit. More is *not* better—you'll coax a little more power out at the expense of efficiency!

That's it! You're on the air. Feedback to date from other builders has been highly favorable. You might be surprised at what you can work on either 40 or 30 meters with only a watt or two. I've had the pleasure of ragchewing with stations from all over the US and have worked about a half-dozen European countries with the 40-meter version alone.

Acknowledgements

Special thanks are in order to Jim Fitton, W1FMR, for his guidance; to Paul Kranz, W1CFI; Wayne Burdick, N6KR; and others for design suggestions and other support. This rig was first described in the April 1994 issue of *72*, the newsletter of the New England QRP Club.

Notes
[1] D. DeMaw, "A Four-Stage 75-Meter SSB Superhet," *QST*, May 1989, pp 25-28.
[2] Kits of parts for the 40-40 and 30-40 are available for $50 postpaid from Small Wonder Labs, 80 East Robbins Ave, Newington, CT 06111.

Be sure to specify either the 40 or 30-meter version. Includes selected crystals, all onboard parts, wire for toroids and manual. Allow three weeks for delivery. (The ARRL and *QST* in no way warrant this offer.)

Circuit boards (only) for this project are available for $6 (plus $1.50 postage) from FAR Circuits, 18N640 Field Ct, Dundee, IL 60118.

Dan's Small Parts and Kits (1935 S 3rd West No. 1, Missoula, MT 59801) carries many of the parts needed for this project. Remaining items may be obtained from Jameco, Mouser Electronics, and Digi-Key Corp. See the List of Suppliers in the ARRL *Handbook* for more information.
[3] R. Llewellyn, "An Optimized QRP Transceiver for 7 MHz," *QST*, Aug 1980, pp 14-19 (an updated version of this project appears in the 1994 ARRL *Handbook*). **QST-**

By Mitchell Lee, KB6FPW, and Dennis Monticelli, AE6C

Revisiting the 40-40

T hose of you who might have passed over the 40-40 QRP article by Dave Benson, NN1G, in November 1994 *QST*, missed a good thing. This little CW rig is well designed, features a stable, varactor tuned VFO, 1-W 2N3553 output stage, QSK, true sidetone, single conversion and crystal IF filter. If you order the kit, be advised it all fits on a high quality 3×4-inch circuit board. The rig uses the same VFO for both receive and transmit, and is based on three NE602 oscillator/mixers. It is essentially equivalent to the popular NorCal 40, but the spectral purity problems associated with that rig's transmitter have been eliminated. The 40-40 schematic and block diagram are reproduced in **Figs 1 and 2**.

Make no mistake: this rig is not a "one of a kind" circuit hack; it is very cleverly and carefully designed, reproducible and highly tolerant of component substitutions. It lends itself to mass ordering of parts for club or school group projects, and is available in kit form for the reasonable price of only $50 for the solo homebrewer.

KB6FPW and AE6C, experienced homebrewers with engineering backgrounds, each constructed a 40-40, but took their projects one step further by making a number of simple modifications and component changes that greatly enhance the performance of the 40-40. If you built, or are contemplating building a 40-40, you're undoubtedly going to want to add these modifications.

KB6FPW built the 40-40 kit and also rolled his own 20-m version, while AE6C opted for a bare circuit board and scrounged his own parts. Let's eavesdrop as they discuss their approach to their projects.

AE6C: Having been a homebrewer and QRPer since my Novice days with a 1-W rock-bound 6AG7 rig, I religiously read every QRP project that passes through *QST*. I learn a little something from each one, but the 40-40 really caught my eye. This diminutive superhet delivered the three S's (sensitivity, selectivity and stability), while being small, low in current consumption and easy to reproduce. I know from experience that doing all this isn't easy. Inasmuch as I felt I could scrounge up just about all the parts locally, I couldn't resist sending for the board this past December. By Christmas I had collected the parts (with liberal substitutions) and got the receiver up and running. And what a nice little re-

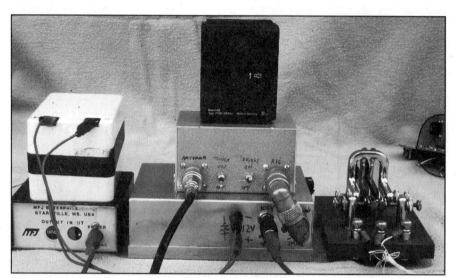

KB6FPW: The most interesting part of any station setup is the rear. Pictured here is the 40-40 hooked up to the SWR bridge/Transmatch, Curtis keyer, 12-V gelcell, and 40-m dipole. Note the UHF U-turn connecting the rig to the SWR bridge/Transmatch. Topping the stack is a Braun travel clock.

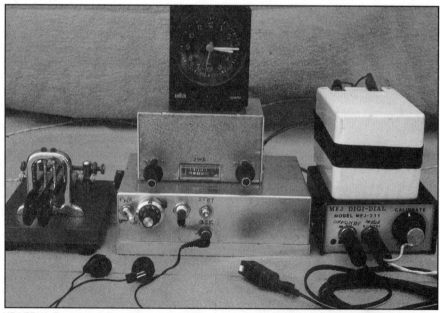

KB6FPW: Reversing the view, we see the user controls for the rig and Transmatch. Earbuds are connected and ready to go, as well as the remote microswitch hand key.

ceiver it was! Dave Benson, NN1G, did a fine job.

The tuning was smooth and the reception single-signal; a real treat for die-hard direct-conversion fans. Sensitivity was decent and selectivity surprisingly good. Sta-

bility was better than I expected from varactor tuning. I played around with it each evening for about a week and it was a delight to operate. Naturally, I couldn't help boasting about the rig during my regular sked with KB6FPW (Mitchell Lee)

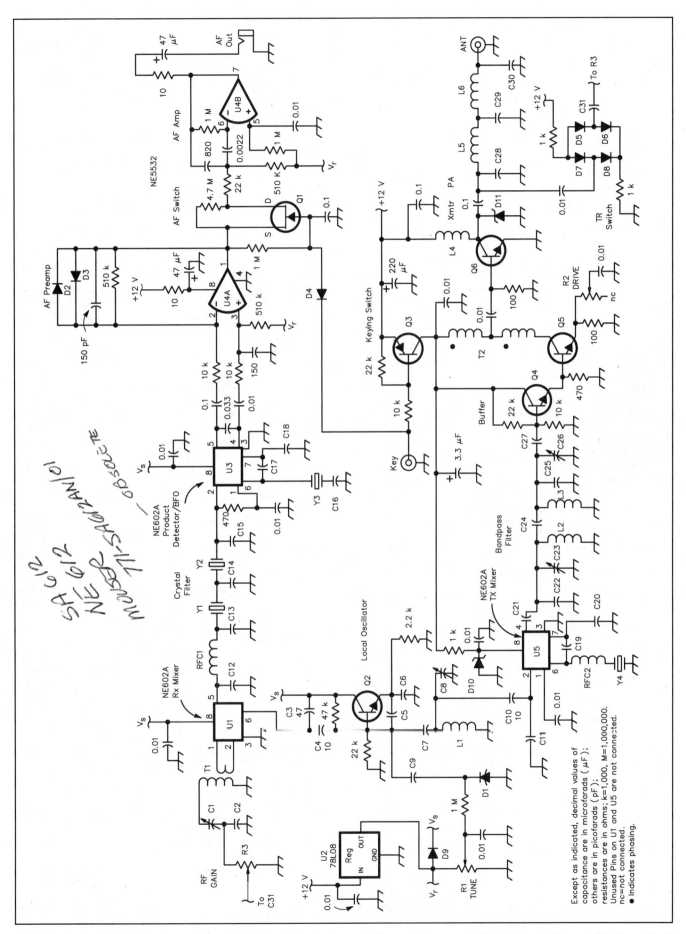

Fig 1—This is the 40-40. You'll want to refer to this schematic as you read along in the text. A 30-m design is discussed in the original article printed in November 1994 *QST*.

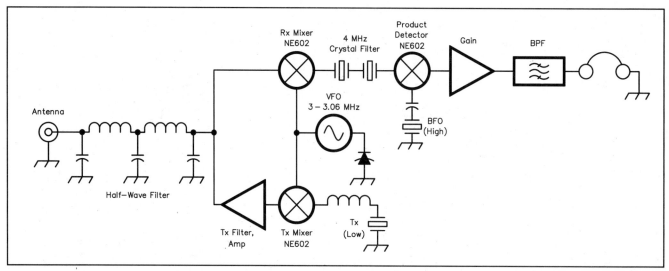

Fig 2—KB6FPW: The 40-40's elegant design is most evident in its block diagram. A single VFO, tuned by a varactor, is used to mix incoming signals to a 4-MHz IF, as well as mix a 4-MHz transmitter IF up to 40 m. BFO and TX LO offsets are obtained by reactively pulling their respective 4-MHz crystals.

and N6CNY (Pete Murphy) Saturday morning. Despite the fact that the transmitter section wasn't yet operational, I succeeded in spreading the infection to my friends. I later traced the transmitter problem to an open driver emitter-bypass capacitor and fixed it easily.

KB6FPW: It was late January when I caught up with AE6C on 80 m. He and Pete, N6CNY, were discussing a QRP rig. I jumped into the QSO in progress and discovered that they were talking about the 40-40 rig described on page 37 of the November 1994 issue of *QST*. AE6C said it was a really great QRP rig. He had ordered a bare board, and now had his receiver going. N6CNY, infected the previous Saturday, ordered the complete kit, but it had not yet arrived.

My recollection of the November 1994 issue was that it was full of construction articles, and I remembered thinking, "This is a good issue, and these are good construction articles." An ATV rig, a great remote-tuned coaxial capacitor and two QRP rigs, all in one issue. I like to see homebrew articles in *QST*, and I like to see how other people design circuits and solve problems. The only downside to the November 1994 issue was our dismal FD showing—the result of our contest software scrambling our 1100+ contacts as it wrote them to the floppy drive. Listening to AE6C's sales pitch, I pulled out the November 1994 *QST*.

I've seen all of these QRP rigs. They either have crummy direct conversion receivers, or drifty VFOs, or they are crystal controlled, or they need special tuning capacitors making them impossible to reproduce. Plus I'm an electrical engineer, and I'm hard to please. The 40-40 would be like all of the others: hum, chirp, clicks, drift, images, coils you couldn't reproduce and RX bandwidth as wide as a barn. AE6C

would use the rig once and then lay it to rest on a shelf in his shack closet.

I studied the schematic and read the text while AE6C shared his thoughts about the rig. I wasted the rest of the day analyzing the circuit, and even running a few *SPICE* simulations of the audio and RF filters. By nightfall I was sold. My order for a complete 40-m kit was in the mail two days later. At the same time I ordered a bare board from FAR Circuits; my kit arrived, was assembled, installed in a box and making QSOs before the bare board showed up. The bare board was held in reserve for a 20-m version. I beat N6CNY and AE6C to putting a 40-40 on the air, even though they had their stuff way before I had mine.

Kit vs Bare Board

KB6FPW: I'm not sure where to start, but since AE6C scrounged for junk box components, I'll cover the 40-40 kit itself (called SW-40 in the kit's assembly manual). I ordered the complete kit because I don't have time to look for all of the parts. (It took me an hour just to select a suitable box and buy a few odds and ends.) Another thing is that most circuit boards are laid out for specific components, often with unique dimensions. Kits contain parts which fit all of the holes properly. And besides, I'd rather be building than shopping. It took about eight days round trip to NN1G to receive my kit. That's fast.

AE6C: I thought I was smart by just ordering the board and scrounging parts, but I think Mitch made the better choice. While I got off pretty cheap and had the satisfaction of doing more homebrewing, it took more time and a little frustration along the way. The FAR Circuits board [identical to the kit's PCB layout] is laid out and drilled for miniature parts of a certain size. The 40-40 is small partly because of this choice of parts and also because it is tightly

packed. Thank goodness I had a deep junk box and ready access to three local surplus stores here in Silicon Valley. Even then, I had to freely substitute in order to populate the board. If you order the correct miniature parts by mail, you will suffer less, but then I doubt you will save much money and you will certainly consume more time. But those of you who prefer to "roll your own" will want to read the rest of this article.

KB6FPW: The board is small (3×4 inches) and the components are packed, making substitutions and maintenance difficult. However, I appreciate the small size. NN1G did an excellent job in layout and compressing the board. Now how about a surface mount version? There isn't anything on that board that can't be found in surface mount, even the crystals, coils and trimmers. The board would be half as big, or less.

Back to the 40-40 kit for a moment... It is well documented, and much of the construction hints are as shown in *QST*. Everything board mounted is included; this means you supply your own gain and tuning pots, key jack, power connector, phone jack, on/off switch, RF connector, wire to hook up all aforementioned items and a box. All of the circuit board stuff is taken care of, even crystals, toroids, wire to wind the toroids, trimmers, transistors and ICs—all the hard stuff—as well as all Rs and Cs. The manual had one or two discrepancies relative to the circuit-board silk screen, but no show-stoppers.

The biggest drawback to kit assembly was the lack of designators for the majority of components. This makes stuffing a matter of filling holes until the components are gone, or until the holes are filled, whichever comes first. The kit assembly instructions don't say "put R1 in holes 1 and 2," but rather "stuff all of the Rs and Cs into the circuit board." If you aren't good at reading schematics and tracing circuit boards, you may find this kit a bit frustrating, but it's worth it. Find an experienced helper to lend you a hand.

AE6C: The lack of component designators is a major problem for homebrewers stuffing the FAR Circuits board. When scrounging components it will be easiest if you make a photocopy of the circuit, label all of the components and make up your own parts list.

Another problem for those bypassing the 40-40 kit is that the stuffing diagram doesn't clearly show the position of the component holes, but rather the position of the component bodies. In addition, the FAR Circuits board has no silk screen or solder mask. This increases the difficulty in correlating schematic to circuit board since you can't clearly determine what pins and leads hook up to which traces—it takes schematic, stuffing diagram, circuit board and parts list all at once to keep things straight. You'll have to do a lot of circuit and schematic tracing and cross-checking to figure out what goes where, and it could be confusing for an inexperienced kit-builder.

KB6FPW: I built my own 20-m "20-40" on a FAR Circuits board and experienced some of these problems, but for me it was more of a nuisance factor than a show-stopper. (See **Fig 3**.) Writing up your own parts list using the original *QST* article as a starting point should be helpful, rather than doing it from memory like I did. Patient hams could even mark the PCB with a felt-tip pen prior to starting construction to facilitate stuffing.

AE6C: When scrounging parts it is important to be able to match each component shown on the schematic to a unique location on the board, so you can find ones that fit exactly and that have the correct electrical characteristics. Let's just say that after buying parts for and stuffing my FAR Circuits board, I was very familiar with the PC layout and the schematic.

FAR Circuits provides a good service to homebrewers by offering a comprehensive catalog of project boards at reasonable prices. But anything more than a simple project requires experience to be successful. And you don't get many chances to rectify mistakes either as the traces have a tendency to lift, even with careful application of soldering heat.

KB6FPW: Free of the parts-scrounging process, it took me only two nights to build the 40-40 kit. I wound the toroids and installed a few items one night (two hours), and finished construction the next night (three hours?), skipping the part that said "before applying power check the following..." That's for sissies. I jammed in 12 V, put it on the air, and immediately contacted NA5N/QRP, in Socorro, New Mexico. I gave his 4-W MFJ rig a 599; he gave my sub-320 mW output a 459 (I thought I was running a watt). I spent a Saturday afternoon picking up a suitable box, various bits

Fig 3—KB6FPW: Here is the 20-m version I built, prior to packaging. Note that toroids smaller than those specified for the 40-40 are used.

and pieces, drilling holes and installing the stuffed board. I was done.

Alignment

KB6FPW: There are three sections to be aligned: VFO, driver band-pass filter and receiver input. I had no problems making these adjustments, and used no test gear, aside from a second receiver with S-meter.

As for the VFO, my initial tuning range was from 7020 to 7053 with C8 almost fully meshed. I set this by monitoring 7020 in a second receiver, and keying the 40-40 into a dummy load with the tuning pot set to the lowest frequency. Then I adjusted C8 until I was on 7020.

Driver band-pass filter tuning is peaky—maybe too peaky. But after 85+ QSOs and several business and backpack trips, it still doesn't need an alignment. I peaked the filter while watching my second receiver's S-meter. You could also watch the output power with an SWR meter (if you have a sensitive one), or build a simple detector (see the 40-40 construction manual), or monitor the input current to the final.

Receiver alignment is a no-brainer: adjust for maximum received signal somewhere in the middle of the tuning range.

Hot Transistors:

KB6FPW: When aligning the transmitter, use caution because driver Q5 gets warm. Some copper or brass shim stock could be soldered to the transistor can for a heat sink. Under normal QSO conditions, the temperature rise will be only slight and is nothing to be concerned about. Q6 doesn't get hot when correctly loaded. I did add a small press-on heat-sink to Q6—maybe I'm superstitious; I happened to have one that fit nicely.

Component Substitutions

KB6FPW: Although I built the 40-40 and operated the stock version for a short time without modification, I compiled a list of changes I wanted to make. Some are

component substitutions, others are slight design changes.

AE6C: Since I built mine from scratch with scrounged components, I tended to anticipate and make changes during initial construction.

Capacitors:

KB6FPW: The 10-nF ceramic disc capacitors in the kit had 0.25-inch lead spacing, but the holes were spaced 0.2 inch. The instructions suggested breaking away the excess ceramic and narrowing the spacing; I opted to use some 0.2-inch spaced units I had in my junk box. All other kit components fit like a glove. No holes too big; none too small. Very professional job, and very high-quality circuit board complete with solder mask and silk screen.

AE6C: The only problem I had here was with size. Half the time, the cap I wanted to use was either too big for the holes or the space allocated on the board. So I would either find another part or get creative in mounting it. Fortunately, the values are relatively common and the types well known. Don't mix types unless you really know what you're doing. For example, the disc ceramics are best for RF bypass and remember to use the NP0 variety around the VFO. I stuck with Polystyrene where recommended in the VFO. You can use silver mica there if you wish, but the holes aren't set up for that style cap.

KB6FPW: I just couldn't bear to pass audio signals through ceramic capacitors, so I replaced the 10 and 100-nF caps feeding U4A with films, and I did the same for the 820 pF (actually I put in a SM) and 2.2-nF caps in the U4B audio filter. I substituted a few films elsewhere for better bypassing, where it made sense. RF stuff is best bypassed by ceramic. This I learned the hard way. . . see my comments on the transmitter stage.

AE6C: I also sought out the better quality ceramics for the PA harmonic filter. The trimmers gave me some trouble but only because of the space constraint. Don't be afraid to use slightly different values here. I used some nice surplus trimmers at C1 and C8 that were 15-60 pF and 8-26 pF, respectively. For C23 and C26 I used a couple of tiny Radio Shack 5-60 pF trimmers from my junk box that unfortunately are no longer carried by that chain. Like Mitch, my instincts told me not to use a ceramic for the 820 pF in the audio active filter. I too stuck in a silver mica instead.

KB6FPW: I used silver mica capacitors on my 20-m version for the output filter. It is possible to find half-sized silver mica capacitors in the surplus stores which have very thin leads—sort of like a Polystyrene in that regard—and these fit nicely into the 40-40 circuit board.

Main Bypass Capacitor:

KB6FPW: The day after I stuffed the board, I was sitting at my bench at work and spied a slightly used Sanyo OS-Con capacitor. I wasn't very satisfied with the low-quality 220-µF electrolytic bypass cap supplied in the kit, so I put in that OS-Con instead. These are hard to find, but a Panasonic HF or HFQ-series cap would be a better choice than the kit's no-name electrolytic—especially in cold weather.

Inductors:

AE6C: I have a reasonable supply of cores in the junk box, but I sure struck out for this project. Being too impatient to or-der them and not finding them available locally, I decided to design my own. In all cases they turned out just fine. Here is what I did.

L1, VFO Coil: Fortunately, I had a T50-2 so I used 25 turns for the inductance I needed [original design calls for 27 turns]. You can substitute a mix 6 (yellow), but you will need to use more than a single layer of wire.

L2 and L3, Driver Filter: I had no T37s, and since you have to use something smaller than a T50 here, I designed with my stash of T30-6. 26 turns of #28 gave me the desired inductance of 2.5 µH.

L4, Collector Choke: Just my luck to be almost all out of ferrite going into this project. Instead of a T37-43, I used 47 turns of #28 (single layer) on a T50-10. This gave me only 7 µH instead of 10 µH, but my calculations showed that this would be ad-equate for the impedance at that node. Any-thing more on that toroid would risk high frequency self-resonance behavior. Pow-dered iron was a bit of a force fit here, but it worked out just fine.

L5 and L6, Output Pi Filter: I made use of those T30-6s again by winding 17 turns of #28 on them to make the required 1 µH for the output filters. My calculations showed that the smaller cores were in no danger of saturating under worst case load conditions.

T1, Tuned Receiver Input Transformer: Another case of applying powdered iron where ferrite was called out. However, this was a narrow-band application (the input fil-ter), so I felt good about using a T50-2 here. Fortunately the board could handle the extra room. 48 turns on the primary and 12 turns on the secondary, both #28, did the trick.

KB6FPW: In spite of the Secret Knowl-edge (see the **sidebar** entitled "Secret Tor-oid Knowledge Revealed"), winding the toroids is one of the most time-consuming chores. The kit includes not only the cores, but also the wire. The instructions say to scrape away the insulation of the enameled wire. As I was scraping the wire, wishing they had instead supplied Polythermalese or Solderese-insulated wire, I absentmind-edly picked up my soldering iron and balled up some solder on the end of the wire. To my amazement and delight, the insulation retracted—it was directly solderable wire after all! This made the job much easier and saved me a lot of time.

The toroids supplied with the 40-40 kit were oversized for the power levels in-volved, so for the 20-m version, I pulled much smaller units from my junk box, scal-ing the inductances and number of turns to compensate for frequency and differences in A_L.

Back to the 40-40 kit: Some of the coils and some capacitors end up a little on the floppy side, given the size of the parts rela-tive to the wires holding them down. A small bit of paraffin can be melted and dripped over any loose components to help secure them to the board. Superglue or RTV works

---

Secret Toroid Knowledge Revealed

KB6FPW: If you work in the electronics industry, and work anywhere near toroids, then you have undoubtedly been "inducted" into the Secret Circle of Toroid Winding Knowledge Keepers. But for the rest of the plebiscite, I will now reveal this secret knowledge, breaking the vows that have for so long bound me to silence.

Winding a toroid can be done two ways: the right way, and the wrong way. With the exception of those in the Secret Circle, everyone winds toroids the wrong way. Winding is accomplished by first passing an appropriate length of wire through the center of the toroid, thereby forming turn 1. Next, one end of the wire is passed through the toroid to form turn 2. This process continues for turns 3, 4, 5 and so on, until the appropriate number of turns have been wound. Un-fortunately, the Uninformed Technique causes the wire to kink, and causes much frustration and cramping of the hands.

The Right Way is as follows (refer to **Fig A**):

a) pass the appropriate length of wire through the toroid.

b) bend the wire tightly around the toroid so the ends point in opposite direc-tions, forming the first turn.

c) pass the Secret Tool (a bent piece of heavy-gauge wire or paper clip) through the toroid, and hook the wire.

d) pull the wire back through the toroid.

e) using either the hook or you finger, pull the wire all the way through the toroid, and pull now-complete turn 2 tight.

f) return to step (c) for turn 3.

Using this technique of "backing" the wire through the toroid, rather than passing the end of the wire through the toroid, prevents kinks and frustration. This is the way electronics professionals in the industry hand-wind toroids in the lab.

The process can be sped up by clamping about a third of the toroid in a soft-jaw (wood or plastic) vise, and using one hand to operate the tool and the other to handle the wire. An experienced winder can apply about one turn every two or three seconds using this method.

By the way, the Secret Tool is simply a hook made out of 12, 14, 16 or 18-gauge wire (depending on the size of the toroid and the size of the wire you're pulling), long enough to hold onto, and bent to a radius tight enough to pass through the toroid. Paper clips work, too.—*KB6FPW*

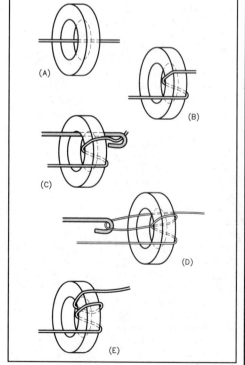

Fig A—KB6FPW: (A) Pass wire through toroid; (B) wrap turns around in opposite directions. (C) pass Secret Tool through toroid and hook wire. (D) Pull Tool and wire back through toroid. (E) Pull wire clear through, and wrap back around toroid.

Table 1
Performance Summary

Receiver	AE6C	KB6FPW
Tuning Range:	70 kHz	63 kHz
Sensitivity:	0.26 µV	0.31 µV (10 dB (S+N)/N)
Gain:	89.5 dB	89.0 dB (into 80-ohm headphones)
Image Rejection:	53.3 dB	46.1 dB

Note: The image falls within the AM broadcast band (950 kHz in the case of a 4.000 MHz IF and 7.050 kHz receive frequency), so an input filter or trap may be necessary if you live close to broadcasters.

Selectivity	340 Hz	360 Hz (–3 dB points; combined IF plus AF response)
Unwanted Sideband	–48.5 dB	–44 dB
Stability	–360 Hz	–13 Hz (for 30 minutes, following a 10 minute warm-up)
Supply Current	6.5 mA	6.3 mA
	(9.5 mA with 78L08)	

Transmitter		
Power Output	1.2 W	1.0 W
Supply Current	215 mA	260 mA

too, but these methods are a little more permanent. Whatever method you choose, take care to keep the substance out of the IC sockets and well away from variable capacitors.

Crystals:

AE6C: I thought the use of four matched crystals in this design was really clever. Small microprocessor crystals in the HF range are commonplace and readily available surplus. I took my Kenwood Dip Meter (it has a socket for exciting a crystal) and a portable shortwave receiver to the local surplus store. Within 10 minutes I had matched a little pile of 3.932-MHz rocks to within 50 Hz. You can't beat that for 50 cents each.

KB6FPW: The kit included matched crystals, so I had no work to do here. Note that offsets for the BFO and transmitter LO are provided by a capacitor and inductor. In my assembled kit, the BFO offset was centered right down the middle of the IF passband and the transmitter LO offset was frighteningly symmetrical. When I built my 20-m version, I thought I'd get smart and find two matched crystals for the IF, and use high and low crystals for the BFO and transmitter LO. This was a mistake. I had to play with the components of both crystal oscillators to get proper alignment.

Transistors:

AE6C: This design is pretty tolerant except for the PA [treated in the next section]. I used 2N5669 for the audio switch Q1; 2N2222A TO-18 cans for Q2, 4 and 5 (VFO and drivers); and a 2N4403 for the transmit switch Q3.

KB6FPW: Except for the final, I made no substitutions for the transistors in either my 40-40 kit or my 20-m version.

Transmitter Stage Comments and Modifications:

AE6C: Lacking the 2N3553 called out, I first tried an MRF475 left over from my 40-m Cubic Incher project (July 1982 *QST*). That device was designed for CB service so it's rugged and beefy enough for 4 W output. But being a relatively large chip, it turned out that a simple class A driver wasn't enough to excite it. So I then dropped down to the smaller commonplace 2N3866.

The 2N3866 worked out okay, but I kind of got interested in the experimentation game and started plugging in all kinds of transistors (by this time I had gravitated to a socket on the board). It turned out that the best junk-box transistor I found was a TO-18 style device that was originally designed for core memory driving. It had lots of breakdown (translation: tough to destroy with high SWR), and was capable of relatively fast switching. Low saturation (0.5 V) was possible up to 0.5 A and drive needs were modest. This transistor comes under several part numbers such as 2N4014 and 2N3725. But it may be as hard to find today as the core memory it used to drive. Mitch did a more thorough search for a good PA and has a better recommendation.

KB6FPW: I initially had my R2 throttled all the way back, because this resulted in about 100-125 mA transmit current—just right for a pack of eight AA alkaline cells. Later I decided it was worth turning up to 160-170 mA, which I thought put out about 1 W. I was wrong. The figure is closer to 330 mA for 1 W output from a 2N3553 operating on a 12-V supply. This was not portable-friendly.

Transmitting efficiency was poor, but the final transistor wasn't getting particularly warm. I surmised that it took a lot of drive power to reach 1 W.

Like Denny, I too conducted a transistor bake-off. I tried the 2N5108 (315 mA for 900 mW—couldn't reach 1 W with 12.0 V supply); Denny's core memory driver—he sent me a sample—(280 mA for 1 W); a 2N3866 (same basic results as the 2N5108); and finally a 2N3924 (260 mA for 1 W output). Of course not all of the supply current actually reaches the final, but this is still a valid means of comparing final transistors. By the way, the circuit board supplied with the kit survived all of

my soldering and de-soldering intact without resorting to a socket.

You'll notice Denny gets more output for less current with his 40-40, as shown in **Table 1**. The difference is in the driver (I ran stock bias; Denny reduced his), QSK (in transmit some power is lost in the QSK switch, and Denny eliminated his altogether), and supply voltage (my 40-40 has a diode in series with an external supply used for the power output test). The important thing is that all transistors were tested under the same conditions.

So what's wrong with the 2N3553 used in the original design? The problem, I discovered, is that the 2N3553 is designed for 28-V service. As a result, the transistor has an unnecessarily high breakdown voltage at the expense of collector resistance, resulting in poor performance on 12-V supplies. I spent some time looking at an old edition of the Motorola *RF Device Databook* before finding the 2N3924 and deciding to give it a try. All of the favorites, such as the 2N3866 and 2N3553, are designed for 24-28 V supplies, where higher collector resistance has only a minor impact on efficiency in Class C service. At 12 V collector resistance is critical.

Finding a 2N3924 posed a problem, however, as Motorola has obsoleted most of the RF transistors in the 1-10 W class, retaining only a couple of dice in eight-pin surface mount packages—unusable at full power. Put another way, Motorola's two-volume *RF Databook* set has been reduced to one volume in the latest edition. The 2N3924 was available in March 1995 through Richardson Electronics from a mystery manufacturer. Although the packaging quality isn't up to Motorola standards, mine won the 40-40 efficiency bake-off as expected. It beat AE6C's core memory driver by a percentage point.

By the way, if you have a personal affection for any of the old favorites such as the 2N5160 (the world's fastest power PNP and complement to the 2N3866 NPN), MRF475, MRF476, MRF479, MRF237, 2N5108, 2N5179, 2N3866, 2N3553 or any RF transistor sold in a TO-5/18/39/72/99 or other metal can package, or if you have any projects or equipment containing these devices, you'd better buy now, because they are as obsolete as the 807. Purchasing activity in March 1995 was brisk on these devices; I called perhaps eight major distributors before locating anyone who could quote 2N3866s, 2N3553s and 2N3924s. Unfortunately, I was too late for 2N5160 PNPs. Boy, there are going to be a lot of function generator owners out there with scrap to sell if they blow their output stages!

One last thing I did was add a back-biased 1N4148 across the base-emitter junction of my final transistor (it fit nicely on the copper side of the board). This precludes exceeding the emitter-base breakdown rating of 3 V under conditions of high drive. It makes less than a 1 percentage point dent in

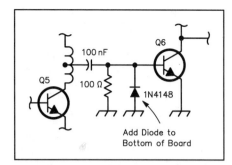

Fig 4—KB6FPW: A protection diode isn't a bad idea for the final, especially for those transistors with 3 V_{ebo} maximums.

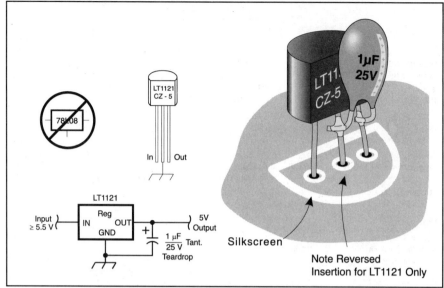

Fig 5—KB6FPW: Save and extend battery life two ways; with reduced operating current and lower dropout. The LT1121, if used, must be inserted opposite to the keyed package outline of the silkscreen. Note the difference in pinouts. Also, a 1-μF tantalum teardrop should be added to the regulator, either on the bottom of the board or as I did, directly to the leads.

the transmitter's efficiency. See **Fig 4**.

As an aside, when I adjusted my output power, I noticed a slight hysteretic effect in the control pot at the highest output levels. I wasn't sure what caused it, but I eventually traced it to poor bypassing on V+, in and around Q6. I had substituted a Mylar unit for the input bypass cap on the voltage regulator. That's good for the regulator but bad for the final. (Here's an example of where component designators would have saved me some time, because I would have paid more attention to the physical location of the capacitor, instead of just trying to find its location.) I added a 10-nF disc ceramic under the electrolytic power supply bypass capacitor, eliminating this effect.

QSK:

KB6FPW: The first time I keyed the rig (using a Super CMOS Keyer II) I thought, "Hey, this isn't QSK; I've got an HW-7 that sounds like this." The 1-MΩ/100-nF combination on Q1 slows receiver recovery to "semi-QSK." By wetting a finger I was able to selectively "recover" Q1 at a faster rate, discovering a happy medium where I got QSK, without too much pop. Later I changed to 2.2-M and 10-nF film. With the RF gain at zero, the pops sound a little annoying. However, real signals going through the receiver mask the pops and the QSK sounds great.

AE6C: I eliminated the QSK switching to reduce current consumption, and instead added a manual SEND/RECEIVE switch (more on this later). Maybe we ought to talk about quiescent current first, since we both added a number of mods to reduce it.

Q Current:

KB6FPW: A big defect in the original design is the receiver's copious quiescent current of 22 mA. I measured this current in the receive mode with no input signals before making any modifications; my supply was 12.0 V at the circuit board. 5 to 8 mA of the 22 are wasted away warming the NE5532 (a JRC device was supplied as a substitution in the kit).

AE6C: You don't have to use the current-hungry op amp in the kit. The dual pinout is an industry standard and many newer products will give you equivalent or better

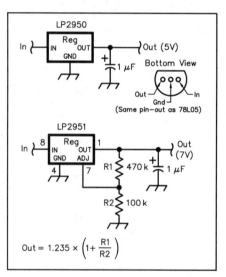

$$Out = 1.235 \times \left(1 + \frac{R1}{R2}\right)$$

Fig 6—AE6C: A couple of ways to improve on the battery-unfriendly 78L08 regulator. The LP2950 is virtually a drop fit. The DIP style LP2951 lets you choose your optimum operating voltage; I recommend 7 V.

performance for far less current. I chose an LMC662 (Digi-Key #LMC662CN-ND; price $2.28) which is a CMOS part that can literally drive rail-to-rail at the output. Its CMOS inputs do not generate current noise that manifests as voltage noise across the large input resistors. Supply current consumption is only 750 microamperes vs many milliamperes for the older bipolar NE5532. Do not use just any CMOS op amp here as most have feeble output stages that are not able to drive headphones.

KB6FPW: AE6C identified the op amp as a likely candidate for replacement (the kit comes with sockets, making substitution and A/B comparisons easy). Although

I had a junk box device that worked well, Denny sent me a '662 and since it beat mine by 50 μA, I condescended to use it.

AE6C: The voltage regulator in the design was evidently chosen because of its availability and small size, but there are two major drawbacks to the 78L08. First and foremost, it will begin to dropout when the battery voltage sags to only 10 V.

KB6FPW: When that happens, the VFO is going to pull badly. The second major drawback is the 78L08's battery-hostile quiescent current. You'll hear a sucking sound when you apply power.

AE6C: Better, newer devices of the "low dropout" variety are available. You can use an LP2950 (Digi-Key #LP2950CZ-5.0-ND; price $2.07) for 5 V output or the adjustable LP2951 (Digi-Key #LP2951CN-ND; price $2.52) for 8 V or anything in-between.

KB6FPW: My junk box produced an LT1121CZ-5 (5 V micropower regulator), and I substituted this in place of the 78L08. As a bonus it offers protection for downstream circuits against accidental reverse battery. Note that the LT1121 pinout is opposite that of the 78L08; I had to mount it backward relative to the 40-40 silk screen. See **Fig 5**. Don't worry, if you insert it incorrectly and apply power, no harm is done to the regulator or the downstream circuits. Just pull it out and put it in the right way.

AE6C: Equivalent parts and alternate sources are available from several manufacturers. The TO-92 style LP2950 is the best board fit, but you are pretty much stuck with 5 V. A little more voltage is better because the receive mixer will give an extra dB of large signal handling when at the higher voltage. The 40-40 needs every dB it can get in this regard. **Fig 6** shows the circuit options.

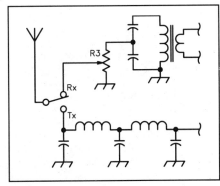

Fig 7—AE6C: A low-tech alternative to the diode gated QSK scheme. This conventional TX/RX switch consumes zero current and provides maximum sensitivity.

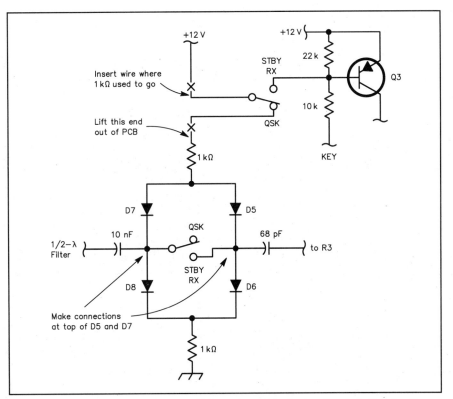

Fig 8—KB6FPW: Save 6 mA with a DPDT toggle switch. Keying the rig in the standby mode will cause no harm since the TX/RX switch is disabled.

KB6FPW: Both the LT1121 and LP2950/1 need 1 μF output capacitors for stability. I used a dipped tantalum—a very tiny unit that fit right on the regulator's leads (Fig 5). Although changing the regulator has a ripple effect on the VFO, the circuit will still function perfectly well with a 5 V regulator. We'll get into the VFO later. This regulator also supplies the receiver mixers through D9. According to NN1G, D9 serves to keep the mixer supply voltage below 8 V, which is uncomfortably high for the NE602. With a 5-V regulator, there is no need for D9's 700-mV drop, so I shorted it.

Hey, we can't forget to talk about the QSK feature. A full 6 mA is wasted away in the receiver's QSK switching. This is more than ¼ of the original power budget.

AE6C: Diode gating burns current if large signal handling is to be preserved. A low cost rig cannot afford to use costly PIN diodes. QSK is a deluxe feature to have on a relatively simple rig, but the implementation on the 40-40 does have another drawback of which you should be aware. The receive sensitivity is adversely affected and this IF-stageless design does not have gain to burn. So, I opted for a simple TX/RX changeover switch (**Fig 7**), eliminating the diode switching altogether.

KB6FPW: No wonder it took you so long to come back the other night during our QSO.

AE6C: You're not so quick with a micro-switch style key yourself. It is not elegant, but it works well. Mitch has a good idea to implement current savings when not in "QSO Mode."

KB6FPW: I fixed this by using the circuit shown in **Fig 8**. All it takes is a DPDT switch. In the QSK position everything operates as originally intended, but in the STANDBY RX mode the TX/RX switch is locked in receive, and I remove bias from the diode bridge, instead passing signals through directly with the second switch section. 5.5-6 mA saved. If you key the rig in STANDBY RX no harm is done and you won't hear any sidetone.

Incidentally, sensitivity suffers about 1 dB in the QSK position.

AE6C: My total receiver current is 6.5 mA—outstanding for a rig of this quality.

KB6FPW: My receive current in STANDBY RX is now 6.3 mA—very respectable.

The rig will run continuously for more than two weeks on a load of AA alkalines, perfect for portable camping/backpacking operation. D cells would last three months or more.

VFO:

KB6FPW: There were several improvements to be made in the VFO. My initial tuning range, before modification, was 33 kHz, not 40 kHz as claimed in the original article. Changing the regulator took the varactor potentiometer reference voltage from 8 V down to 5 V, further reducing my tuning range to about 22.5 kHz. I wasn't happy with 33 kHz to start with, so to increase the tuning range, I dropped C6 to 1.8-nF Polystyrene, increased C9 to 160 pF SM and reduced C11 to 100 pF SM. I added a 12 pF SM across C8, the VFO trimmer, and now my rig tunes from 7005 to 7068, a range of about 63 kHz. Dropping the value of C11 also restored my injection level to U5. See **Fig 9** for a summary of the changes.

AE6C: I had Motorola HEP2503 and MV209 varactor diodes on hand, so I thought I might give those a try. Although they proved to be good stable tuning devices, they lacked the capacitance swing necessary to give the frequency range I wanted. Even when I took C9 all the way up to 300 pF, I maxed out at 32 kHz of tuning range. Further, the tuning was very non-linear. It

wasn't until Mitch rescued me with a genuine MV1662 that I got the 70-kHz range I was seeking. The non-linearity was less as well. Stick with the recommended unit.

KB6FPW: I steered clear of the bottom of the band for fear of operating outside the band edge owing to VFO drift. In three months of operating the VFO has shown no long-term drift; my only drift is less than ±300 Hz temperature drift. Now that I'm more confident in the oscillator, I may eventually go back and adjust for 7001 to 7064.

AE6C: Maybe that will get your country total up. You missed out on Kermadec.

KB6FPW: I didn't take the tuning range as far as Denny; operation above 7065 is mostly RTTY modes anyway and there is nothing to be gained.

Nevertheless, if you want to also cover the Novice band, the VFO should swing 150 kHz by juggling the frequency-determining capacitors, and possibly reducing the VFO coil inductance. I have no idea what the drift performance will be like afterward. The receiver input and driver band-pass filters are quite narrow and can be expected to show some roll-off over a 150-kHz bandwidth.

VFO Potentiometer:

AE6C: The best decision I ever made on this project was the use of a nice, smooth 10-turn pot for tuning. Wow, what a difference! Mine was a 100k Helipot. These babies can set you back $10 to $20 (for example, Clarostat Series 73JB from Digi-Key, #73JB104-ND; see also Circuit Specialists, DC Electronics or Hosfeldt Elec-

Inf = 1000 pf

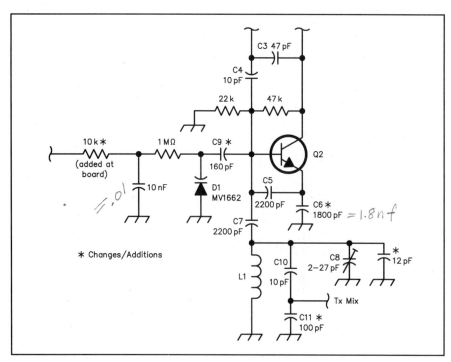

.01

C6 * 1800 pF = 1.8 nf

Fig 9—KB6FPW: After modifications for a wider tuning range, here is what my VFO looked like. It tunes from 7005 to 7068, and is very stable.

tronics) if you can't find a surplus source, but you will be glad should you spring for one. Mitch applied a turns counter (also expensive) to his potentiometer to allow a direct readout. This is a nice feature, but can interfere with the velvety smooth tuning of a quality multi-turn pot.

KB6FPW: With 33-kHz tuning range, a single-turn pot really does have enough resolution, as long as the pot is mechanically sound. But I also decided to go to a 10-turn pot for my widened tuning range. I added a 10-kΩ resistor in series with the wiper to clean up pot noise. Initially I made a simple calibration chart showing the operating frequency for each complete rotation of the pot. This works well, giving about 4 kHz per revolution at the bottom of the tuning range and closer to 8 kHz per revolution at the top end.

Ultimately I added a turns-counting dial and made a calibration chart in 1-kHz steps to keep track of my frequency. The addition of the dial didn't impede the feel of my 10-turn pot very much, and it has a mechanical brake to lock the tuning knob—a great feature for use in a sleeping bag. (See the **sidebar** entitled "Linearizing the 40-40 Tuning Dial.")

Linearizing the 40-40 Tuning Dial

The first thing I did when I got my 40-40 on the air was compile a calibration chart to help me keep track of my operating frequency. Connected to a Dentron dummy load and Heathkit IM-4100 frequency counter, I tuned the 40-40 from one end to the other, stopping at 1-kHz intervals and recording the reading on my turns-counting dial.

Unfortunately, the tuning was not linear. At the bottom end of the band the tuning rate was about 23 counts per kHz, and at the top end of my tuning range the rate was about 11 counts per kHz. The problem is complex, involving not only the non-linear characteristic of the tuning diode, but also the effect of the oscillator's various series and parallel capacitors that make up the frequency determining components.

Another problem was that at mid-scale, my turns counting dial (1002 counts full-scale) had an "integral linearity error" (INL) of approximately 125 counts. In other words, when tuned half-way between the top and bottom of the rig's tuning range, the dial reads 626, not 501. Most operators wouldn't care, but my curiosity led me to stumble upon an amazingly simple and current-conscious solution to the problem.

After much algebra and computer simulation, I found that by adding a resistor from the potentiometer's wiper to the reference regulator's output (see **Fig B**), I could reduce the INL to about ±35 counts—an improvement of about 4×. The error would peak at approximately ¼ and ¾ full scale, for an error of 2 kHz by dead reckoning. Error at

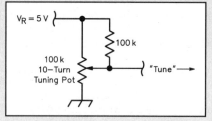

Fig B—KB6FPW: By simply adding a resistor, the tuning linearity can be improved by a factor of 4.

mid-scale is essentially zero. In my case the potentiometer is 100k ohms, so I would need a 100-kΩ resistor. At the bottom end of the tuning range this resistor adds 50-μA current consumption to the circuit.

Upon further investigation I discovered that a current source of 20.5 μA, injected into the wiper of the pot, would reduce the INL to less than 25 counts—more complicated, but a definite improvement over the resistor. **Fig C** shows a possible implementation using an LM334 constant current source. Temperature compensation is introduced with a 1N4148 diode. Note that this solution adds 20.5 μA to the receiver's current budget, regardless of tuning.

I added this modification to my 40-40 and improved my INL to about 27 counts (less than 2-kHz error) at mid-scale, in close agreement with predicted performance. There are a number of variables, including the accuracy of the current source (I did no trimming), the accuracy of the potentiometer (100 kΩ

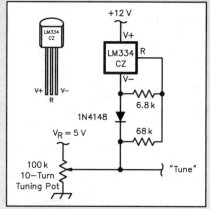

Fig C—KB6FPW: Taking it one step further, this temperature-compensated constant current source will improve tuning linearity by a factor of 5. With this in your 40-40, you have full on-the-air bragging rights.

±5%), and the linearity of the potentiometer (3%). My potentiometer must be a good one, because my current source ended up just a bit on the low side, and this would account for the INL being slightly greater than 25 counts. Note that my tuning rate is about 66 Hz per count.

These modifications are strictly fringe optional, but if you're a perfectionist, you'll no doubt be eager to implement at least the resistor fix. Don't forget to make a new calibration chart. And if you add the 20.5-μA current source, you'll definitely have on-the-air 40-40 bragging rights. —*KB6FPW*

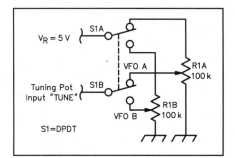

Fig 10—KB6FPW: Dual VFOs for pseudo-memory or manual split operation.

You can have dual VFOs by simply adding a pot and a switch (see **Fig 10**). This is a nice feature. Since most battery-conscious QRP operation involves tail-ending QSOs, you can leave one VFO parked on a strong QSO, while scanning up and down the band with the other. Another idea is to use a 10-turn pot for high-resolution tuning on one VFO, while using normal, single-turn pot for quick scanning on the other. I was going

to add this mod, but ran out of room in my 2×4×6 box. Small size was ultimately more important. See the **sidebar** entitled "Further Tuning Tricks for the 40-40" for more VFO tuning ideas.

RF Gain Potentiometer:

KB6FPW: While I was building the kit I figured I'd leave the volume control out. No IF amp, QRP rig, crystal filter—I was going to be lucky to hear anything. Wrong. It is loud, and very sensitive. S6 noise will leave you deaf if you run wide open. Use the 5k pot and save your ears.

AE6C: The 5-kΩ attenuator pot, R3, is of linear taper. I used an audio taper instead and found the range more gradual.

KB6FPW: I didn't think the control range with a linear pot was that bad, although there is a shelving effect in mine over about a 90-degree rotation, and it is highly compressed right at the bottom of the control range where I'm likely to set it for a really strong signal. I'll have to look for a log pot in my junk box and try it out.

As far as sensitivity, Denny already touched on this in his opening comments; I've heard KP4, Cuba, Italy, Korea, Russia, Philippines, Australia, KH6; wish they could hear my 1 W! I was able to work JH1EHO with 1 W output, through about 50 feet of RG-58 and another 65 feet of RG-213, into a Butternut HF-9V. I was elated.

Reverse Battery:

KB6FPW: The kit instructions say U2 and Q6 will be toast. Well, my LT1121 is reverse battery proof, but the best solution is to add a blocking diode in series with the supply (see **Fig 11A**). I added this on my rig, plus the switch shown in **Fig 11B**. Note that I don't waste the internal batteries on a diode drop. If I plug more than 50% of my AA cells in backward, I deserve to lose Q6. The switch is a locking toggle type, and can't accidentally turn on in my backpack or suitcase. It serves as either an on/off switch, or an internal/external power selector.

Further Tuning Tricks for the 40-40

Dual VFOs (see text) is only one possibility for 40-40 tuning options. Another enhancement that may be of interest to many operators is a crystal switch. Well, not a real crystal switch, but one such as shown in **Fig D**. Crystals are replaced by 10-turn Trimpots, picked off by a selector switch. This switch enables the operator to choose among any of several preset frequencies, or one or more conventional tuning knobs. This way popular frequencies such as 7040, or net frequencies can be "programmed" into the rig, and selected instantly without resorting to a frequency chart or look-up table. This option requires no modification of the basic 40-40 circuit board.

Some operators may miss the availability of big-rig features such as RIT, or separate VFOs for transmit and receive. While the fixed-tuned option requires no modification, you'll want to reduce the size of the varactor control voltage bypass cap for this one, to about 1 nF.

Two potentiometers, serving as transmitter and receiver VFOs, are selected by an analog switch. The smaller 1-nF capacitor is necessary to allow the frequency to settle before the transmitter is up and running, thereby eliminating chirp. A selector switch allows "reverse" operation or selection of either VFO A or B. While this example uses three front panel holes (one switch, two pots), a clever operator could reduce the front panel space used to two holes by using a dual pot with concentric shafts.

The entire circuit can be assembled as a module at the back of the tuning pots and grafted into the 40-40 via three wires (V_r, Key and V_{tune}), plus ground. I didn't use this circuit in my

40-40 because I wanted minimum size and simple controls, but I have added it to my 20-m "20-40," where size isn't

important and split operation and QRP DX are a more likely combination than on 40 m.—*KB6FPW*

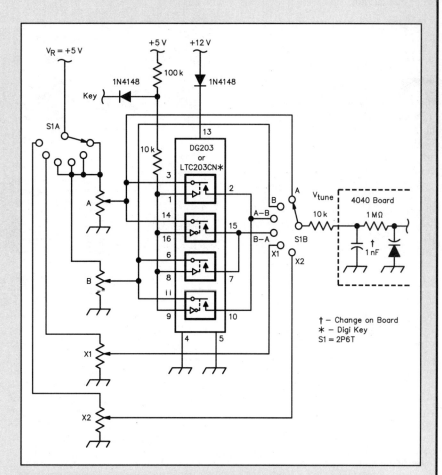

Fig D—KB6FPW: Deluxe frequency control with two VFOs, reversible split operation, and two crystal positions. X1 and X2 are 10-turn Trimpots.

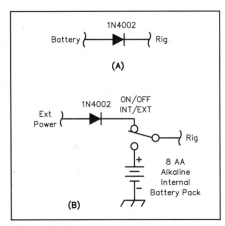

Fig 11—KB6FPW: (A) Simple reverse battery fix to protect final. (B) This is what I ended up with, but protecting against reversed external supply connections only.

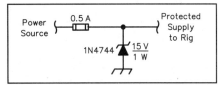

Fig 12—AE6C: A simple three-way input voltage protector. The fuse blows if either (1) the polarity is reversed, (2) the voltage is above 15 V or (3) the rig draws excessive current.

Fig 13—AE6C: Photo of interior PCB style cabinet during assembly. Small heat sinks are evident on Q5 and Q6 as is the 10-turn tuning pot. The rear panel houses, from left to right, connectors for ant, key, phones and power.

AE6C: I always include some kind of input voltage protection in my projects. My favorite is the three-way circuit in **Fig 12**. The Zener protects against overvoltage by blowing the fuse. And the diode action of the Zener protects against reverse battery by also blowing the fuse. This simple circuit adds no extra voltage drop in the battery line.

KB6FPW: I like Denny's scheme, but I'm not sure I have room for any kind of fuse holder. They do have very small fuses nowadays that look like $1/4$-W resistors—that would fit but would be hard to change.

Construction

Box:

AE6C: I am fond of things small, so I decided to craft a custom box built out of single-sided PCB material and tack solder it together (**Figs 13 and 14**). It measures 4.2 inches wide by 4.5 inches deep by 1.4 inches high. Along the front (from left to right) is the miniature ON/OFF toggle switch, the 10-turn tuning pot, the RF attenuator and the TX/RX changeover toggle switch.

Along the rear (from left to right as viewed from the rear in Fig 13) is the power connector (Radio Shack 274-1577), the chassis-isolated headphone jack (Radio Shack 274-250), the 3.5-mm key jack and the BNC antenna connector. I stood the

Fig 14—AE6C: Photo of the assembled rig before labeling. From left to right are the ON/OFF switch, the 10-turn tuning pot, the RF attenuator and the manual TX/RX toggle switch.

PCB on top of $1/4$-inch standoffs and used $5/8$-inch standoffs above the board to accept the 6-32 bolts that secure the top lid.

KB6FPW: My finished rig squeezes into a 6×4×2 LMB chassis (#642C), including key and eight AA alkaline cells. With no batteries it weighs just under a pound, 1.5 pounds with (see **Fig 15**). Along the front (**Fig 16**) I mounted a locking toggle power switch, 10-turn pot, RF attenuator, RX STBY/QSK switch and 3.5-mm headphone jack. On the back (**Fig 17**) I put bananas for power, $1/4$-inch 2-conductor jack for key input and SO-239 antenna connector.

Connectors, pots and switches are a big space and weight factor in a small QRP rig. There is a temptation to use tiny little connectors on QRP rigs so that the finished

product is impressively small. Unfortunately, small connectors, pots and switches are usually frail, flimsy and prone to failure at inconvenient times. I want something sturdy that won't break in the field.

I learned my lesson long ago not to compromise the hard work that goes into a homebrew project with inferior controls and connectors. Take my advice: use quality heavy-duty connectors, pots and switches with solid, non-metric hardware (a sure sign of low quality consumer-grade components). You can determine the quality of the inside by checking the finish on the outside. Precision machined and finished bushings and hardware are indicative of quality product, as well as high cost.

Speaking of cost, the prices of high quality potentiometers have gone up by a factor of 6 over the past 5 years (wish I could say that about my paycheck!). The cost of decent connectors and controls can double the price of a simple QRP project, but it's worth it.

I broke my rule and used a small, plastic 3.5-mm stereo headphone jack. Big mistake. Yes, now I can scratch a $1/4$-inch to 3.5-mm stereo adaptor from my checklist (see **sidebar** entitled "40-40 Accessories"), but I can also scratch using my 40-40 in the middle of a skiing trip if the 3.5-mm jack fails. It is a rather meager, minimum-geometry affair, guaranteed to be the first to fail (contacts are already getting flaky). My only consolation is that it will be easy to replace.

AE6C: One definite advantage of big connectors is that adapting a small plug to a large jack is easier than the other way around. Try converting a 3.5-mm head-

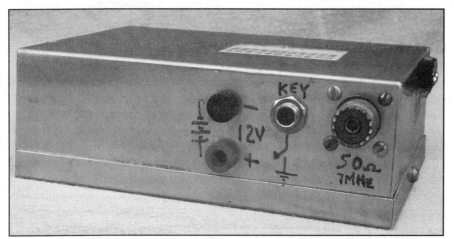

...ell, here is the inside of my 40-40. Eight AA ...)-40 circuit board and controls and connectors ... The white, curlicue wire connecting the audio ...ows up quite clearly on airport X-ray machines.

...Fig 16—KB6FPW: 40-40, front view. From left to right, locking power toggle switch (switching to the right selects external power, switching left selects internal power); 10-turn dial for tuning; RF attenuator (volume control); RX STANDBY/QSK switch; and 3.5-mm insulated headphone jack. To the left at the end of the box you can see the built-in microswitch key.

Fig 17—KB6FPW: Available on the rear skirt (left to right) external 12-V input bananas; ¹/₄ inch external key input; and SO-239 antenna connection.

phone jack to accept a ¹/₄-inch plug. You can do it, but it isn't as clean and rugged as adapting a 3.5-mm headphone plug to a ¹/₄-inch stereo jack.

Keys:

KB6FPW: I used a tiny microswitch, mounted on the end of my enclosure as a key (you can see it pretty well in Figs 16 and 17). This way I don't have to remember to pack an external one, or carry the added weight. I can go a solid 18 wpm in short bursts with the microswitch, without cramping my hands and fingers.

AE6C: No argument here. Who wants to lug around a key as big as the entire rig? Microswitches can be pressed into service if you find one with the right feel. I searched around the local surplus shops until I found one that felt good and was large enough (⁵/₈×³/₄×1⁷/₈ inches) to hold with the other hand. Its lever extends beyond the body where I attach a small plastic knob for a grip. It works pretty well up to about 15 wpm, but not for long stretches. I wouldn't recommend it for contesting either, but it travels really well and collects lots of funny comments.

KB6FPW: Mike Agsten showed a really nice homebrew, built-in key on page 33 of November 1994 *QST*, but I didn't want anything sticking out that might snag or bend in my pack. I went through a lot of microswitches at a surplus store to find just the right one. Keys have to feel right to the user. Wires pass through a couple of holes under the switch terminals. Of course the ¹/₄-inch jack is always there should I decide to use a straight key or keyer.

Circuit Changes

AE6C: Aside from the parts substitution, I made a few circuit changes that are worth passing along for consideration.

Mixer Injection Levels:

AE6C: Both the receive and transmit mixers get their oscillator drive from Q2. Buffering is via two small 10-pF coupling caps, C4 and C10. I found the NE602 injection levels to be marginal on the low side. Perhaps this was just due to my particular oscillator being a little soft; I don't know what was typically expected of Q2 in the design. I found injection levels to be only 20 to 100 mV P-P, which is below optimum for the NE602.

KB6FPW: The NE602 data sheet says 200 mV P-P is the optimum injection level for the top quad (pin 6) of the Gilbert multiplier cell.

AE6C: Increasing C4 to 22 pF boosted receive gain and large signal handling. Correspondingly, lowering C11 at the transmit mixer to 47 pF boosted drive to the final. Don't go any lower than 47 pF for C11 or the VFO will pull excessively during key-down due to the dynamic loading of the keyed transmit mixer.

KB6FPW: I boosted my U5 injection

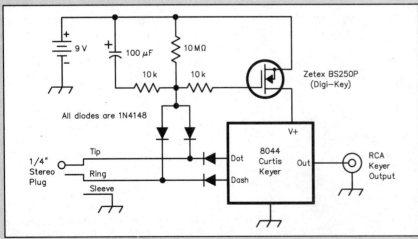

Fig 18—AE6C: Rebiasing the driver to both reduce the power dissipation in Q5 and save a little transmit current.

level to 50 mV P-P by reducing C11 to 100 pF. The VFO pulls about 38 Hz in transmit. I left my receiver's mixer injection level at 50 mV P-P (stock), and my sensitivity numbers compare favorably with Denny's. In my 40-40, a 91 pF C4 brings it

up to 200 mV P-P, but I elected not to make this change.

Driver Dissipation:

AE6C: The PA driver, Q5, runs Class A and quite warm (to the extent that I put a small heat sink on it as well as Q6, which runs much cooler).

KB6FPW: I noticed this too...see my comments under "Alignment."

AE6C: You can run Q5 closer to Class B by rebiasing the base of Q4 (**Fig 18**) at a lower potential. As an experiment I paralleled the 10k resistor from the base of Q4 to ground with 15k. The emitter voltage of Q5 dropped from 2.2 V to 1.1 V, which halved the collector standing current. This trick saved 120 mW (10 mA) of battery power and cooled down Q5 at the same time. Going still lower, however, would risk loss of drive and increase harmonics feeding Q6 as Q5 would cut off during part of the cycle as the battery sags.

KB6FPW: I tried a more complicated

modification, moving the 22k resistor biasing Q4's base to the 7.5-V Zener diode regulating U5's supply. This also drops the bias as Denny suggests, while regulating against changes in the supply voltage. You cannot bias Q4's base from the 5-V regulator because Q4's collector would then draw power 100% of the time. I reduced my transmit current from 260 mA to 250 mA, in agreement with Denny's prediction.

Headphone Connections:

AE6C: I have gotten into the habit of connecting the ubiquitous stereo headphones in series so as to boost the combined impedance 4 times to roughly 80 ohms (at 800 Hz).

KB6FPW: I like this idea, and I've used it in the past on other projects. The official impedance is 2×32 ohms, or about 64 ohms total, but I have measured "Walkman" type headphones with both lower and higher impedance.

AE6C: The higher impedance is much

Tip for Reducing Current Drain in Electronic Keyers

As an accessory for use with my 40-40, I completed a project that had been collecting dust for a long time: a Curtis keyer chip (8044) and matching circuit board from FAR Circuits. These were held in reserve for the day when I needed them, and that day had arrived. I populated only half of the FAR Circuits board, eliminating the weight control, sidetone and relay functions. This left a speed pot, 1/4-inch jacks for straight key and iambic paddle, and an RCA connector for keyer output—a very compact unit.

Since the time when the Curtis keyer chip came on the market, some improvements have been made to the ubiquitous 9-V transistor battery. Present alkaline renditions boast a three-year shelf life, suggesting that the 50-μA quiescent current of the 8044 may be excessive. I devised a simple scheme for automatically disconnecting the battery when the keyer is not in use.

Shown in **Fig E**, my circuit uses a P-channel MOSFET to switch the battery voltage to the keyer board. When either paddle of my key is depressed, steering diodes pull down both the appropriate keyer input, and the gate of the MOSFET. This turns on the MOSFET, instantly applying power to the keyer. While a single dit is enough to

get things going, one or two letters will store enough charge on the 100-μF capacitor to hold the MOSFET on for about 30 minutes.

The reason for holding the circuit on is that at power up, the Curtis keyer chip outputs a false dash or dot. This renders the circuit unusable if, say, power was applied for the length of only a letter or word. With a nearly 30 minute hold-up time I don't have to worry about a "wake up" call to the keyer, even after listening to the most monologulous over. The Curtis chip outputs no false keying as the power supply voltage slowly decays.

When not in use (the keyer could sit on the shelf for weeks or months between uses), the P-channel MOSFET shuts off and eliminates the 50-μA static current drain, allowing the battery to realize its full potential shelf life.

This technique can be extended to other keyer designs where the power supply voltage is high enough to enhance the MOSFET. On lower supply voltages, such as the 4.5-V supply of the CMOS Super Keyers, try substituting a Zetex ZVP4105A or frustratingly small International Rectifier IRF7202. Both have guaranteed enhancement (and accompanying low ON resistance) at 4.5-V gate drive.

Yes, the venerable Curtis Keyer Chip is still available, although now marketed by Mouser Electronics and others. The CMOS Super Keyer III is available from Idiom Press, PO Box 1025, Geyserville, CA 95441.—*KB6FPW*

Fig E—KB6FPW: Eliminate quiescent current in the Curtis keyer chip with this automatic supply switch.

40-40 Accessories

While I tried to make my 40-40 completely self-contained, including batteries and key, and as small as possible, I've added a collection of accessories for use in a variety of operating situations. See **Fig F**. Perhaps building and gathering together these items was as much fun as building the 40-40 itself, and they add to the functionality of the rig. You may want to consider some for your own QRP station.

Outboard Equipment

Transmatch: Perhaps the most important station accessory is a means of resonating antennas and transforming the resultant impedance to 50 ohms. I must have a Transmatch for certain portable operation because my antennas are never ideal. The one I like best is described on page 228 of *QRP Classics* (from September 1988 *QST*). A Transmatch is useless without an SWR bridge, and my favorite follows roughly along the lines of the one shown on page 48, Fig 3-6 of *QRP Notebook*. I put a 40-m-only version of the Transmatch in a 2×2×4 aluminum box together with my SWR bridge (**Fig G**). The matcher has no trouble tuning up antennas that would have otherwise been 50 ohms, but for various installation reasons exhibit some unknown, often wild impedance.

One of the best things about the SWR bridge is that no inductors or transformers or trim caps are needed, and it isolates the final from severe mismatches. It doubles as a 6-dB attenuator for 250-mW QRPp operation. It has no problem indicating full scale with 1 W and a high SWR.

I made a few mods to the original published SWR circuit. I substituted 51-ohm resistors in place of the 47-ohm resistors shown, I used a 1N914 instead of a 1N34A, and I eliminated the CAL position and pot. The bridge resistors dissipate only 250 mW each with 1 W applied, so I used quarter-watt carbon film resistors. These are completely adequate for tuneups, QRPp operating (as an attenuator), and brief key-down tests, and they are easier to find than carbon composition resistors of higher wattages. This little accessory has more than paid for itself in several hotel rooms. For up to 2 W, parallel two 100-ohm, ¼-W resistors to replace each 51-ohm unit.

–20 dB coupler: I mention a coupler here because there is no reason you couldn't build it into the SWR bridge/ Transmatch with a little advanced planning. A digital frequency readout is an especially welcome addition to any analog rig. It's nice to glance at a counter instead of poring over a calibration chart when logging the frequency of a QSO. A –20-dB coupler is the ticket. I put two SO-239s back to back in a small aluminum box with a single insulated wire running between them (see Fig F). Threaded onto this connecting wire is a ferrite toroid wound with 10 turns of hook-up wire. I used an FT-114-64; an

Fig F—KB6FPW: This is the entire 40-40 accessory lineup. This stuff isn't used all at once, but I draw upon these items to satisfy various operating requirements such as business or camping trips, trips to visit relatives, RFI investigation, or operation at home. I've even operated mobile. Progressing from lower left to upper right are pictured remote microswitch hand key; ear buds in carrying case; spare final; SWR bridge/Transmatch with removable knobs; Braun QRP station clock; adaptors ¼ inch to RCA, UHF to F, BNC, RCA and five-way banana; UHF U-turn consisting of two elbows and one male-male adaptor; the 40-40; log book; pen; Gates Cyclon 12 V/2.5 Ah six-pack; banana to alligator clip pair; shaving kit bag (black); tuned, shielded loop; Vibroplex iambic paddle; homebrew Curtis keyer in a gutted MFJ aluminum box; –20 dB coupler; RCA patch cord; Ault Model 5000 12 V/300 mA wall cube; lastly, in the back, a 40-m dipole with 50 feet of coaxial feed line and choke-style balun wound on an extension cord holder.

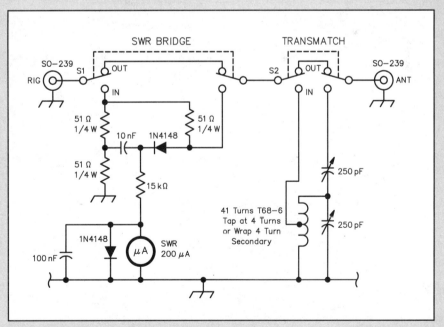

Fig G—KB6FPW: An SWR bridge and Transmatch will be one of the first accessories you'll want to add to any QRP rig. I cobbled this circuit together with material from several different sources, along with a little of my own ingenuity. There are two switches: one selects or bypasses the resistive bridge, and the other selects or bypasses the versatile tuner. Often times my portable dipole needs no tuning and I take the SWR bridge/Transmatch out of circuit altogether. The two 250-pF variable capacitors are fishpaper capacitors, #24TR222 (Mouser, Circuit Specialists, DC Electronics); parallel sections.

FT-114-A-61 is more readily available (Amidon) and will do nicely, as well as any number of type 43 or 61 toroids and sleeves.

The 10-turn secondary passes out of the box through a BNC to a 50-ohm terminator at my frequency counter. This absorbs only 1/100 (10 mW) of my output power—a small price to pay for a digital readout—but gives solid counts. If you want to get fancy, use a short length of 50-ohm coax to bridge the gap between the SO-239s. The braid acts as an electrostatic shield, but be sure you ground the braid at one end only, or it will shield the magnetic field too. Another option is to use a chassis isolated BNC connector and float the secondary winding. This keeps the counter from injecting ground noise into the 40-40's receiver.

Key: Although I built a microswitch into (onto) my 40-40, this wasn't especially convenient in a sleeping bag. Either I'd have to stick the cold rig in my bag, or stick my arm out of the bag into the cold air to operate the built-in key. For my brand of fourth-season mountaineering, I devised a simple key consisting of a 1/4-inch plug and small microswitch joined by a couple of feet of light zip cord. The microswitch can be operated from inside my bag, while the rig remains outside. Some people may find this key difficult to operate, but 30 years of playing violoncello, 20 years of touch typing, and 10 years of operating

a Vibroplex iambic paddle haven't exactly hurt my dexterity. AE6C built one too.

Keyer: Although I already had CMOS Super Keyers II and III, I decided to pull out an old 8044 Curtis Keyer chip and matching FAR Circuits circuit board and installed them in the smallest box I had on hand. I was able to out-do the other keyers in terms of size and weight, and now I don't have to tear down my home station when I need to take a keyer portable. Perhaps I'll next build a miniaturized version of the CMOS Super Keyers. See the sidebar entitled "Tip for Reducing Current Drain in Electronic Keyers" for a way to conserve keyer battery life.

Ear Buds: These are a great innovation. Headphones without a head-band. They roll up in a small coil and can be stowed in any little nook or cranny in a suitcase, pocket, or briefcase. They'll even fit inside the rig, if necessary.

Operating Aids

Logbook: Much to my dismay, Newington says that the *ARRL Mobile Logbook* is now out of print and no more will be produced. My XYL came to the rescue with a "Marble Memo" (The Mead Corporation, Dayton, OH 45463). This looks just like the lab notebooks I use at work; you know the kind—a green marbley cover with quadrille paper—but this one is only 4.5x3.5 inches. It compares favorably with the 4x6-inch footprint of my 40-40, and contains a full

80 sheets (160 pages). Nevertheless, scratch it off your Dayton list, because the binding allows pages to fall out after a little exercise. The binding isn't sewn like my lab notebook. A spiral-bound notepad may be a better choice. Try a Memo Book, No. 524352, from the Union Camp Corporation, Wayne, New Jersey 07470. It measures 5×3 inches and also contains 80 sheets.

Pen or Pencil: Now that you've got a log book, don't forget to pack a pen or pencil too. Pens run out of ink, pencils get dull or break. I don't know what the solution is other than to take a spare or check the ink tube inside the pen to see how much is left.

Flashlight: Not pictured. I keep a Mini-Maglite AAA (operates on two AAA cells) for use at night when ac-powered lighting is not available, such as when camping or emergency communications. Other flashlights abound that are much more "QRP" than a Mini-Maglite, such as key-chain types, and small single AAA cell flashlights built in the form of a pen.

Station Clock: This idea is not new, but it bears repeating here. Stick-on digital clocks are available for less than $5 at any variety or auto parts store. One can be attached to the rig or an accessory chassis. It's amazing that what once was a $100 station luxury is now a throwaway accessory for a QRP rig. I particularly like the ones supplied with a Velcro fastener, allowing for easy removal or

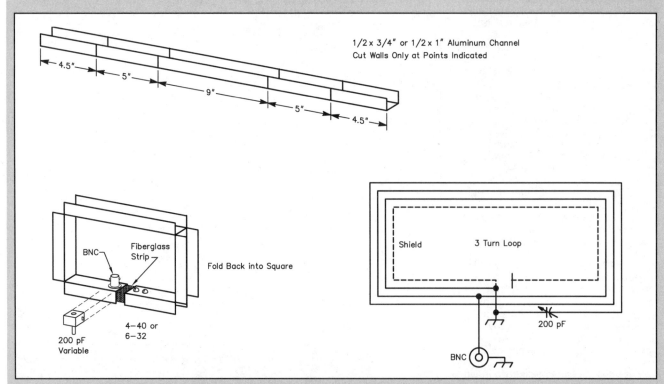

Fig H—KB6FPW: A tiny rig begs use as an RFI crime fighter. You can search out BCI, TVI and RFI from a variety of sources such as rectifying joints, the neighbor's television set, or a street lamp with this tuned loop. Simply cut the walls of a length of aluminum U-channel in four places and fold back into the shape of a square. I used a piece of stripped fiberglass and screws to secure the gap. This one is wound with three turns, tuned with a 200-pF air variable, and the output is sampled with a BNC tapped one turn up from the grounded end of the loop.

Table A
KB6FPW: Handy Adaptors to Have on Hand

Source	From Type	To Type	For Connecting
Transceiver or Transmatch	PL-259	Fem. BNC	Short runs of RG-58 or BNC-equipped accessories
	PL-259	Fem. F	TV-grade coax with crimped F connectors
	PL-259	RCA jack	RCA equipped coax or accessories
	PL-259	5-way banana binding post	End-fed antennas
External key input	1/4 inch plug	RCA jack	RCA-equipped external keyer or keys
External power input	Banana plug	Alligator	External 12-V batteries or power supplies

Also:

UHF U-turn; consists of two elbows and a male-male adaptor; used to connect rig directly to SWR bridge/Transmatch.

RCA Patch Cable; 1 to 3 feet long, shielded, with RCA plug at each end; used to connect external keyers (RCA is almost universal in this regard).

replacement of the clock. You can also find pens with clocks built in—this is a great way to combine two accessories. Now if I could just find a pen with a built-in clock and light I'd have it made. When traveling I just use my Braun travel clock. It's the QRP equivalent to a 12-inch wall clock, and it has built-in incandescent illumination, but no pen.

Checklist: This should be compiled while the 40-40 is installed and in use, so that you don't forget any essential elements. Although my checklist (inventory, actually) is hand written inside my logbook, it could be compiled on a computer and printed in shrunk form and taped inside the logbook or taped to the bottom of the rig.

Calibration Chart: I attached an abbreviated calibration chart this way, but taped to the top of the rig. The log is another handy place to keep it.

Transportation and Repairs

Shaving Kit: How could this be a radio accessory? I can carry my 40-40, and any necessary accessories all in a small zippered shaving kit. Small pouches and containers like this abound, at low cost. Look for food/beverage totes, camping pouches and packs, bicycle accessories, and commercial airline overnight kits and bags.

Spare Parts: AE6C suggests taping an extra final transistor and fuse to the inside of the box, just in case your luck runs out and you're not at home. I also put the small tuning tool, which was included as part of the 40-40 kit, inside my rig for field adjustments should they become necessary.

Tools: Not pictured. For opening the rig, I carry a very small blade-type screwdriver. This way I can change batteries or get in to make adjustments should they become necessary.

Antennas

Dipole: I fabricated a dipole using *Handbook* dimensions as a guide. The dipole itself is made out of stranded twisted pair for strength and flexibility, with nylon strings attached to the ends. A center 1:1 insulator/balun feeds 50 feet of TV-grade RG-59 coax pre-wired with type-F connectors. I also attached about 50 feet of Dacron cord to the balun for inverted-V use, or to support the weight of the coax. All of this is wound on an extension cord holder for easy transportation and deployment.

Portable Loop: A small, compact QRP rig like the 40-40 begs service as a QRM fighter, searching out local man-made interference like broken power poles and other neighborhood malfunctions. I took a 28-inch length of 1×1/2" aluminum U-stock and cut the walls of the channel at 4.5, 9.5, 18.5, and 23.5 inches; then folded the U-stock back on itself to form a rectangular frame (see **Fig H**). The gap was secured with a strip of insulating fiberglass PCB material (stripped of copper) and 4-40 hardware. I added a 200-pF air variable and BNC, attached right to the loop frame (the BNC can pass through the fiberglass to secure the fiberglass at one end). Lastly I added three turns of insulated hookup wire with a tap at one turn up from [frame] ground.

A BNC male-to-male barrel completes connections to the 40-40. This loop is just sensitive enough to pick up strong signals (I haven't tried a QSO), and perfect for sleuthing neighborhood QRM. It also couples well into household conductors such as rain gutters and water pipes, simplifying the search for rectifying joints.

End-fed Wire: Not pictured...You can make contacts with nothing more than a 1/4-wave (33 foot) wire strung up to the nearest skyhook. Don't forget you need a ground. I carry a matching 33-foot radial made out of light zip cord, and a shorter length of heavy wire with a large alligator clip for connecting to water pipes, car chassis, or whatever ground I can find nearby.

Connections

Adaptor Kit: For the antenna connections, you can never tell what you'll run into, so I keep an assortment of UHF-to-whatever adaptors on hand. These include BNC, F, RCA, and a five-way banana binding post for end-fed wires. Other adaptors get me in and out of the 1/4-inch key jack and banana power jacks. See **Table A**.

Power Sources

Power Supply: This rig is a lot of fun, and you're going to want to operate it at home, but without wasting money on batteries. A power supply is required. I should give up building power supplies, what with the ready availability of wall cubes. These run from 50 cents to $2, depending on whether you buy them at a flea market or retail store, regardless of condition or size. Normally despised because of their proliferation in the consumer industry, these are a handy source for ready-made power supplies.

I bought a wall cube at the store for $1.50. Manufactured by Ault, it is an exceptionally nice one weighing about twice what it should, and it puts out a clean, regulated +12 V. The heavy-duty output cable also contains a ground connection that is handy for picking up a free ground path in hotel rooms. Unlike direct-conversion rigs, the 40-40 is hum-free even when connected to an unbalanced antenna and ac ground. By the way, I cut off the weird connector on the end of my wall cube and installed some banana plugs to mate with my 40-40 external power jacks.

Infinite Power Source: Clearly, the load of eight AA alkalines is for use only in the most portable of circumstances, such as when skiing or backpacking, or perhaps for emergency communications. But for portable operation away from power lines where I'm not carrying the weight on my back, I take a rechargeable battery.

With only 6.3-mA receive current and 260-mA transmit current, I couldn't resist mating my 40-40 with a 2.5-Ah six-pack of surplus Gates rechargeable "Cyclon" gelcells. This is equivalent in capacity to the AA alkalines, with enough reserve to last an entire contest or through a weekend of intense operating. 2.5 Ah will supply the 40-40 through 38.5 hours' worth of QSOs, or two weeks of monitoring. See the **sidebar** entitled "Batteries" for further information on battery operation.—*KB6FPW*

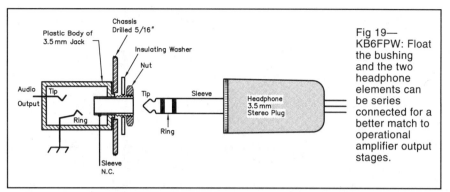

Fig 19—KB6FPW: Float the bushing and the two headphone elements can be series connected for a better match to operational amplifier output stages.

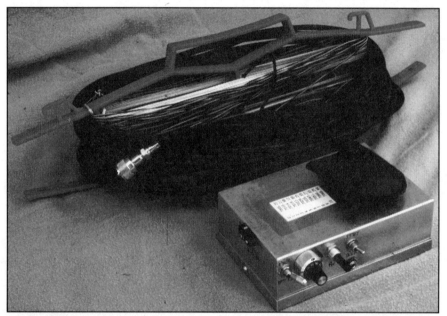

Fig 20—KB6FPW: The bare essentials. This is the minimum configuration for a weekend (or longer) trip. Only three items need be packed: ear buds, 40-40 and 40-m dipole on extension cord holder. Forgetting the ear buds isn't a show-stopper as a new pair, sold in a wide variety of stores, can be purchased almost anywhere anytime day or night for well under $5. My calibration chart is affixed with packing tape to the top of the rig.

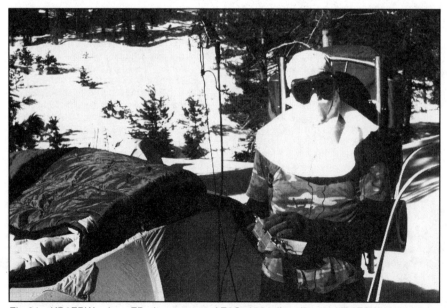

Fig 21—KB6FPW relays FD site status to AE6C, 150 miles distant. KB6FPW got a 589 using a dipole only 6 feet off the 8-foot snowpack, and what was later verified as 320-mW output power. The little 40-40 is well-suited for these harsh conditions.

more friendly to op amps and low power discrete audio circuitry, often mitigating the need for current-hogging IC audio amps. Most op amps have plenty of voltage compliance, but little output current.

KB6FPW: Even driving 80 ohms, most op amps will current-limit before hitting the rails, but you'll get 4 times the peak audio power (+6 dB) by putting them in series. Sort of like having an "11" on your volume control. See **Fig 19**.

AE6C: When the protective overcurrent clamps engage, boy, is it hard on the ears.

KB6FPW: But the extra output is handy in noisy environments, like in a tent during a windstorm.

AE6C: You don't have to rewire your favorite headphones to make the series connection, just use a headphone jack that is electrically isolated from the chassis. The "shell" of the plug is allowed to float and the signal is fed across the tip and ring sections.

KB6FPW: Radio Shack makes an ideal 3.5-mm headphone jack (#274-249) which when installed in a 5/16-inch hole, becomes isolated from ground. Be sure to use an insulating washer under the nut. It's a good thing there are two per package, because the connectors are flimsy.

I've noticed a slight amount of BCI from local stations with my floating headphone ground. A solid ground at the rig minimizes this pick-up. It has only been a problem at home in the middle of RF Gulch.

Headphone Selection:

AE6C: To carry miniaturization to its logical conclusion, the headphones should be small. This suggests the use of "earbuds" as supplied with many of today's portable radios, tape players and CD players.

KB6FPW: I agree with AE6C. "Earbuds" are the way to go. Unlike conventional 'phones with a headband, you can wear earbuds under a warm, wool watch cap in a sleeping bag. They are also small and easy to carry in a backpack. And you can rest the side of your head on a pillow while wearing them. Try that with a pair of Sennheisers.

Conclusions

KB6FPW: I took the 40-40 on a cross-country ski trip in February with my family and N6CNY. We skied to our Field Day site to see if essential trees had survived January's 135-mph winds and record snowfall. We were able to report good news to AE6C with the 40-40 and a dipole only 6 feet off the 8-foot snow pack. The path was about 150 miles, and we made contact at both 9 AM and 4 PM. It was nice having the rig along to pass wakeful periods during the long nights. See **Figs 20 and 21**.

AE6C: I'm taking mine camping, too. I've built a lightweight dipole to complement the 40-40.

KB6FPW: Not long after building my 40-40, I ran across a Ø using the same rig!

Batteries

While my 40-40 contains a load of eight AA alkaline cells for portability, these are costly to replace so I use them only when necessary, such as when skiing, backpacking, wandering the neighborhood in search of RFI sources, or for on-the-spot emergency communications.

For sustained non-ac operation, a rechargeable battery of one type or another makes the most sense. NiCd batteries, while readily available, are the worst possible choice for emergency and portable power because they have high self-discharge rates, their charging efficiency is low, they cannot be "topped off" to maintain a full state of charge, they give no advanced warning of end-of discharge, and there is no way to know their state of charge without actually discharging them.

Lead-acid "gelcells" eliminate most of these problems. They have good shelf life, and can be topped off once a month or float charged indefinitely. The state of charge is simply monitored by measuring the terminal voltage (for a cell at rest 12.8 V full, 11.8 V empty, linearly extrapolate in between). The Gates Cyclon series includes two practical cell sizes that often show up in surplus stores and catalogs. The 2.5-Ah cell is about the size of a D cell alkaline, and the next size up is 5 Ah, which has the same form factor. These cells are often packaged in blocks of six (12 V), with the terminals spot welded together and housed in a plastic box.

Other gelcell types are potted in a plastic block or cube, with their capacity and voltage ratings printed on the side. They are available from many manufacturers including Yuasa, Sonnenschein, Panasonic, Globe and Power Sonic, to name a few. Potted cubes are available up to capacities of 48 Ah and more—too big for a 40-40.

Care for gelcells as you would any other lead acid battery. I've had good success charging gelcells at 14.4 V (2.4 V/cell), and floating at 13.8 V (2.3 V/cell). **Fig I** shows a circuit you can use to charge gelcells of up to 6 Ah capacity (larger batteries can be charged, but slowly). A low dropout regulator is used to extract as much power as possible from a 12.6-V transformer. Typically the peak rectified voltage is close to 18 V, but the LT1086 needs only 16 to 16.5 V to overcome the diode (D3) and still make 14.4 V at the battery.

The charging voltage is controlled by a center-off toggle switch. In position 1 the circuit floats at 13.8-V, position 2 "equalizes" the battery at about 14.8 V, and position 3 charges the battery at 14.4 V. Although gelcells can be floated indefinitely, long-term degradation can result if a fully charged battery is left in the charge position for many days, such as a week or more.

Equalizing should be done infrequently, and for only a few hours (2-6 hours on a fully charged battery) at a time. Equalizing essentially force-feeds the weaker cells in an attempt to completely restore all of the active plate material. If you use your gelcell often enough to charge it every week or two, equalize after every two to four charging cycles. If the gelcell gets less use, or if it is float or solar charged, equalize perhaps once every six months.

At 14.8 V damage occurs much more quickly than at 14.4 V—the curve is steep—so don't equalize for more than 6 hours or so. Discontinue equalizing (or any charging, for that matter) if the battery becomes noticeably warm to the touch.

A six-pack of 5-Ah Gates Cyclon cells will go forever. After modification, my 40-40 would operate on a 5-Ah battery for three days of solid QSOing, or a month of continuous reception. Such a large capacity would only be justified for, say, a two-week camping trip or if the charging source was undependable, such as a solar charging system riding out a month's worth of fog.

Solar Charging

Years ago solar panel prices ran around $20/W new, and about $10/W for surplus seconds. This put them out of reach for most amateur use. Owing to improvements in fabrication cost, new panels today run about $8/W, and less than $4/W for seconds and used panels. These prices (for large panels) are well within reason for powering a QRP station. Cost per watt peak power is a little higher for small panels, since the manufacturing cost is dominated by packaging, and the total available market is much smaller than for mass-produced large panels.

As a very rough rule of thumb, solar charge gelcells with a panel that puts out about C/10 (ampere-hour capacity divided by 10). For example, a 2.5-Ah gelcell matches well with a 250-mA solar panel. Assuming an equivalent of six hours of full insolation per day, two days' worth of sunshine would fully charge the battery. In the winter, or during periods of adverse weather, it might take a week.

Solar panel ratings are normally based on the peak available power, measured in full sunlight at sea level, in a place like Arizona. This doesn't mean much for charging 12-V batteries, because the panel's terminal voltage is in the 16 to 17-V region at peak power. Since solar cells are largely constant current devices at lower voltages, the maximum available output current at 12 V is approximately equal to the peak power rating divided by 17 V. My surplus Solarex panel is rated at 6 W, and in full sunshine it delivers 330 mA into a 12-V battery. Altitude does make a difference, as I've measured as much as 400 mA at 7000 feet. On cloudy-but-bright days, I can still get 100 mA out of the panel. This panel isn't a bad match for my 2.5-Ah six-pack.

For panels of C/10 or greater, some form of charge-control is recommended. Most commercial charge controllers use a shunt regulator to limit the maximum battery voltage to a safe value. **Fig J** shows a simple shunt regulator you can build. I have designed all kinds of charge controllers using op amps, MOSFETs, hysteretic control, and even peak-power tracking switching regulators, but this one can't be beat for cost and foolproof operation.

This circuit dissipates full panel power once the battery is charged, so a heat sink is necessary. A 10-W, 10-ohm resistor is added in series with the Darlington transistor to help share the dissipation. Still, the transistor must be heat-sinked as it will dissipate a maximum of about 5-6 W at 1 A. The maximum voltage can be calibrated with the

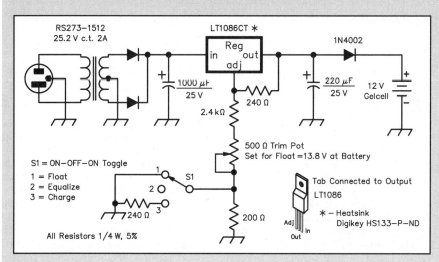

Fig I—KB6FPW: Here is a simple constant voltage charger suitable for floating, charging or equalizing 12-V gelcells.

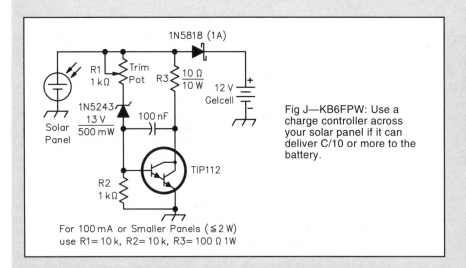

Fig J—KB6FPW: Use a charge controller across your solar panel if it can deliver C/10 or more to the battery.

In the schematic:
1N5818 (1A)
R1 1 kΩ
Trim Pot
R3 10 Ω / 10 W
12 V Gelcell
1N5243 13 V / 500 mW
100 nF
TIP112
R2 1 kΩ
Solar Panel

For 100 mA or Smaller Panels (≤ 2 W)
use R1 = 10 k, R2 = 10 k, R3 = 100 Ω 1W

trimpot to compensate for Zener voltage, V_{be} variations and Schottky forward drop at current. The knee of this circuit is relatively soft, eliminating stability problems. You can use this circuit up to about 1 A maximum. For sub-100 mA panels, increase R1, R2 and R3 by a factor of 10 each. R3 can be a 1-W unit, and the heat sink can be eliminated.

Sizing a QRP Solar Panel and Battery

Accurately sizing solar panels and batteries requires a series of educated guesses and compromises. Your operating habits must be considered to reach a reasonable solution. A general technique that works for most amateur habits is to add up a week's worth of operating current and self-discharge current; select a battery that can store this amount, and find a panel that can deliver anywhere from one to two times this amount, spread over a week's time. Here are the equations:

Battery capacity (Ah) = (total required ampere-hours per week) × 1.084

Panel capacity (Watts) = [(total required ampere-hours per week) × 1.1/42] × 17

Fudge factor explanation:
1.084 = battery self-discharge per week for a new battery, up to 1.2 for an old battery.
1.1 = battery ampere-hour charging inefficiency.
42 = average hours of maximum weekly insolation.
17 = panel voltage at rated power.

You can change the fudge factors to fit operating parameters peculiar to your situation. This method works great for those who concentrate their operating time in one or two chunks per week, but results in oversized batteries for those whose operating time is spread out evenly throughout the week.

These equations result in a "break-even" panel; it just keeps up with the demand under predicted insolation. After several days of cloudy weather the panel may get behind and since it can only keep up at best, it will never fully recharge the battery when fair weather returns. This is why the power of the panel should be as much as double the value calculated above.

Because the 40-40 uses so little current, a 1.2-Ah gelcell (this is about the smallest you can find) and a solar panel ranging from ¹/₂ to 2 W (depending on your operating habits and insolation) will work for everything from Field Day, to a daily net or sked, to one evening a week. If you oversize the battery, the self-discharge current becomes a major portion of the ampere hour budget, increasing the size and cost of the solar panel. Undersize the battery and you'll surely run out of power in the middle of a contest or DXpedition. Expect to pay a premium for such a small panel—as much as the rate of old, $20/W.

Throwaway Sources

A pack of eight D cell alkalines, although expensive to replace, will give their full 14 Ah at 40-40 current levels. This means three months of continuous reception, or 215 hours of continuous QSOing. The casual operator can easily expect a year's worth of use, filling a page in the log every two weeks.

I like to think of it in terms of total QSOs. A pack of D cells is good for 861 15-minute QSOs—that's more operating than I do in an entire year, all modes and bands combined! And alkalines are ideal for something like the mountain cabin scenario, because they have excellent shelf life. This attribute is essential for emergency communications.

A QRP rig like the 40-40 begs use for emergency communications. Although most of the local and regional traffic nets in my area are conducted on 80 m, 40 m has come alive with health and welfare traffic during major emergencies like the recent San Francisco and Los Angeles earthquakes. For emergency backup power you might want to consider a load of alkalines, or a gelcell, which can be solar charged, float charged, or topped off once a week.

In an emergency, don't forget about your car's battery. Typical capacities range from 50 to 75 Ah—months of continuous QSOing. Other impromptu household sources of emergency 40-40 power include motorcycle, snowmobile, lawnmower and camcorder batteries.—*KB6FPW*

His signal was strong, so I found it hard to believe I was listening to 1-1.5 W almost 1000 miles away. I've worked about four 40-40s so far.

A few weeks' casual and random operating netted 8 states and 23 QSOs. I think WAS would be a good goal for this rig. With falling solar activity, it should be possible. I now stand at 22 states, 3 provinces and 3 countries. Summer QRN is slowing my progress...

The most effective operating tactic, given my 1-W output power, is to tail-end QSOs. This is a common technique employed by veteran QRP operators that I was quick to adopt. I've called CQ with a memory keyer for up to an hour before getting a response. Tail-ending works almost every time. Also, I scan up and down looking for stations calling CQ, but there are more tail-endable QSOs in progress than loud stations calling CQ.

AE6C: Tail-ending is taught in QRP boot camp. You can't survive without it, particularly if you like to chase DX.

KB6FPW: You'll find a lot of like-minded QRPers on 7040, plus 7037 and 7030. While I concentrate on the strong ones (they're likely to hear me), I don't hesitate to answer a weak "/QRP" station calling CQ. I've even worked a couple of weak ones that were actually QRO. They must have much better receiving conditions than I have here in RF Gulch.

AE6C: Antenna tune-up can be a problem, as 1 W output isn't compatible with most commercial SWR bridges.

KB6FPW: None of my commercial SWR bridges showed any deflection with 1 W applied. An excellent QRP SWR bridge is described in the July 1986 issue of *QST*, "The SWR Twins—QRP and QRO," and one tailored for the 40-40 is detailed in the June 1995 issue. For the SWR Twins, you can use a 25 or 50 µA movement for greater sensitivity, and R1-R5 can be eliminated. See the sidebar entitled "40-40 Accessories" for a schematic of my matching SWR bridge/Transmatch.

Countless times, after exchanging the usual RST HR IS... NAME HR IS... QTH

HR IS. . . I get to the part where I send RIG HR IS 1 W QRP 4040 FM NOV 94 *QST*, and I get the response "TT RIG SOUNDS GREAT... CANT BELIEVE UR HOMEBREW... UR NOTE PURE ES NO CHIRP OR CLIX... FB SIG FER 1 WATT... UR RIG DOING FB JOB..." always unsolicited and without prompting. This rig is great.

Our 40-40 modifications increased battery life by a factor of more than 3, increased the tuning range by a factor of 2, and saved 70 to 115-mA supply current in transmit. I haven't had this much fun with a rig since I spent $2000. And this one cost much, much less.

AE6C: Having access to good test equipment in the home lab, I made a few measurements on my version (Table 1).

KB6FPW: I have so-so test equipment, and I made the same measurements.

I also checked the spectral purity. The 2nd harmonic was 34 dB down, and spurious responses were down more than 40 dB. These figures are in close agreement with those quoted by the ARRL Lab in the original article.

Yes, even in this simple, synthesizerless design there are some in-band spurs, but they represent less than 100 microwatts of output power. Part 97.307(d) says the limit is 30 dB down minimum; 4 dB is a comfortable margin, as the relative strength of the distortion products isn't particularly sensitive to output power or loading.

Dennis Monticelli, AE6C, 44533 Parkmeadow Dr, Fremont, CA 94539-6528, was first licensed at age 16 in 1967. His Amateur Radio activities spurred his interest in electronics and led to the pursuit of a BSEE, which he earned from the University of California in 1974. Since graduation Dennis has worked for National Semiconductor Corporation, collecting 20 patents as an analog IC designer. He presently serves as the Vice President of the Power Management Business.

Dennis's favorite ham radio activities include homebrewing, HF DXing, antennas, QRP and CW. He lists his greatest accomplishments as DXCC, the Cubic Incher and cajoling a semi-legal, incorrigible low-band experimenter into becoming KB6FPW.

Now in his 12th year of hamming, Mitchell Lee's (172 N Twentyfourth St, San Jose, CA 95116) interest in Amateur Radio was spurred after earning a BSEE at California Polytechnic State University, San Luis Obispo, in 1980. Mitchell presently works at Linear Technology Corporation as an Applications Engineer.

Mitchell has also held the call VK4CFL, operating AM from the Brisbane area. Past QRP activity includes operating 10-m AM motorcycle mobile as KB6FPW/VE7, /VY1 and /VE8 from a large, dual-purpose enduro. He attributes much of his QRP interest to 15 years of completely legitimate 1750-m operation and Elmering from QRP folk hero W6TYP (SK), the first ham to break the "Million Mile Per Watt Input" barrier—accomplished on 40 m—and later 70 million miles per watt on 70 cm. Mitchell's father, Ed, is KB6JQK.

In addition to competing against each other at work and on the air, Dennis and Mitchell share an intense interest in the 40-40, both hold Extra Class licenses, and since 1984 they have annually joined forces operating AE6C Field Day.

From QEX, October 1990, p 3:

Modifications and Improvements to the HW-9

By S. W. McLellan, ND3P
RD 1, Box 149H
Kempton, PA 19529

Several articles have been written dealing with modifications and improvements to the HW-9.[1,2,3,4] After reading them and making my own changes/improvements/corrections to the rig, I thought I would share the modifications I made and the difficulties with the changes suggested by others.

Although the HW-9 "out of the box" played well, several problems were detected and many enhancements were desired. Most importantly, problems, such as instabilities, had to be overcome to make the HW-9 stable and reliable.

To avoid duplicating the entire HW-9 schematic, portions of the schematic are redrawn to illustrate the changes I made. It will still be necessary to refer to the complete HW-9 schematic to get the "whole picture." In addition, the original components are referred to by Heath's component designation numbers.

The most annoying (and destructive) problem was instability and overheating in the power output stage. My solution is shown in Figs 1 and 2. I (and others—see Ref 1) have noticed that the power output stage of the HW-9 suffers from instability problems. In particular, I noticed that a mismatch to the rig might "induce" oscillations in the power output stage, sometimes at VHF. The oscillation was evident from excessive current consumption, FM radio interference, or by a sudden increase in output power (as measured by a watt meter) as the drive level is increased. As will be discussed below, I found that I could not rely on the HW-9's output meter to measure the relative output power of the HW-9; AGC and IF amplifier problems interfered with the output meter's readings.

When I asked Heath about the power output amplifier instability problem, they said that Q402 should be a 2N5770 (417-293) and that would solve the problem. They happily sent me the replacement transistor and I installed it; the problem didn't go away.

I found that the main problem with the power output stage is the lack of adequate RF bypassing. Heath provided a single 0.1-μF ceramic bypass capacitor (C445) between the output transformer T403 and the two-

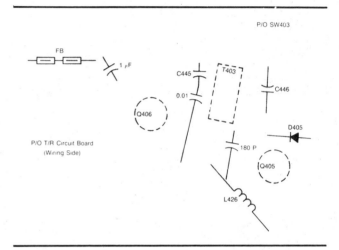

Fig 1—P/O T/R circuit board (wiring side view of power output stage)

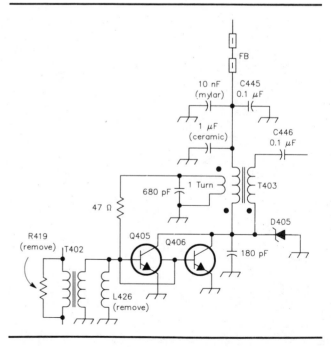

Fig 2—Power output stage

ferrite-bead choke. Further, the ground side of C445 is as far away from the emitters of Q405, Q406 (the power output transistors) as seemingly possible. Too much inductance in the ground path can lead to instability. I beefed up the bypassing by adding a low series inductance 0.01-μF mylar capacitor from the "hot side" of C445 to the ground trace nearest the emitters of Q405, Q406. This is shown in Fig 1, a magnified bottom view (wiring side) of the T/R circuit board. Note that the 0.01-μF capacitor provides the shortest possible path back to the ground and the emitters of Q405, Q406. In addition, I added a 1-μF ceramic bypass capacitor to improve the low-frequency bypassing. Both the 0.01 μF and 1 μF capacitors are tack-soldered on the underside of the T/R circuit board in approximately the positions shown.

To reduce the possibility of VHF oscillations, a 180-pF mica (or other suitable, low series-inductance capacitor type, such as a metalized mylar) capacitor was added between the common collectors of Q405, Q406 and ground by the shortest possible path. Again, the 180-pF capacitor was tack-soldered on the underside of the T/R circuit board, approximately in the position shown in Fig 1.

The above modifications are also shown schematically in Fig 2. I further wanted to "flatten" out the gain-vs-frequency characteristic of the power output amplifier so that the amplifier is more stable at low frequencies without reducing the gain thereof at high frequencies. For this I added frequency-dependent feedback. As a result, I have been unsuccessful in coaxing the amplifier into oscillation with the load mismatched. I removed R419 (330 ohms) and L426 (10 μH) and added a 47-ohm resistor to the bases of Q405, Q406. The 47-ohm resistor now acts, essentially, as the base load for the power output amplifier, removing the need for R419. Negative feedback is provided by a loose, one-turn, winding added to T403. In my HW-9, T403 is provided by Heath premade and the one-turn winding is wound such that the lead to the 47-ohm resistor is wound through the center of the toroidal transformer T403 and the other end of the winding is grounded. Check your T403 to make sure of the correct winding direction. The 680-pF ceramic capacitor reduces the negative feedback at high frequencies, such as on the 12 and 10 meter bands. I grounded the one turn winding to one lead of the 680-pF capacitor and soldered that lead to the ground trace in the circuit board by drilling a hole nearest the emitters of Q405, Q406. Remember, use the shortest leads possible to get the job done.

In Ref 1, emitter degeneration resistors are suggested to help with stabilizing the power output amplifier. I found that they were not necessary. Motorola provided emitter ballasting resistors inside of each transistor so external ones are redundant and significantly reduces the available output power of the amplifier.

I also added extra heat sinks to both transistors (I super-glued another finned heat sink onto each existing

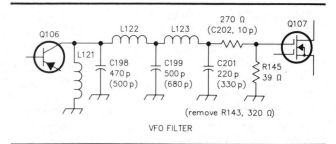

Fig 3—VFO filter

heat sink) which greatly reduced the case temperatures thereof. In addition, I heat sinked the driver transistor, Q404, to cool it down.

Stability of the VFO was greatly improved by soldering one end of a short piece of wire (I used a thin braided wire like Soder-wick®) to the frame of the variable capacitor C1 and the other end to the VFO shield. This was suggested in (Refs 1 and 3) and it went a long way in making the HW-9 easy to tune—especially when using the narrow filter.

One very annoying problem was the dropping off of output power from the HW-9 when tuning to the low-frequency end of each band. Similarly, the sensitivity of the receiver also decreased at the low end of each band. A major contributor to both problems was the VFO filter shown in Fig 3. A computer model of the Heath version of the VFO filter showed an approximately 4-dB variation in output signal voltage over the desired passband (about 5.75 to 6 MHz). Further, the harmonic suppression was not as great as it could be due to a high-pass coupling arrangement between the output of the filter and the first mixer. The new filter design utilizes the old inductors (L122 and L123) and changes the capacitors—only two new capacitors are needed, a 470 pF and a 220 pF. Preferably, the capacitors have a low temperature coefficient (NP0) or are of mica. The 500-pF capacitor (C198) is reused and moved to C199's position. The capacitor C202 is removed and a 270-ohm, ¼ watt, resistor is used instead. R145 is changed to 39 ohms, ¼ watt, and R143 is removed. The 270- and 39-ohm resistors reduce the signal level to the first mixer from the VFO filter to approximately that before the above changes were made. Note that to avoid static discharge problems, C202 should be changed first and then R145. The resulting filter has less than 0.5 dB of ripple over the desired passband and the second harmonic suppression is now about 45 dB below the fundamental. This change reduced the level of "birdies" on all bands and substantially flattened out the output power vs VFO frequency problem mentioned above.

A perplexing problem showed up when I was monitoring the output of the HW-9 on another receiver and the output power varied. As the output power increased, the transmit frequency changed almost 1 kHz from minimum power to full power. Initially I thought it was due to power supply voltage droop. Instead I found that the RIT circuit (C179, D118, R126, etc) was being affected by the T/R circuit. When the output power is increased, the output signal through C443 forces diode D407 into conduction, placing a negative voltage on the R12 control bus. When the voltage on the R12 bus (+ 12 on receive) became sufficiently negative (I measured over 10 volts negative at full power), the emitter-base junction of Q103 breaks down and varies the voltage applied to the RIT control diode D118. Placing a diode in series with the emitter of Q103 would solve the problem but still applied negative voltage across electrolytic capacitors (which I removed anyway, discussed below) on the bus. The solution I chose was to redesign the T/R switch to solve the problem and improve the receiver performance. This is shown in Fig 4. Instead of D407 dragging the R12 bus negative, D407 is reversed, C442 is removed, and the additional transistor passes current to the D407 when in receive and isolates the diode during transmit. D407 is changed to a PIN diode so that it acts less like a rectifier and has a lower series resistance than the old diode when forward biased. Now, more of the input signal gets through to the transformer T404 during receive. Diode D406 is removed (it operated as a clamp during transmit) and another PIN diode is used as a shunt during transmit. During receive, the diode is unbiased, acting as an open circuit. During transmit, the lower forward resistance of the PIN diode further increases the isolation of the transmitted output signal from the rest of the receiver. With this design, only one diode (D403) instead of two (D403

and D404) is used for isolation. D404 is replaced with a strap and R422 is removed as it is no longer needed. The result is that on 10 meters I can now hear the background noise when I attach an antenna. Note that in Ref 1, the author suggests replacing the diodes with Schottky diodes; *don't do it*—it will worsen an already bad problem and the overload characteristics of the receiver will suffer having diode D406 with a lower forward voltage drop as a clamp across the high-impedance secondary of T404.

I also found an interaction between the transmit return adjustment (R131) and the RIT control due to the emitter-base junction of Q104 breaking down. To eliminate it, I placed a diode (here a germanium diode, such as a 1N3666) in series with the emitter of Q104 (anode to emitter).

Stability of the AGC amplifier was another major concern. I notice that the output of the AGC amplifier U302 was weakly oscillating. Heath evidently forgot to add a bypass capacitor across the power supply to U302; tacking a 0.01-μF ceramic bypass capacitor (circled in Fig 5) from pin 7 of U304 to ground solved the problem. The AGC set point had to be readjusted afterward. In addition, no compensation capacitor on U302 is provided. The lack of a compensation capacitor caused U302 to oscillate when it suppled current to C317 during increasing received signal strength. Adding a 100-pF ceramic capacitor from pin 1 to pin 8 on U302 (also circled in Fig 5) on the underside of the T/R circuit board eliminated the oscillation.

In Ref 1, a suggestion was made to increase the capacitance of C317 to slow up the AGC decay rate. I

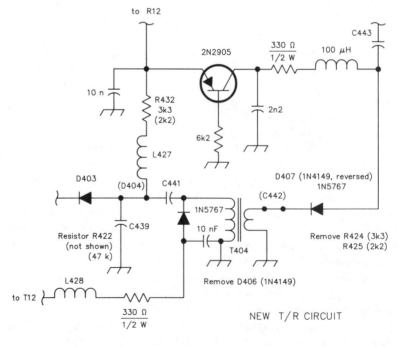

Fig 4—New T/R circuit

NEW T/R CIRCUIT

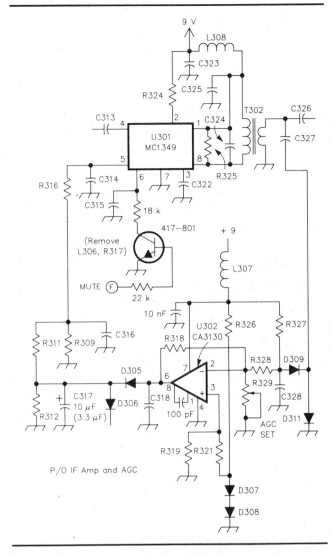

Fig 5—P/O IF amp and AGC

As mentioned above, I could not rely on the output meter to indicate the relative output power of the HW-9. The main difficulty with the output meter was a sudden jump of the meter to near full scale as the output power was increased. Correspondingly, the meter indication would not drop until the output power was nearly zero. The actual output power, as indicated on a watt meter, did not match the output meter's indication. This phenomena occurred mainly on the 80- and 40-meter bands. The problem was traced to RF energy being amplified by the IF amplifier U301 (Fig 5) and upsetting the AGC. I found that the gain of U301 was not being sufficiently reduced during transmit. Decreasing the resistance of R317 (originally 1.5 megohms) reduced the gain of U301 sufficiently to eliminate the problem but the AGC characteristics would suffer because the AGC bias current from pin 5 of U301 would decrease, decreasing the voltage across C317. The meter would then read well below zero when transmitting with low output power. However, by shorting pin 6 through a resistor to ground during receiver mute (further discussed below), the bias current from pin 5 of U301 would not change significantly and the gain of U301 was reduced sufficiently to eliminate the problem. I used the transistor that was Q303 (Heath part number 417-801, discussed below in connection with the audio thump suppression modification), removed R317, and replaced L306 with a 22-kΩ resistor. The base of the added transistor goes into the hole where R317 was to connect to the 22-kΩ resistor. An 18-kΩ resistor is soldered into the remaining hole for R317, the unsoldered end connecting to the collector of the added transistor, and the emitter of the transistor soldered to the ground lead of C315. Now the output meter correctly indicates the relative output power of the HW-9 on all bands even though the meter reads slightly less than zero during transmit with no output power. This modification should be made in conjunction with the audio thump suppression modification discussed below.

A small change that will improve the overload capability of the HW-9 receiver is to add an idler to the second mixer U401 during receive. As shown in Fig 6, I added a 51-ohm resistor in series with a tank circuit, which resonates at approximately the IF frequency (8.83 MHz), across the primary of T301. The resistor/tank circuit combination has low Q so that the resonate frequency need not be at exactly the IF frequency. The idler, during receive, provides a matched load to the IF port of the mixer U401 at all frequencies except at near the IF frequency. At the IF frequency, the tank circuit resonates and the 51-ohm resistor is decoupled. Note that the idler does not couple to the mixer U401 during transmit; steering diodes D301, D302 (not shown) decouple T301, C301, C302, etc, from the mixer during transmit.

A major change I made dealt with the IF filtering. As pointed out in Ref 4, the IF filter bandwidth is too wide for dense signal environments—such as in a contest or on Field Day. In addition, the crystal filter supplied (FL 301) is mismatched so that severe passband ripple

changed C317 from 3.3 μF to 10 μF which slowed the decay nicely. It was also suggested that the resistor R312 (47 kΩ) be changed; *don't do it!* The values chosen by Heath are critical for the proper bias current for U301 at maximum IF gain (minimum AGC). However, after I changed C317, when keying the rig the S-meter would "pin" at the top end even with low output power. But if I hold the key down, the meter reading would fall to the right level. I traced this to the timing of the voltages on the R12 and T12 (+12 on transmit) control busses. The voltages on the busses were not dropping sufficiently when switching from transmit to receive and vice-versa before the other bus went to full voltage. The overlap would leave the receiver IF on for a millisecond or so during transmit and remained transmitting when the receiver was turned back on. Changing C576 to a 0.01-μF bypass capacitor (it was 3.3 μF) solved the receiver turn-off delay problem. Changing R436 from 1 kΩ to 510 ohms solved the transmit turn-off delay problem. Now the meter "reads" correctly even at 35 WPM.

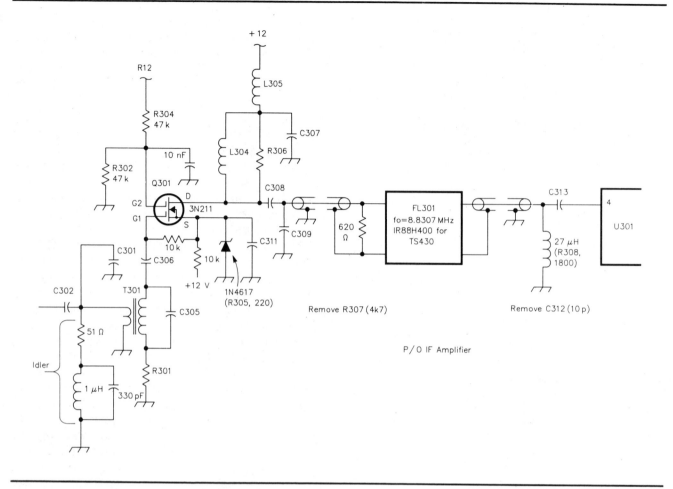

Fig 6—P/O IF amplifier

occurs. It was very annoying to have the S-meter vary more than 3 S units when tuning through a steady carrier in the pass band—the signal peaked when the audio note was over 2 kHz! Instead of trying to properly match the existing filter, I decided to replace it with a good (8-pole) crystal CW filter. Fortunately, the Kenwood TS-430 IF frequency is the same as the HW-9's—8.8307 MHz. I bought an International Radio IR88H400 crystal filter, an 8-pole, 400-Hz wide filter. The new filter is designed to be matched with a 600-ohm resistive load with a 10-pF shunt on both the input and output thereof. The new filter arrangement is shown in Fig 6. I removed the old filter and, because the new filter is much larger than the old one, attached a PC board on standoffs to the HW-9 T/R circuit board and mounted the filter on the new PC board. Short pieces of RG-174 couple the new filter to the T/R board. To properly match the output of the new filter, R308 was removed and a miniature inductor (27 μH) was put in its place. The inductor, combined with the input admittance of U301, provided the equivalent of 600 ohms/10 pF at 8.83 MHz. The input of the filter is matched with the 620-ohm resistor and C309 (10 pF). However, the insertion loss of the new filter is much greater than the old one; the first IF amplifier had to have

its gain increased. Q301 was changed to a high transconductance dual gate MOSFET (3N211) and R307 removed. (Note that R306 could be changed to 600 ohms and the resistor across the input of the filter removed. However, I feel that it is easier to do the matching as shown.) L305 (missing from Heath's schematic) is routed to the +12 line instead of R12. To turn off the first IF amplifier when transmitting, the second gate of Q304 is controlled by R12. To assure that Q304 is completely cut off during transmit (R12 being approximately zero volts), the source of Q304 has a fixed voltage thereon suppled and stabilized by a 10-kΩ bias resistor and a 2.7-volt Zener diode, respectively. A visible LED and a silicon diode in series may be used instead of the Zener diode with a lower resistance bias resistor. R301 is no longer necessary but does not require removal.

As a consequence of using the narrow IF filter, the BFO transmit frequency must now be set correctly or you may not be transmitting on the same frequency you are receiving. Don't attempt to adjust the transmit return (R131) to compensate; you are compensating the VFO and the "compensation" will be good only for the one VFO frequency you adjust it for. Instead, adding a small trimmer capacitor to the BFO circuit will allow for proper

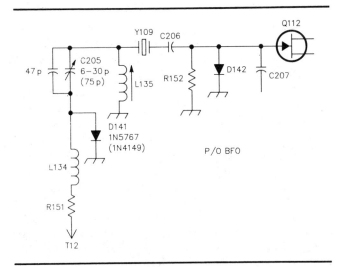

Fig 7—P/O BFO

compensation, as shown in Fig 7. I removed C205 and placed a 6-30 pF trimmer in its place and bridged a 47-pF capacitor across the trimmer. I changed D141 from a IN4149 to a IN5767 (a pin diode) for better, more stable, control of the BFO frequency. Next, I drilled another hole in the BFO shield over the trimmer and reassembled the radio. This change means that the alignment of the BFO is now slightly different from the way Heath suggests. BFO alignment is now as follows: Using a frequency counter, first set the BFO frequency to 8.8314 MHz by adjusting L135. Next, key the HW-9 and adjust the new trimmer (C205) for a frequency of 8.8307 MHz. This gives

you the correct 700-Hz shift from receive to transmit.

Another annoyance was the sidetone pitch being lower than the narrow filter center frequency; often I was off frequency and not "zero beat" since I was tuning the receive pitch to the sidetone pitch. Bridging a small resistor (I used a 270 kΩ) across R366 moved the pitch to near 700 Hz.

Ref 2 suggests changing the components in the narrow audio filter. The new narrow filter design works well and implementing the change is strongly recommended. The design is shown in Fig 3 using 1% resistors and metalized film capacitors for more consistent performance. However, I noticed some "fuzziness" when using the new narrow filter. The data sheets on the device (an LM 324) mentions that when the output of the op amp is AC coupled (here, the output of U304C), crossover distortion may result due to insufficient bias current in the output stage thereof. This was causing the fuzziness I was hearing. Adding a 10-kΩ or so resistor from the output of U304C (pin 14) to ground eliminated the distortion.

Another possible "mistake" is in the design of the low-pass filter of U304B. It is not clear to me what filter type it is; the design suggests a second-order multiple-feedback low-pass filter arrangement. I took the basic circuit from Heath and changed the component values and the circuit topology slightly to provide the second-order characteristic. The new circuit is shown in Fig 8. The resistance values of R348, R349, and R351 have been changed. The capacitance of C338 was not changed but instead of coupling to the junction of R348,

Fig 8—P/O narrow audio filter

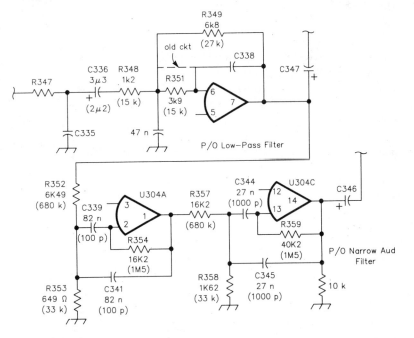

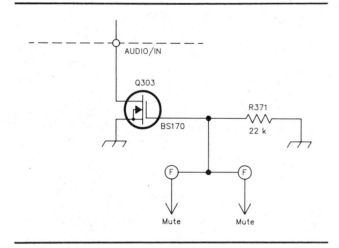

Fig 9—New audio mute circuit

R349, and R351, it couples to the inverting input (pin 6) of U304B. A 0.047-μF capacitor is added from the junction of R348, R349, and R351 to ground to achieve the second-order characteristic. The resulting low-pass filter has a cut off frequency of about 1.4 kHz. Note that capacitor C336 should be reversed per Ref 3 and the capacitance thereof increased to 3.3 μF (or more) for better low-frequency response.

In Ref 2 an elaborate design is presented to remove an annoying audio thump when the HW-9 goes from transmit to receive. A much simpler circuit that completely solves this problem is shown in Fig 9. Q303, originally a bipolar transistor, is replaced with an N-channel MOSFET, such as a BS-170 (Radio Shack 276-2074), with the gate thereof going directly to the mute line and R371, formerly going to the base of Q303, connecting to ground. The thump in the original Heath design results from collector-base junction of Q303 becoming forward biased during transmit. The FET does not have this problem and R371 now acts as a pull-down for the mute line. The thump is now gone. The old Q303 is reused in the IF amplifier disable modification discussed earlier.

Some operators may think that the receive bandwidth using the new, narrower, IF filter is too narrow for just browsing the bands. I feel, however, that the narrower bandwidth is required since the HW-9's narrow audio filter is not sharp enough for our crowded bands and the narrower IF filter avoids AGC pumping from adjacent strong signals. Still, it would be an interesting project to correct the matching to the original Heath crystal filter so that the pass-band ripple is reduced and still have the wider bandwidth when desired.

No reverse power voltage protection is supplied. I inserted an in-line fuse (2 amps) in the red wire coming from the power connector S1 to switch S2. A diode (such as a 1N4001) was bridged from the S2—fuse junction to ground so that the diode would be forward biased upon applying reversed power supply voltage to the HW-9, thus blowing the fuse. If you frequently get the voltages reversed, it may be more practical to mount the fuse in a holder on the rear panel or put it in line with the power cable so that the fuse can be replaced more easily.

I also suggest that you build in a keyer like that mentioned in Ref 2. It makes it much more convenient on backpacking trips if you don't want to bring along your keyer.

Be forewarned that some of these modifications are difficult and tricky; proceed at your own risk. It took over a year and a half to design and complete the modifications described above. It was both fun and frustrating to figure out the problem and solve it—usually the change interacted with other sections of the rig, causing more headaches and changes. I think my HW-9 is now more enjoyable to use both for contest operating and rag-chewing than the unmodified version. Some of the modifications can be made at any time. A few of the changes, such as the power amplifier changes and the AGC bypass capacitor and compensation capacitor additions, should be made at the earliest convenience.

References

[1]"Helping and Hopping the HW-9" by Staudt, *73 Magazine*, February 1988, pp 50 & 52.
[2]"Improving the HW-9 Transceiver" by Hutchinson and Lau, *QST*, April 1988, pp 26-29.
[3]QRP Column by Bryce, *73 Magazine*, February 1989, p 86.
[4]Hints and Kinks column by Newkirk, *QST*, June 1990, pp 40-41.

From QST, November 1995, p 41:

A Small High-Performance CW Transceiver

Can *you* handle full break-in, 1 W output and single-signal direct-conversion reception in a 20-meter package the size of a 35-mm camera?

By Rick Campbell, KK7B
Department of Electrical Engineering
Michigan Technological University
Houghton, MI 49931
e-mail: rlcampbe@mtu.edu

Here is a little radio that I designed as an exercise in cuteness. It is supposed to disappear into my backpack without making a noticeable bulge or increase in weight. Those two constraints dictated a number of engineering decisions. With 1990s RF technology, a radio for any band can be small and light. 1990s battery technology limits the power output of a lightweight rig to about 1 W. A power output of 1 W makes some bands and modes considerably more attractive than others. One watt of VHF FM works well in flat areas, but I don't backpack in flat areas—in fact, my first rule of backpacking is to keep a mountain range between me and civilization. In between mountain ranges, it is nice to bounce signals off the moon or the ionosphere. A backpack EME station requires too many B batteries, so the bouncing mechanism of choice has to be the ionosphere. One watt of SSB on 10 or 12 meters works fine during the sunspot maximum, but that's five years away. SSB on 15 or 17 meters works occasionally these days, but generally during the daylight hours when I would rather be enjoying the scenery. There is nothing technically wrong with 1 W on 20-meter SSB, but it is a bit like riding a bicycle on the rush-hour interstate. Forty meters is a little better, but D-layer absorption is getting high. During the months I like to backpack, 75 and 160 meters are not in very good shape, and efficient antennas for those bands are physically large. Moving over to CW, there are two very good bands: 20 and 30 meters. I flipped a coin and built the radio for 20 meters.

Packaging

I put quite a bit of thought into the packaging. My first inclination was to make the

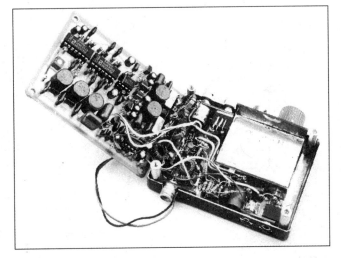

Opened and unfolded, the miniature CW transceiver displays its VFO/transmitter board (ugly construction, right) and miniR2 board (left, available as a kit per Note 1).

whole station the size and shape of a paperback book. Then I remembered that I always have to think about where I put a book in the backpack so it won't poke me, and that the books I take backpacking always get bent. One thing that slips in easily and never gets hurt is my little Minox 35-mm camera. After half a dozen sketches I had a packaging scheme that produced a 1-W, 20-m CW transceiver the same size and shape as my camera.

There is always a question of how much to put in the radio enclosure. Should the batteries, antenna tuner, VSWR meter, key

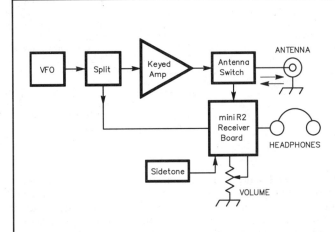

Figure 1—The little CW transceiver's block diagram. All of the radio's circuitry fits on two boards: the miniR2 receiver module, (Figure 3) available as a kit per Note 1, and an ugly-constructed module (Figure 2) containing the balance of the parts.

[1]Notes appear on page 3-38.

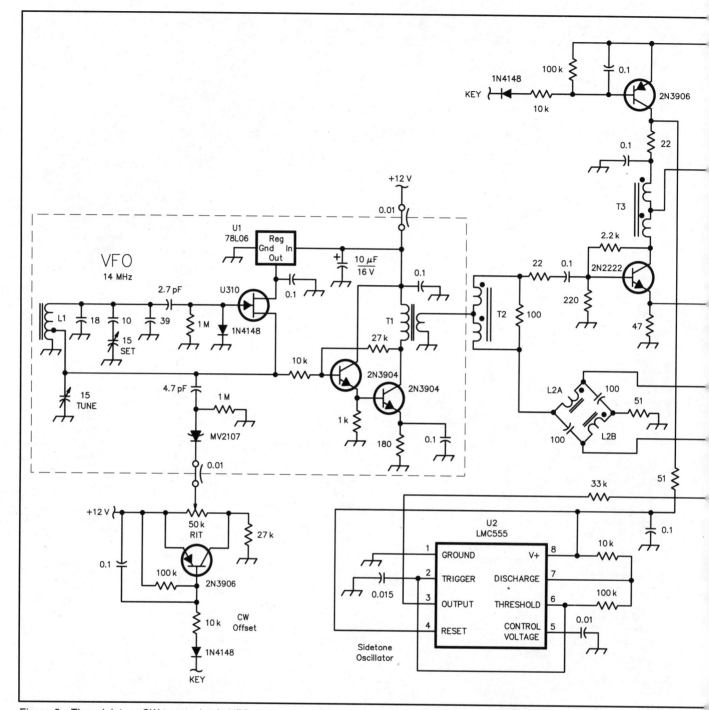

Figure 2—The miniature CW transceiver's VFO, transmitter and sidetone circuitry. All of the circuit's resistors are ¼-W, 5%-tolerance units unless specified otherwise. The protective 33-V Zener diode at the 2N3866's collector is a 1N973 or equivalent; the MV2107 tuning diode used in the RIT circuit has a nominal capacitance of 22 pF at a tuning voltage of 4 V.

L1—24 turns of #28 enameled wire on a T-37-6 toroidal powdered-iron core. Tap at 6 turns from ground end.

L2—14 bifilar-wound turns of #28 enameled wire on a T-37-6 toroidal powdered-iron core. Do not twist wires prior to winding.

L3, L4—10 turns of #28 enameled wire on a T-37-6 toroidal powdered-iron core.

L5—120-mH miniature choke.

L6—35 turns of #28 enameled wire on a T-37-2 toroidal powdered-iron core.

L7, L8—13 turns of #28 enameled wire on a T-37-6 toroidal powdered-iron core.

L9—29 turns of #28 enamelled wire on a T-37-2 powdered-iron core.

T1—Primary (winding on 2N3904 side): 15 turns of #28 enameled wire on an FT-37-43 toroidal ferrite core; secondary: 3 turns of the same wire over the primary.

T2, T3, T4—10 bifilar-wound turns of #28 enameled wire on an FT-37-43 toroidal ferrite core.

U1—78L06 6-V, 100-mA voltage regulator.

U2—LMC555 (or equivalent) CMOS timer.

and speaker be external or built-in? For that matter, there are lots of very good reasons to dis-integrate the radio even more, with separate VFO, transmitter and receiver modules. I decided on external batteries because disconnecting them positively turns off the radio, and they can be used in my flashlight if needed. An antenna tuner and VSWR meter are not always needed, so they are left out. Sometimes it is nice to use a "real" key (bigger and heavier than the whole radio!) so I left that out too. I use headphones to keep battery drain low, so there is no speaker. Everything else is in the little package.

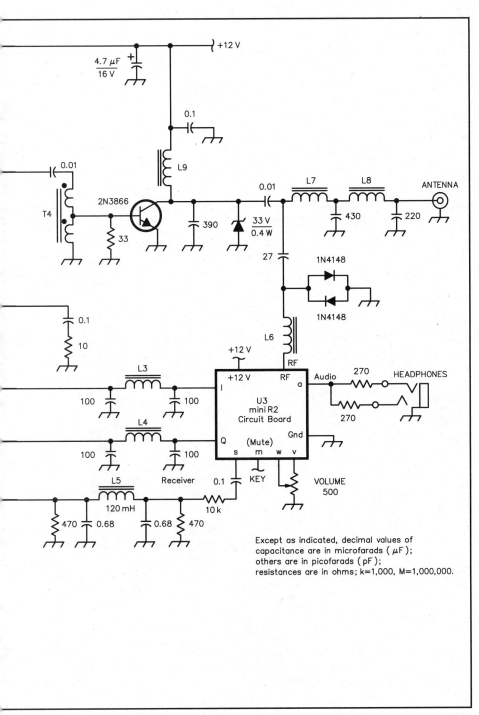

Except as indicated, decimal values of capacitance are in microfarads (μF); others are in picofarads (pF); resistances are in ohms; k=1,000, M=1,000,000.

brass with soldered corners. Don't try this at home, kids. I have built almost as many sheet brass boxes as radios, and the first few hundred were pretty ugly. Even if you build one that looks nice, it still has a problem: It weighs more than the radio it contains. Next time I will make the case out of foam-sandwich-wood-epoxy composite. Trips to the local hobby shop for a sheet of ¹/₁₆ inch aircraft plywood and the local boat store for a West System Maxi Repair kit and a little fiberglass cloth will provide the materials. I have built a bunch of those, too, and they started looking pretty good after about number 10. Rounded corners are a good idea for anything that is going to bounce around in a cloth bag.

Circuitry

Figure 1 shows the transceiver's block diagram and Figures 2 and 3 show the schematic. I call this circuit the "generic low-power transceiver," or "G-QRP rig" for short. It is full of ideas contributed by several generations of homebrew transceiver artists over the past few decades. I have used the same basic circuit for a number of different radios because it works well. The only significant departure from such classic QRP rigs as Roy Lewallen's "Optimized"[1] and Wes and Roger Hayward's "Ugly Weekender"[2,3] is the use of an image-reject receiver. Sometimes I call this circuit "The Imposter" because it is impossible to tell that it is not a superhet just by operating it.

The circuitry in Figure 2 is all built "ugly style" on a piece of unetched copper clad board cut to the same dimensions as the miniR2 circuit board, with small vertical pieces soldered on and a shield enclosure soldered completely around the VFO. Ugly construction takes optimum advantage of the available space, builders talent and available parts, and generally outperforms printed circuitry in RF applications. "Ugly" radios can also be real original works of art, and their builders are justifiably proud of their creations.

Receiver module U3 (Figure 3), is a miniR2 kit, available from Kanga Products.[4] The circuitry is described in detail in references cited at Notes 5 and 6. The miniR2 is half the size of the R2, has headphone-only audio output, and doesn't need any hand-picked parts. It sacrifices a little skirt selectivity and close-in dynamic range, but its improved noise figure makes its dynamic range, measured using ARRL's standard spacing of 20 kHz, a little better than the R2. I recommend the miniR2 for portable applications and the R2 for base-station operation in crowded bands.

The dashed line around the VFO is shielding. It is part of the circuit and is *not* optional. When a transmitter operates on the same frequency as its VFO, the VFO tank circuit acts as an antenna and picks up a little of the transmitted signal. The transmitted signal adds to the VFO signal, and

There are four controls: **VOLUME**; bandset (**SET**); tuning (**TUNE**); and **RIT**. The band-set control is a very stiff capacitor that sets the tuning range somewhere in the 20-meter ham band. Normally, it is set to the CW portion. The tuning control then tunes from 14.000 to 14.070 MHz with a mark every 10 kHz. The tuning rate is quick, but acceptable. The combination of RIT and excellent skirt selectivity makes a very effective interference-fighting tool during contacts. Since full-break-in CW is used, no manual TR switch is needed.

There is a flaw in the ergonomics. Conventional radios have a "front panel" with controls and a "rear panel" with connectors for power, antenna, headphones and key. Hand-held radios are designed to be conveniently operated while being held. This radio is neither, but it is much closer to a hand-held. Because of its conventional "rear panel" connections, there is no easy way to hold the radio while operating, and it needs to be propped up somewhere in the tent, with as much weight holding it in place as possible. The next time I build a back-pack radio, I will make the box first and then find out how I want to operate it before blindly following conventional wisdom.

I made the clamshell case out of sheet

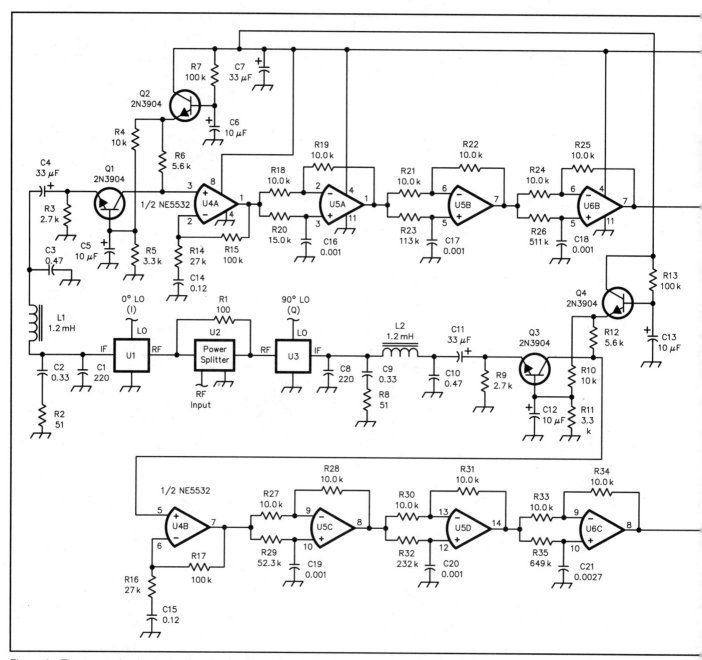

Figure 3—The transceiver's receiver portion consists of a miniR2 (miniature single-signal direction-conversion receiver) module (see Note 1). All of the circuit's resistors are 5%-tolerance, ¼-W types unless otherwise indicated.

C1, C8—220 pF, chip
C2, C9—0.33 µF, 50 V, 5% (Panasonic V Series)
C3, C10—0.47 µF, 50 V, 5% (Panasonic V Series)
C4, C7, C11, C24, C39—33 µF, 16 V, 20% (Panasonic KA Series)
C5, C6, C12, C13, C22, C23, C36—10 µF, 16 V, 20% (Panasonic KA Series)
C14, C15—0.12 µF, 50 V, 5% (Panasonic V Series)
C16-20—0.001 µF (Xicon 102 FT)
C21—0.0027 µF (Xicon 272 FT)
C25—0.18 µF, 50 V, 5% (Panasonic V Series)
C26—0.022 µF, 50 V, 5% (Panasonic V Series)
C27—0.27 µF, 50 V, 5% (Panasonic V Series)
C28—0.033 µF, 50 V, 5% (Panasonic V Series)
C29—0.15 µF, 50 V, 5% (Panasonic V Series)

C30, C31—1.0 µF, 100 V, 10% (Panasonic ECQ-E Series)
C32, C35—0.1 µF, 50 V, 5% (Panasonic V Series)
C33, C37—0.12 µF, 50 V, 5% (Panasonic V Series)
C34, C38—390 pF, 63 V, C0G (Panasonic monolithic ceramic)
C40—100 µF, 16 V, 20% (Panasonic KA Series)
D1—1N4148 diode
L1, L2—1.2 µH (Toko 10RB, Digi-Key TK4401)
L3, L4—33 µH (Toko 10RB, Digi-Key TK4418)
L5—120 µH (Toko 10RB, Digi-Key TK4426)
Q1-4—2N3904 NPN BJT
Q5—2N5457 N-channel JFET
R1, R52—100 Ω, ⅛ W chip
R2, R8—51 Ω
R3, R9, R36, R37, R51—2.7 kΩ
R4, R10, R39, R41, R42, R43, R47, R49—10 kΩ

R5, R11—3.3 kΩ
R6, R12—5.6 kΩ
R7, R13, R15, R17, R44, R50—100 kΩ
R14, R16—27 kΩ
R18, R19, R21, R22, R24, R25, R27, R28, R30, R31, R33, R34—10.0 kΩ, ¼ W, 1%
R20—15.0 kΩ, ¼ W, 1%
R23—113 kΩ, ¼ W, 1%
R26—511 kΩ, ¼ W, 1%
R29—52.3 kΩ, ¼ W, 1%
R32—232 kΩ, ¼ W, 1%
R35—649 kΩ, ¼ W, 1%
R38—1 kΩ, 10-turn trimmer pot (Spectrol 74W or equivalent)
R40—470 Ω
R45, R48—4.7 kΩ
R46—1 MΩ
U1, U3—TUF-1 mixer (Mini-Circuits)
U2—TK2818 splitter (Toko)
U4, U7—NE5532 dual low-noise op amp
U5, U6—NE5514 quad op amp

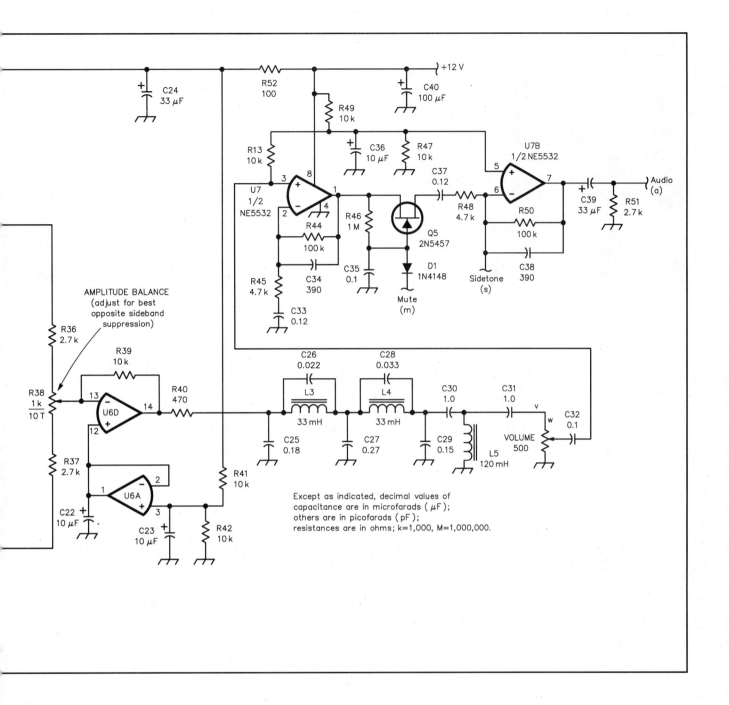

Except as indicated, decimal values of capacitance are in microfarads (μF); others are in picofarads (pF); resistances are in ohms; k=1,000, M=1,000,000.

the phase of the vector sum of both signals differs from that of the VFO signal by itself. To satisfy the Barkhausen criteria for oscillation,[7] the VFO quickly changes its frequency to maintain 0° of phase shift around the loop. This is called *chirp* (in polite company). There are several good ways to eliminate chirp. One is to operate the VFO on a different frequency than the transmitted signal, either by using a frequency multiplier or a heterodyne scheme. Another is to properly shield the VFO, so that the transmitted signal can't get in. Since shielding is inexpensive in a home-brew radio and also improves thermal and mechanical stability, it is a good approach.

The LO phase-shift network shown in Figure 1 is different than those shown in the original R2 article. It provides 90° of phase shift over a very broad bandwidth, and acceptable amplitude balance when used to drive saturating LO ports. With the component values shown, it works nicely from 13 to 15 MHz, after tweaking at any frequency in the 20-meter band. The lumped-element eighth-wave transmission lines in each leg provide a means of tweaking the relative phase of the output ports. This network was described in *SPRAT*.[8]

The Complete Station

The complete station consists of the radio, a dipole antenna with tuned feed line, a microswitch key, Walkman headphones, and an 8-AA-cell battery pack. It all fits in a little camera bag. I stuff all the pieces in zipper-lock bags—a habit I picked up in the rainy Pacific Northwest. The entire

package weighs about as much as one good meal, and is small enough that I don't have to leave anything home to make room in the backpack.

Operation

I try to get the antenna up as high as I can in the trees. Then I listen and see if the band is open. If there are lots of loud signals, especially up near 14.060 MHz, I tune around for a loud CQ to answer. Full break-in and a good clean CW signal just like the appliance at home make for easy contacts. When the band is open, 1 W of CW to a dipole works out just fine—there is no need to go begging "alms for the weak" by sending "QRP" every other word. (Opinions run strong on the HF bands, and some stations hear much better if they think you are run-

A look into the transceiver's VFO before the VFO shield enclosure was soldered closed. Air-dielectric trimmer capacitors serve as the VFO's SET and TUNE controls; the VFO tuned-circuit inductor (L1) is between them.

RICK CAMPBELL, KK7B

ning 100 W.) When 20 meters is in bad shape, I put the batteries in the flashlight and dig out the bent-up paperback that has been poking me in the ribs all day.

Conclusions

This little radio works well. Its audio distortion is low; its two-tone, third-order dynamic range is better than most commercial transceivers; and its full-break-in CW makes it easy to operate. The combination of ugly construction for the RF stages and a commercially available PC board kit for the receiver signal processing is an attractive approach to high-performance custom radio engineering. In the past, I only put radio equipment in the backpack for special events like Field Day. This rig is small and light enough that I can throw it in just in case I feel like operating.

I named this radio the "Passport" be-cause it has been all the way around the world. I carried it with me to the Asia-Pacific QRP conference in Kuching, Sarawak, East Malaysia, in November 1994, and loaned it to the Reverend George Dobbs, G3RJV. He carried it back to England, and then returned it to me at Dayton. It has also made two trips to the West Coast and back. Judging by the amount of travel this little radio has done, my original goals for its design must have been met!

Acknowledgments

Once again, I thank the Reverend George Dobbs, G3RJV, for twenty years of publishing delightful little radio circuits. Much of the circuitry presented here is a natural evolution of material from the past two decades of *SPRAT*.[9]

This radio has "Wes Hayward" written all over it. From the first inklings of ultraportable backpacking radios to his review of this manuscript, he has been a part of the entire process. Wes made significant contributions to the development of the miniR2 board from the R2, and did an extensive performance evaluation of the radio.

Notes

[1]Roy Lewallen, W7EL, "An Optimized QRP Transceiver," *QST*, Aug 1980, pp 14-19; also see Feedback, *QST*, Nov 1980, p 53.

[2]Roger Hayward, KA7EXM, and Wes Hayward, W7ZOI, "The 'Ugly Weekender,'" *QST*, Aug 1981, pp 18-21.

[3]Roger Hayward, KA7EXM, "The 'Ugly Week-ender' II: Adding a Junk-Box Receiver," *QST*, Aug 1992, pp 27-30.

[4]Kanga US, 3521 Spring Lake Dr, Findlay, OH 45840, tel 419-423-5643. A miniR2 kit that includes the circuit board and the parts that mount on it is available for $95; a board by itself is $20. Add $4.50 for shipping and han-dling. More information on Kanga kits is avail-able by e-mail (kanga@bright.net) and from Kanga's World Wide Web home page (**http://qrp.cc.nd.edu/kanga/**), which includes the full Kanga catalog.

[5]Rick Campbell, KK7B, "High-Performance, Single-Signal Direct-Conversion Receivers," *QST*, Jan 1993, pp 32-40.

[6]Rick Campbell, KK7B, "A Single-Board No Tune Transceiver for 1296?" *Proc of Micro-wave Update '93*, pp 17-38 (Newington: ARRL, 1993).

[7]See, for example, the How Oscillators Work section of Chapter 14, AC/RF Sources (Os-cillators and Synthesizers), in *The ARRL Handbook for Radio Amateurs*, 1995 edi-tion.—*Ed.*

[8]Rick Campbell, KK7B, "KK7B SPRAT Techni-cal Cartoon #1, A Passive Phase-Shift Net-work to Cover the Whole Band," *SPRAT*, Winter 1994/5, pp 20-22.

[9]*SPRAT* is the membership journal of the G QRP Club, annual dues for which are US$10 (MasterCard and VISA payment is acceptable). For details, a sample of the journal *SPRAT* and an application form, write to George Dobbs, G3RJV, St Aidan's Vicarage, 498 Manchester Rd, Rochdale, OL11 3HE, United Kingdom, or use e-mail (g3rjv@gqrp.demon.co.uk). Membership re-newal facilities are available in the US. *SPRAT* is airmailed 4 times a year to each member.

QST-

From QST, May 1993, p 29:

Single-Conversion Microwave SSB/CW Transceivers

No-tune transverters have made it easy to get on the UHF/SHF bands—as long as you have a commercial 2-meter transceiver you can dedicate to that application. Here's how to put two other recent *QST* projects, the R2 direct-conversion receiver and T2 transmitter, to work with a transverter as an inexpensive and lightweight, high-performance, all-home-brew station.

(photos by Kirk Kleinschmidt, NTØZ)

By Rick Campbell, KK7B
Department of Electrical Engineering
Michigan Technological University
Houghton, MI 49931

In January, I described a high performance SSB/CW receiver called R2,[1] and last month I presented a companion multimode transmitter, T2.[2] These two modules can be used to build high-performance, direct-conversion (D-C) transceivers for *any band* below 500 MHz.

One of my favorite activities is weak-signal microwave work on mountaintops using small, portable SSB/CW systems. Using the R2 and T2 boards as a tunable IF for a no-tune microwave transverter, I can build high-performance microwave SSB/CW transceivers that are smaller and use less battery power than systems using commercial multimode 2-meter transceivers and transverters. This article describes some of the design philosophy behind single-conversion microwave systems, and presents a complete 1296-MHz transceiver and an IF system using a choice of two VFO circuits and the R2 and T2 boards.

Basic Design Considerations

Fig 1 is the block diagram of the SSB/CW transceiver. The transceiver has an SSB/CW generator and IF receiver, a pair of mixers and a local oscillator (LO) to perform the IF-to-RF frequency conversion, and RF amplifiers to set the receiver noise figure and increase the transmitter power. The same arrangement can be used for signal frequencies from a few kilohertz to hundreds of gigahertz.

The choice of intermediate frequency (IF) is determined by the selectivity of the RF filtering and the available IF-filtering components. An IF of about 10% of the signal frequency permits good image rejection with a reasonable number of noncritical RF tuned circuits. Conventional SSB/CW superhets for microwaves need to use several frequency conversions to reach a narrow-bandwidth crystal filter operating near 10 MHz. Each frequency conversion adds system complexity, spurious responses, and internally generated receiver signals ("birdies").

We can eliminate the need for crystal filters by using the R2 and T2 boards to build a tunable IF. Since both R2 and T2 work fine at 1/10 the frequency of any microwave band below 6 GHz, we can build single-conversion microwave transceivers that cost less and have fewer spurious responses and outputs than a traditional scheme.

Block Diagram

A complete microwave transceiver using a no-tune transverter board[3] and the R2 and T2 boards is shown in Fig 2. Fig 3 shows the first prototype of this system, and Fig 4 shows IF2, a 144-MHz transceiver intended for direct connection to a no-tune transverter. It's relatively easy to build a transceiver with these boards, because the two share no functions other than the LO. In fact, the interconnections between the boards are almost identical to the cables that interconnect a Collins S line and 62S-1 transverter for VHF-transceive operation!

Each board needs a +12-volt supply at the points marked +. Since the T2 board includes transmit-receive switching and R2 has a muting circuit, both boards are normally powered continuously. R2 requires an external speaker, volume control and filter, options for which were discussed in my January 1993 and August 1992 *QST* articles.[4]

T2 has microphone connections, a push-to-talk (PTT) solder pad marked **P** on the circuit board, and a solder pad marked **K** for key. **P** is grounded for transmitting SSB or CW. To disable audio modulation when transmitting CW, the audio preamp output marked **A** is shorted to ground. A grounded solder pad is etched next to **A** for conve-

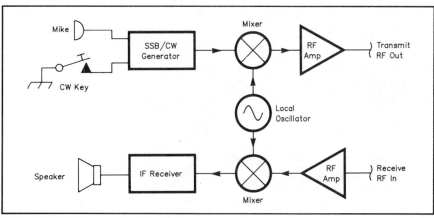

Fig 1—SSB/CW transceiver block diagram.

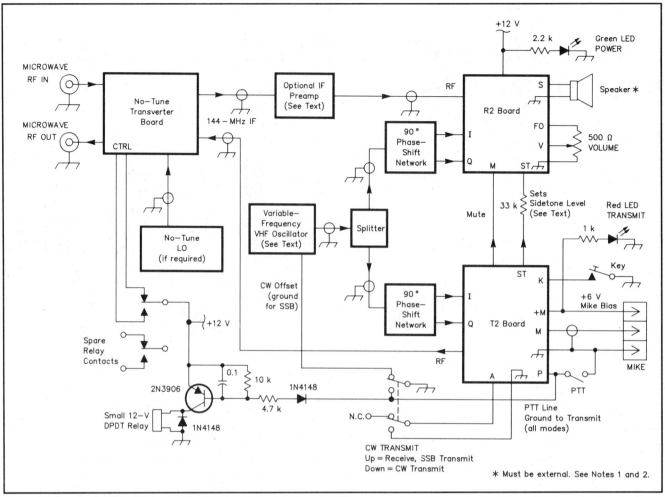

Fig 2—Interconnecting the T2 transmitter board, R2 receiver board, VFO and a no-tune transverter creates a direct-conversion, no-tune microwave transceiver. All of the no-tune transverters except the 903-MHz version use external local oscillators. Set the resistance value in the **ST** line to an appropriate level for your listening environment; 33 kΩ works well for relatively quiet locations. The volume connection (**FO** on the R2 board) *must* be terminated in 500 Ω (see Note 1).

nience in doing this. I use a DPDT **CW TRANSMIT** switch on my radios that simultaneously grounds the audio-preamp output, grounds the PTT line and offsets the local oscillator from zero beat.

Only two wires connect the R2 and T2 boards: mute and sidetone. To mute the receiver during transmit, connect a wire from the unmarked solder pad to the right of **P** on the T2 board to the solder pad marked **M** on the R2 board. The sidetone generator is on the T2 board, with an output marked **ST**. The sidetone input on the receiver board is also marked **ST**. Directly connecting these two points results in a very loud sidetone! For a more comfortable sidetone level, experiment with series resistor values between about 10 kΩ and 100 kΩ. I settled on 33 kΩ for portable operation in quiet locations. Of course, a 100-kΩ sidetone-level pot is an acceptable alternative.

Each board requires a pair of quadrature LO signals, as discussed in the R2 and T2 articles. The first transceiver I built used a

Fig 3—The first no-tune, single-conversion 1296-MHz transceiver that follows the block diagram of Fig 2.

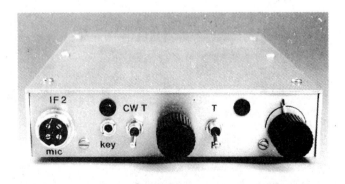

Fig 4—IF2, a D-C transceiver with an integral VXO (Fig 5). This 1¼ × 5¼ × 7½-inch transceiver can be directly connected to a no-tune microwave transverter to create a single-conversion microwave transceiver.

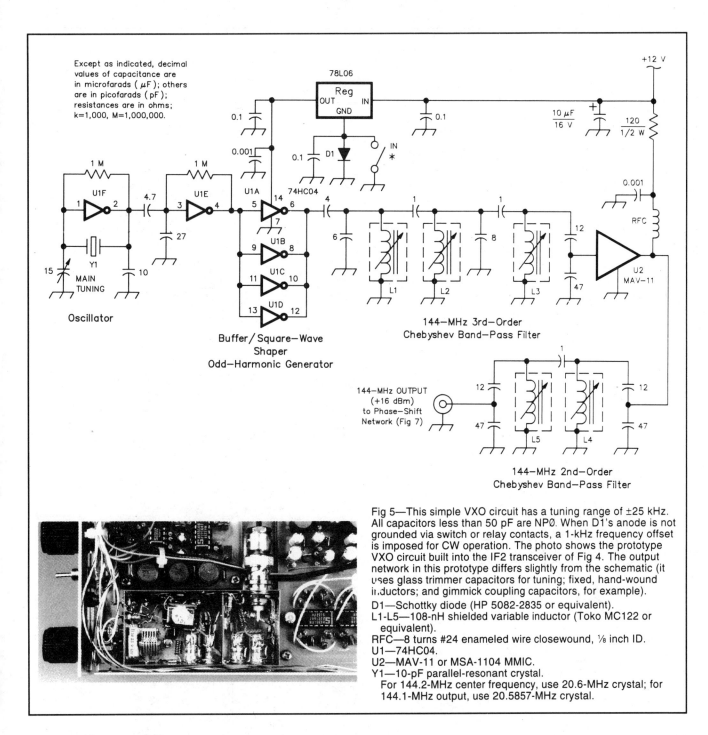

Fig 5—This simple VXO circuit has a tuning range of ±25 kHz. All capacitors less than 50 pF are NPØ. When D1's anode is not grounded via switch or relay contacts, a 1-kHz frequency offset is imposed for CW operation. The photo shows the prototype VXO circuit built into the IF2 transceiver of Fig 4. The output network in this prototype differs slightly from the schematic (it uses glass trimmer capacitors for tuning; fixed, hand-wound inductors; and gimmick coupling capacitors, for example).

D1—Schottky diode (HP 5082-2835 or equivalent).
L1-L5—108-nH shielded variable inductor (Toko MC122 or equivalent).
RFC—8 turns #24 enameled wire closewound, ⅛ inch ID.
U1—74HC04.
U2—MAV-11 or MSA-1104 MMIC.
Y1—10-pF parallel-resonant crystal.
   For 144.2-MHz center frequency, use 20.6-MHz crystal; for 144.1-MHz output, use 20.5857-MHz crystal.

Local Oscillators

The superhet system in Fig 2 uses single conversion with a crystal-controlled front end and a tunable IF. To make the IF tunable, we need a tunable LO. It's easy to build a stable VFO for frequencies as low as 5 or 10 MHz, but not quite as easy at VHF. Several approaches to VHF VFOs that are stable enough for SSB and CW have been used in custom and commercial equipment over the years. The simplest approach is a variable crystal oscillator (VXO), and the simplest VHF VXO I've seen appeared on the back of my napkin at lunch a few months ago. The most recent iteration is shown in Fig 5. This oscillator has a 50-kHz range at 144 MHz, reasonable stability, and spurs that are suppressed more than 72 dB. I obtained a CW offset of about 1 kHz by raising the 74HC04 supply from 6.0 to 6.4 volts by switching a Schottky diode in series with the

6-volt, three-terminal regulator's ground lead. This is about the minimum-parts-count CW-offset circuit I've seen, and it emphasizes the need for voltage regulation on crystal oscillators followed by frequency multipliers!

Another tunable VHF local oscillator, a *premixed* VFO, is shown in Fig 6. This circuit achieves oscillator and image spurious levels about 45 dB below the desired output, when properly shielded. A premixed VFO is simply a high-frequency VFO followed by a low-level transverter. *The ARRL Handbook* shows several examples of VFOs and transverters that can be combined to provide a stable, tunable LO for VHF. If the VFO frequency is less than about 10% of the

single 90° LO phase shifter with a splitter on each output port to drive the I and Q ports of the R2 and T2 boards. I found that I could adjust the phase-shift network for good opposite sideband suppression from *either* the transmitter or the receiver, but not both! A better approach is to split the LO output first, then use separate phase-shift networks for transmit and receive. This allows independent adjustment of the receiver and transmitter for best opposite-sideband suppression.

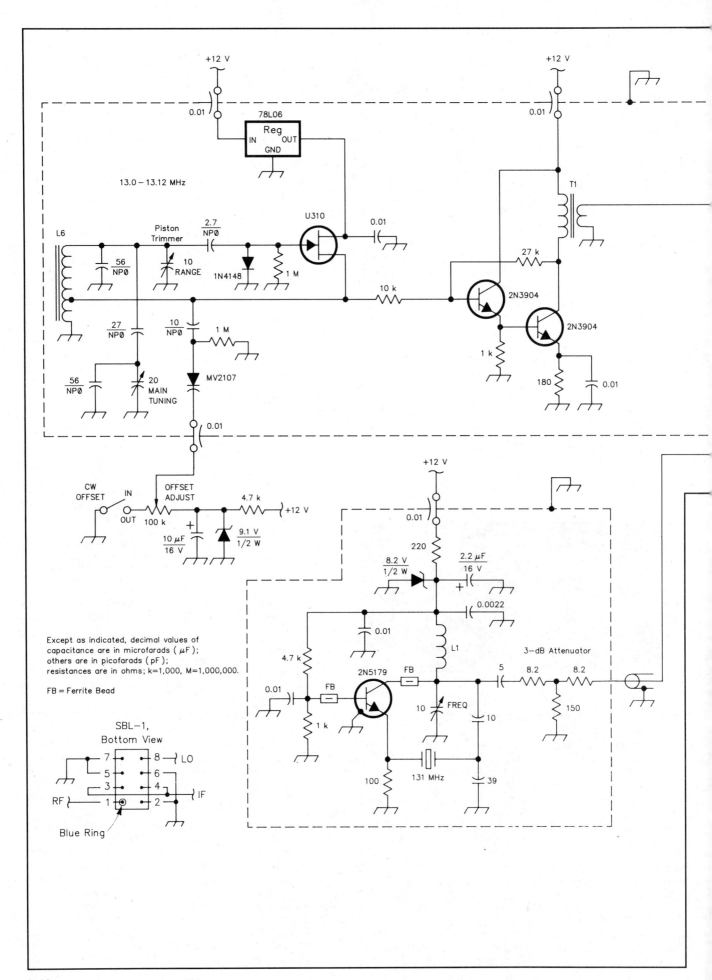

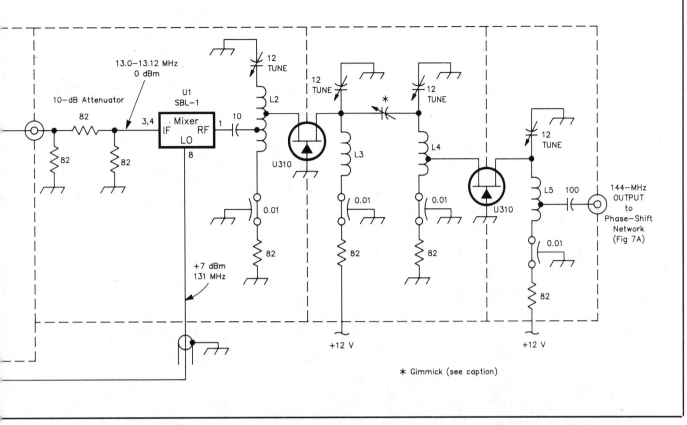

Fig 6—The premixed VFO circuit. The **CW OFFSET** switch is opened to enable the offset. This function can be handled by a relay contact or the front-panel **CW TRANSMIT** switch. The *gimmick* capacitor that provides interstage coupling consists of a ½-inch-long tightly twisted pair of #24 insulated wires.

L1—5 turns #24 enameled wire, ⅛-inch ID, ⅛ inch long.

L2—8 turns #24 bare wire, ¼ inch ID, ⅜ inch long. Tap input 2 turns from ground end; tap U310 source 3 turns from ground end.

L3—8 turns #24 bare wire, ¼ inch ID, ⅜ inch long.

L4—8 turns #24 bare wire, ¼ inch ID, ⅜ inch long. Tap U310 source 3 turns from ground end.

L5—8 turns #24 bare wire, ¼ inch ID, ⅜ inch long. Tap output 2 turns from ground end.

L6—24 turns #24 enameled wire on a T-37-6 core, tapped at 6 turns from ground end. For best stability, boil L6 in water for 2 minutes after winding it.

T1—Core: FT-37-43. Primary: 15 turns #22 enameled wire; secondary, 3 turns #22 enameled wire.

desired output frequency, then the transverter needs very good selectivity to remove the image and oscillator spurs. Helical filters, often used in VHF receiver front ends, can be used to obtain the necessary selectivity.

Another option for a stable variable VHF LO is a frequency synthesizer using a PLL, DDS or some other combination of letters. I have built a few of each type, but they were more complicated and didn't work as well as my VXOs and premixed VFOs, so I stopped playing with them for a while.

Whatever VFO type you choose, use lots of shielding. Commercial radios never have enough shielding, because it's expensive to manufacture and causes problems on the assembly line. Mount your VFO or VXO in a rigid, RF-tight box, and premix circuitry in a separate RF-tight box. Then enclose the whole radio in another RF-tight enclosure. Proper shielding eliminates many of the problems we have learned to tolerate in commercial radios, and once these bugs are gone, it's hard to go back to store-bought gear. Shielding is cheap in a custom radio, so use lots!

The VFO drives a splitter and phase-shift network (Fig 7). This circuit routes the VFO drive to the T2 and R2 boards, as well as handling phase-shifting for the I and Q ports on each board.

Interconnecting T2 and R2 with a No-Tune Transverter Board

The R2 and T2 boards interface directly with the receive and transmit IF ports of the no-tune transverters. The 1296-MHz transceiver in the title photograph follows the block diagram in Fig 2, without the optional IF preamplifier. The R2 noise figure is about 17 dB without the amplifier stage, so it may be useful to add a single MMIC amplifier stage if the transverter gain is low. The R2 receiver can hear signals at reduced sensitivity at odd harmonics of the VFO frequency, so the R2 input needs a simple low-pass filter. Since the 1296-MHz no-tune transverter board includes plenty of RF gain and a low-pass coupler at the mixer output, a piece of RG-174 can be connected directly from the transverter's receive-IF port to the R2's RF input.

The transmitter board contains an MMIC and low-pass filter, so a direct connection works with any of the no-tune transverters.

The no-tune transverters require a continuous 12-volt supply for the LO and multiplier circuitry, and switched 12-volt supplies for transmit and receive. I use the relay circuit in Fig 2, with a spare set of contacts available for hard-switching an external preamplifier and power amplifier.

Fig 8 shows the measured output spectrum of the 1296-MHz transceiver with the premixed VFO. It's a little cleaner than the no-tune 1296-MHz transverter driven by an ICOM IC-202, and *much* cleaner than the transverter slightly overdriven by a badly

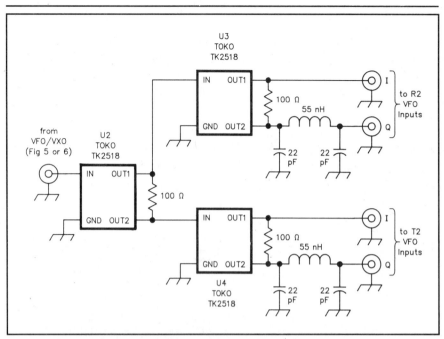

Fig 7—The power splitter and phase-shift network at A drive the R2 and T2 boards with either the VXO (Fig 5) or the premixed VFO (Fig 6). Phase delay in each phase-shift network is optimized by squeezing or spreading the turns of the two 55-nH inductors. Each inductor consists of 7 turns of #22 enameled wire spacewound on a 0.113-inch-ID form (#33 drill). "Piggyback" phase-shift networks are used in IF2 (Fig 4); a photo of the R2 board's network is shown below.

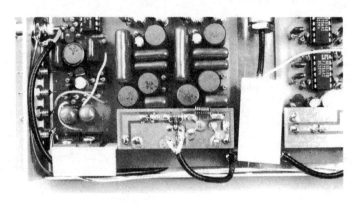

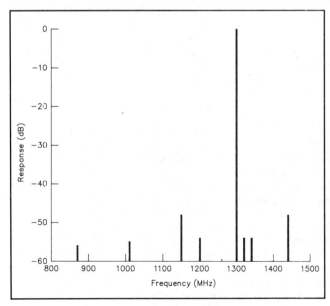

Fig 8—Measured output spectrum of the prototype no-tune 1296-MHz transceiver of Fig 3.

aligned FT-290R. The home-brew setup has higher transmit spurious levels than an ICOM IC-1271, but it also sounds better on both transmit and receive, and it has no birdies over the receiver's entire tuning range.

On transmit, the carrier and opposite-sideband suppression are comparable to VHF multimode radios, and the audio quality is far superior. On receive, the combination of high fidelity, low-distortion audio, decent opposite-sideband suppression, and no AGC is a real eye-opener. Loud, clear signals 40 dB above the noise simply disappear on the other side of zero beat. Weak signals at the noise level may be heard without the distractions of audio distortion and an AGC system that resets the gain on every noise peak.

The radio in the small aluminum box (Fig 4) shown in the photos is the 144-MHz IF for a 903.1-MHz SSB/CW system. It contains only an R2 board, T2 board, VXO and phase shift networks—simple! The no-tune 903 transverter is mounted at the antenna. Separate coax lines connect the transmit and receive IF to the T2 and R2 boards.

I didn't put RIT in either of these radios because I don't use RIT in portable microwave work. Battery-powered microwave radios on cold, windy hilltops tend to be pretty drifty, and it's better to follow other stations around the band than to try operating "random split." For radios with larger front panels, it's easy to add your favorite features.

Conclusions

This article describes one of my favorite applications for the R2 and T2 boards. The January *QST* article showed a 40-meter QRP CW transceiver using an R2 board. With the basic transmitter and receiver circuitry contained on a pair of small printed-circuit boards, the possibilities for custom-built radios are limited only by our imaginations.

I would like to thank the many hundreds of readers who have written to me since the R1 article appeared last August, and to apologize for not having enough time to respond to all of you. I am greatly encouraged by your thoughtful comments; it appears that the technical side of Amateur Radio is very healthy. Keep up all the good work—this stuff is fun!

I would also like to thank my family for tolerating all the evenings I've spent at the bench turning ideas into working radios, and all the times the telephone interrupted a bedtime story.

Notes

[1]R. Campbell, "High-Performance, Single-Signal Direct Conversion Receivers," *QST,* Jan 1993, pp 32-40.
[2]R. Campbell, "A Multimode Phasing Exciter," *QST,* Apr 1993, pp 27-31.
[3]No-tune transverter boards and kits for 432 through 5760 MHz are available from Down East Microwave, RR 1 Box 2310, Troy, ME 04987, tel 207-948-3741, fax 207-948-5157. Catalog available.
[4]R. Campbell, "High-Performance Direct-Conversion Receivers," *QST,* Aug 1992, pp 19-28.

QST

From QST, April 1993, p 27:

A Multimode Phasing Exciter for 1 to 500 MHz

In January, *QST* introduced you to R2, a single-signal direct-conversion receiver for the '90s. This month meet T2, a matching transmitter that generates SSB, CW and more.

By Rick Campbell, KK7B
Department of Electrical Engineering
Michigan Technological University
Houghton, MI 49931

The high-performance direct-conversion receivers described in the references[1,2] may be easily paired with a CW transmitter to make a simple transceiver of very respectable performance. For QRP operation and VHF through microwave weak-signal work, CW is the preferred mode. Whether you enjoy CW operation, or simply use it as a tool to make otherwise impossible contacts, it's nice to be able to switch to a voice mode when the signals are strong and the technical ideas are flowing hot and heavy. Here is a little multimode exciter that makes a perfect companion to a direct-conversion receiver.

Circuit Description

Fig 1 is the block diagram of a direct RF phasing-type SSB exciter. This block diagram has appeared in every *ARRL Handbook* for 40 years, and readers are encouraged to review the basics in those pages.[3] In the 1950s, the blocks contained vacuum tubes, paper capacitors and possibly a Barker and Williamson 2Q4 audio phase-shift network plugged into an octal tube socket. The schematic in Fig 2 is an implementation of Fig 1 using modern components.

Close-up of the top of the 2.5 × 3.5-inch T2 PC board. The power combiner (U6) and mixers (U4, U5) are at the left-hand edge of the board. The audio phase-shift networks (U2, U3) are arranged along the upper half of the board. The audio high-pass (C11, L1, C12) and band-pass (C13-C15, L2, L3) filters are arranged along the right edge. The mike amplifier and sidetone generator (U1) are in the lower right portion, and the control and power-supply circuitry is at the lower left. The MMIC amplifier (U7) and low-pass filter components are located on the back side of the board.

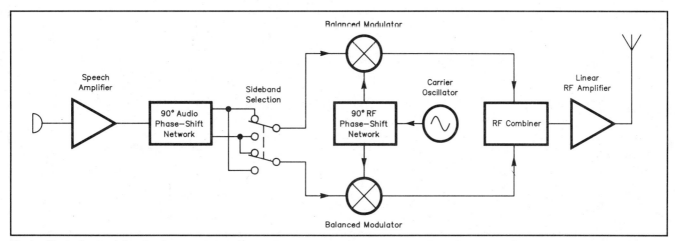

Fig 1—Block diagram of a phasing-type transmitter.

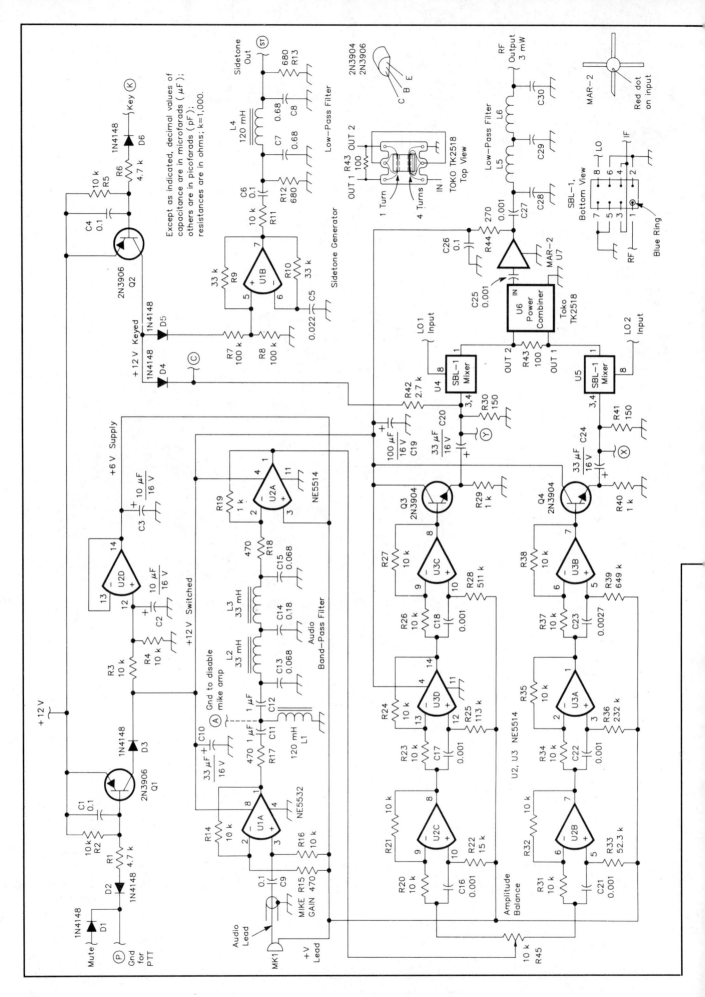

Fig 2—The T2 transmitter circuit diagram. The local oscillator and LO phase-shift network are located off the board. The resistors in the audio phase-shift networks (R20-R28 and R31-R39) are 1%-tolerance metal-film units. Other resistors are 5%-tolerance carbon-film or -composition units. Inductors are Toko 10RB series fixed inductors. Polarized capacitors are aluminum electrolytics rated at 16 V dc. The capacitors in the audio phase-shift networks (C16-C18 and C21-C23) are 1%-tolerance XICON polyester-film units available from Mouser. C7, C8 and C13-15 in the audio band-pass and sidetone low-pass filters are Panasonic V-series 50-V, 5%-tolerance metalized film capacitors. C28-C30 in the RF low-pass filter can be small 5%-tolerance leaded or chip components (see text). The other capacitors can be metalized polyester or ceramic-disc capacitors. See Note 7 for part sources.

C28-C30—See text and Table 1.
L5, L6—See text and Table 1.
MK1—Electret mike (Radio Shack 270-092 or Mouser 25LM045).
R45—10-kΩ, single-turn, PC-board-mount control (Panasonic MAG14 or equivalent).
U4, U5—Mini-Circuits SBL-1 double balanced mixer. Other mixers may be substituted if other frequency ranges are desired.
U6—Toko TK-2518 power combiner/splitter (this part is called a balun transformer in the Digi-Key catalog). See text.
U7—Mini-Circuits MAR-2 MMIC. See text.

Table 1
Fifth-Order Butterworth Low-Pass Filter Values

Frequency (MHz)	C28, C30 (pF)	L5, L6 (µH)	C29 (pF)
7	273	1.8	884
28	68	0.447	220
50	39	0.257	127
144	13.6	0.0803	44.1
222	8.9	0.0579	28.7
432	4.5	0.0298	14.7

Historians may enjoy comparing Fig 2 with Fig 11-5 on page 307 of the 1959 ARRL Handbook. The functions are identical, but virtually all the parts have changed! Following the op-amp microphone amplifier (U1A) is an LC audio band-pass filter, just like the old days, but designed using modern network theory and a computer circuit analysis program (PSPICE).[4]

The audio phase-shift networks (U2B, U3A, U3B and U2C, U3C, U3D) are the same as in the R2 receiver (see Note 2). Second-order (like the old 2Q4), third-order and fourth-order networks were explored for the audio phase-shift networks. Fourth-order networks work very well with ideal components, providing more than 45 dB of opposite-sideband suppression in my computer model. The third-order network with ideal components can provide more than 40 dB of opposite-sideband suppression. When 1% component variations were included in the computer models, the fourth-order network model degraded to within a few decibels of the third-order model. For this design, third-order networks with 1% off-the-shelf components are specified. This provides better opposite-sideband suppression than the phasing exciters of the 1950s and '60s, without requiring hand-selection of any components.

One critical area in a phasing SSB generator is the pair of audio amplifiers between the audio phase-shift network and the balanced modulators. These amplifiers have three requirements:

1) They must have identical phase shifts. This is most easily achieved by making them very broadband, by using large-value coupling capacitors.

2) They must have stable gain. If the gain of one of the amplifiers changes, the opposite-sideband suppression is reduced. Stable gain is most easily obtained by using feedback to set the gain, or using emitter followers with a gain slightly less than one.

3) They must have exceptionally low distortion. Any distortion introduced at this point has two equally undesirable effects: The distortion sends high-frequency audio harmonic energy into the balanced modulators; and the distortion products no longer have the desired 90-degree phase relationship.

The successful implementation of point 3 is what separates an acceptable phasing-type SSB generator from an unacceptable one. A phasing-type generator with 10% total harmonic distortion (THD) sounds pretty good on the air, because most of the 10% distortion falls outside the desired signal bandwidth and is rejected by the receiver. On either side of the transmitted signal, however, is a wide spectrum of garbage, kindly referred to as "splatter." To eliminate splatter, a phasing-type SSB generator must have audio amplifiers with THD well below 1%.

In contrast, a filter-type SSB generator may have large amounts of distortion in any of the stages preceding the filter. Distortion ("clipping") is often introduced intentionally to increase the average-to-peak-power ratio, or unintentionally by operators who turn up the mike gain to squeeze out the last milliwatt. A phasing-type SSB generator requires low-distortion audio and RF design from the input of the audio phase-shift network to the output of the RF combiner. This is why phasing-type SSB transmitters have a reputation for exceptional audio quality.

The emitter-follower drivers used here (Q3, Q4) were modeled on PSPICE, and have less than 0.3% THD when driving the IF ports of the SBL-1 double-balanced mixers (U4, U5). The onset of distortion in the emitter followers occurs above the desired drive level for the SBL-1s. The 150-ohm resistors (R30, R41) were added from the mixer IF ports to ground after I burned out a pair of SBL-1s by dumping the charge on the 33 µF coupling capacitors (C20, C24) through the mixer diodes.

The two double sideband (DSB) signals from the SBL-1 balanced modulators are combined in a Toko TK2518 splitter-combiner. This part is rated from 20 to 600 MHz, but it seems to work as low as 7 MHz in this application. A better choice for lower frequencies is a Mini-Circuits PSC2-1, which must be mounted off the board, or a homebrew replacement as shown in Fig 4 of the January QST receiver article (see Note 2).

After the combiner, the signals are amplified by U7, a Mini-Circuits MAR-2 MMIC (monolithic microwave integrated circuit). Readers unfamiliar with MMICs are in for a treat—this part has 50 ohm input and output impedances, boosts the signal up to a few milliwatts with low distortion, is unconditionally stable, and costs 99 cents. It also provides a constant load impedance for the combiner, so that opposite-sideband suppression is not a function of the following circuitry. You can read more about these remarkable devices in the 1987 QST series by Al Ward, WB5LUA.[5]

Following the MMIC amplifier is a fifth-order low-pass filter. I debated whether to include the low-pass filter on the PC board, since it is the only part of the exciter that must be changed for different bands. I finally included it because it allows the exciter to directly drive an antenna for milliwatt QRP work, or a transverter for the microwaves, or the IF port of a mixer in a heterodyne transmitter. For multiband applications, or for directly driving a linear amplifier, the low-pass filter components can be omitted, with jumpers replacing the inductors. Design equations for low-pass filter elements are given in Chapter 2 of any recent ARRL Handbook, and Table 1 gives typical values for a few amateur bands.

The PC-board low-pass filter artwork will accommodate chip capacitors or small leaded components. I prefer chip caps for frequencies above 30 MHz. The inductors can be air core at VHF and small toroids at HF. For lower frequencies, the low-pass components may be too large to fit on the PC artwork. A separate low-pass filter may be built off the board in that case.

Several different mixers were tried at U4 and U5 in the prototype exciters. Mini-Circuits SRA-2CM mixers will work up to 1000 MHz, and SBL-3s will work down to 25 kHz, with no other changes in the exciter. Options for LO phase-shift networks are discussed in January QST's receiver article (see Note 2) and The ARRL Handbook.

Close-up of the back side of the T2 PC board opposite the mixers. The MMIC amplifier (U7), its coupling capacitors (C25, C27) and the low-pass filter components (C28-C30, L5, L6) are soldered to this side of the board. R43 is also mounted on this side of the board, underneath the power combiner (U6). Although I used chip components for C25, C27-C30 and R43, small leaded components will work as well.

signals at X and Y, but that's another story.

Performance and Applications

A 2-meter version of this exciter has 40 dB of carrier and opposite-sideband suppression. Distortion products are more than 30 dB down at +3 dBm (2 mW) output. The distortion spectrum falls off very rapidly outside the desired passband. The audio quality is about average for an AM broadcast station—noticeably superior to the average SSB signal on the ham bands. The +3 dBm output level is ideal for upconverting to the microwave bands, heterodyning with a VFO to the HF bands, working across town on 222.1 MHz or driving a linear-amplifier module.

For some applications (running the legal limit on a wide open HF band comes to mind), the casual use of a direct phasing exciter is inappropriate. The potential for interference is too high. A carrier suppressed 40 dB below 1500 watts is 150 milliwatts, and that is enough to work the world on a wide-open HF band. For rock-crushing signals on crowded bands, I recommend operating the phasing exciter at a fixed frequency, following it with a crystal filter, and heterodyning to the desired output frequency, as is done in the Kenwood TS-950SDX. Personally, I'd rather operate a really big bulldozer at a landfill than a legal limit amplifier on a crowded band (the two have a lot in common), but I can find dozens of applications for a multimode exciter that's smaller than most microphones and works on any ham band below 1000 MHz!

A phasing "QRP Gallon" (five watt) transmitter will only have 500 microwatts of carrier and opposite-sideband signal, and conditions have to be really good for 500 microwatts to interfere with anyone. See the sidebar "More Power for T2" for references to some suitable previously published power amplifiers.

On VHF through microwave frequencies, it is routine to make SSB and CW contacts out to a hundred miles or so with very low power from hilltops. A crystal-

Frosting the Cake

I like to build portable VHF and microwave rigs, and as soon as I work somebody on a 10-mile path I always go farther away and try again. That means at some point I have to switch from SSB to CW. Then we get our antennas aligned and switch back to SSB. The first prototype used just a resistor to unbalance one of the mixers for CW. I hand-wired all the TR switching and didn't put in a sidetone generator because it was too much trouble. I then had a really cute little microwave transceiver and a great big Morsematic keyer that I have to haul up the mountain because I was too lazy to put sidetone in the little microwave rig.

After the second prototype, I decided to put some convenience circuitry on the exciter circuit board to make it easy to build a transceiver.[6] The extra stuff includes Q2, for CW keying; Q1, the TR-switch transistor; and U1B, a sidetone generator. Since I have low tolerance for bad audio, I added a low-pass filter on the sidetone generator to convert the square wave output of the relaxation oscillator to a fairly decent sine wave. Point P is grounded to transmit, Point K is connected to the key for CW, and Point ST is a high-impedance sidetone output that can

be routed to an appropriate spot in the receiver audio amplifier. Point A is grounded to disable the mike amp for CW. Interconnections will be discussed in more detail next month.

Other Modes

Old timers may remember that some of the early phasing transmitters offered CW, USB, LSB, AM, DSB suppressed carrier, and narrow-band FM (or PM) at the flip of a front-panel switch. It is possible to generate other voice modes besides USB and LSB with the T2 exciter.

• To generate AM, apply 12 V to point C (to insert carrier) and break the circuit at point X to disable the quadrature modulator.

• To generate narrowband PM, apply 12 V to point C and break the circuit at point Y to disable the modulator that is in phase with the carrier. Mathematicians may want to verify that a DSB suppressed-carrier signal plus a 90° phase-shifted carrier is in fact narrowband phase modulation. The more experimentally inclined can simply listen to the various signals on a multimode receiver (I did both!).

All kinds of advanced digital modes can be generated by injecting the appropriate controlled phasing exciter makes a nice companion to a multimode scanner at a scenic overlook. For the higher bands, the phasing exciter can serve as the IF for a transverter—details next month.

Tuning

The LO phase-shift network (not included on the board; see the January *QST* article referenced in Note 2) and **AMPLITUDE-BALANCE** pot (R45) can be set for best opposite-sideband suppression while listening to the wrong sideband on a receiver with good selectivity. I tack-soldered a 100-kΩ resistor from the output of the sidetone generator to the mike input to provide a tune-up tone. By alternately adjusting the LO phase-shift network and **AMPLITUDE BALANCE** pot, it should be possible to reduce the wrong-sideband tone by about 43 dB.

It is difficult to judge the carrier suppression in a direct phasing transmitter by listening to the signal in the station receiver unless the carrier oscillator and receiver are very well shielded. The carrier oscillator puts out at least 10 milliwatts, and the carrier signal will probably be loud in the receiver even with the antenna disconnected. I measure carrier suppression by heterodyning the exciter to a different frequency using a separate crystal oscillator and high-level double-balanced mixer.

I chose the audio amplifier gain for low-distortion SSB with the Radio Shack electret microphone shown in the schematic. For different microphones (or different operating habits), the value of R15 should be changed while listening to the audio and opposite sideband in the station receiver. I recognize that the absence of a front-panel mike gain control is an inconvenience, but the consequences of audio distortion in a phasing rig are far more serious than in a filter rig. R15 should be selected and then left alone. There is just too much temptation to turn up the gain a little to get that last half decibel out when working a weak signal!

The opposite sideband may be selected by reversing the LO connections at the mixers. It may be necessary to readjust the LO phase shift network and amplitude balance pot when changing sidebands.

Conclusions

The photos show how the parts are arranged on the PC board. This little SSB exciter board looks nice and works well from VLF to the low microwaves. The first prototype worked the first time I applied 12 V and an audio input signal. The problem with a fine-looking PC board layout is that it discourages further experimentation.

One of the requirements I impose on my projects is that they must be reproducible. In most cases that implies an engineering cycle that starts with a concept, explores lots of options, creates a block diagram and schematic, tests all of the circuitry on the computer and at the bench, lays out and etches a PC board, builds a prototype, debugs and tests the prototype and then lays out a second, third and often a fourth PC board. When I am finished, I am confident that anyone can put the parts on the PC board and build a working copy of my project.

That is not the only way to build a radio, and it is not necessarily the best way. Most homebrewers are familiar with a technique called "ugly" construction, in which the circuit is built, designed, tested, modified, redesigned, optimized, used on the air, and reoptimized in a continuous creative process. "Ugly" equipment is never finished, and always makes the best use of available parts and the homebrewer's talent. Ugly circuits often work better than nice-looking PC boards for two reasons:

• The continuous ground plane and short ground connections reduce or eliminate ground-current problems and improve shielding.

• The fact that the circuit is already ugly encourages further experimentation and improvement.

Building and improving ugly constructed RF projects is the best way to learn about RF design. As soon as you read about a new technique you can try it out on the bench. Ugly construction allows the homebrewer to be creative all the way through a project, and for me, that is the fun of ham radio.

Next month, I'll give more details about integrating the R2 and T2 boards into a station and show some interesting VHF and microwave applications.

Notes
[1] R. Campbell, "High-Performance Direct-Conversion Receivers," *QST*, Aug 1992, pp 19-28.
[2] R. Campbell, "High-Performance Single-Signal Direct-Conversion Receivers," *QST*, Jan 1992, pp 32-40.
[3] This discussion appears in Chapter 18 of the 1985 through 1993 editions of *The ARRL Handbook*.
[4] *PSPICE1* Circuit Analysis Software is available from the Microsim Corp, 20 Fairbanks, Irvine, CA 92718, tel 714-770-3022.
[5] A. Ward, "Monolithic Microwave Integrated Circuits," *QST*, Part 1—Feb 1987, pp 23-29, 32; Part 2—Mar 1987, pp 22-28, 33.
[6] Etched, plated and drilled PC boards (double-sided, with plated through-holes) for the T2 board are available from Applied Radio Science, PO Box 225, Houghton, MI 49931 for $10 postpaid (send an SASE for a catalog with current kit information). For individuals who want to make their own PC boards, an etching template/part-overlay package for the T2 PC board is available from the ARRL for an SASE. Address your request for the CAMPBELL T2 BOARD TEMPLATE to Technical Department Secretary, ARRL, 225 Main St, Newington, CT 06111.
[7] One source for SBL-1 mixers and MAR-2 MMICs is Oak Hills Research, 20879 Madison St, Big Rapids, MI 49307, tel 616-796-0920. XICON 1%-tolerance polyester-film capacitors used in the audio phase-shift network are available from Mouser Electronics, 2401 Hwy 287 N, Mansfield, TX 76063, tel 800-346-6873, 817-483-4422, fax 817-483-0931. All other parts are available from Digi-Key, PO Box 677, Thief River Falls, MN 56701-0677, tel 800-344-4539, 218-681-6674, fax 218-681-3880.   ▮QST▮

From QST, October 1994, p 64:

Build a One-Watt Transmitter in a Kodak Film Box

By Robert S. Capon, WA3ULH
322 Burlage Circle
Chapel Hill, NC 27514

A fun project for beginners that really works!

Have you ever thought about building a miniature one-watt CW transmitter in an unusual enclosure? Well, try a Kodak film box. If you're a novice kit builder, this project can be a lot of fun. It's easy to build, inexpensive, and does not require alignment. Even if you're a veteran kit builder, this project will amaze your friends, amuse your radio club and tantalize your children. When band conditions are good, one watt is plenty of power for you to work DX. And when band conditions are poor, this little gem will look great on your bookshelf.

Selecting a Kit

The basic circuit for the radio is the *Oner* transmitter. It was designed by the legendary British QRP (low power) enthusiast Reverend George Dobbs, G3RJV.

There have been many implementations of the Oner, but the one that I recommend is offered by 624 Kits in Spartanburg, South Carolina. This particular version is an ex-cellent value, because for $13 it includes an output filter *and* a crystal. With the addition of five inexpensive parts available from Radio Shack, you can build the complete transmitter in the film box and be on the air in no time.

The kit is available for bands from 17 through 160 meters. I chose the 20-meter kit, which is my favorite band for QRP DX. The 20-meter version comes with a crystal for 14.060 MHz, the international QRP calling frequency.

The kit is nicely documented. It comes with step-by-step instructions, a schematic (see Figure 1) and a well-prepared parts-layout drawing. The documentation also comes with component information to help you identify the parts. For example, you're told that a 100 kΩ resistor is marked with brown, black and yellow stripes.

The Oner is an interesting little radio. To avoid chirp, for example, the driver os-cillator remains on all the time. When you key the transmitter, you are actually keying the final amplifier. As a result, nearby sta-tions will hear two signals: a steady carrier transmitting at milliwatt power levels, and a stronger CW signal with an output power of about 1 W. Stations that are not nearby, however, won't hear the oscillator unless conditions are *very* good.

The Oner is crystal controlled. Because a little trimmer capacitor is used in series with the crystal, however, you're not tied to a single frequency. Rather, the capacitor can "pull" the crystal about 3 kHz above or below its primary frequency.

Unfortunately, because of the capaci-tance in the circuit, I discovered that the transmitter operates several kHz *above* the crystal frequency. My unit, which uses the 14.060 MHz crystal supplied with the kit, works at 14.066 MHz. As a result, the lowest that I can pull the frequency is 14.063 MHz, which is somewhat above the

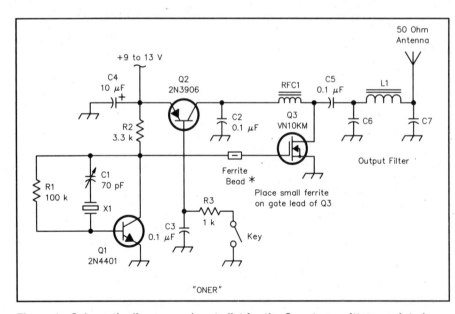

Figure 1—Schematic diagram and parts list for the Oner transmitter, reprinted with permission from 624 Kits.

C1—70pF trimmer capacitor.
C2, C3, C5—0.1 μF, 25-V disc ceramic.
C4—10 μF, 16-V electrolytic capacitor.
C6,C7—
   820 pF disc ceramic (160 meters)
   470 pF disc ceramic (80 meters)
   220 pF disc ceramic (40 meters)
   150 pF disc ceramic (30 meters)
   100 pF disc ceramic (20 meters)
   82 pF disc ceramic (17 meters)
L1—33 turns, #30, T37-2 (160 meters)
   23 turns, #30, T37-2 (80 meters)
   17 turns, #26, T37-2 (40 meters)
   14 turns, #26, T37-2 (30 meters)
   12 turns, #26, T37-2 (20 meters)
   10 turns, #26, T37-2 (17 meters)

Q1—2N4401
Q2—2N3906
Q3—VN10KM MOSFET
R1—100-kΩ, 1/4 W.
R2—3.3-kΩ, 1/4 W.
R3—1-kΩ, 1/4 W.
RFC1—6 turns #26 wire on a ferrite bead
X1—Crystal

Replacing the ferrite bead with a 10-Ω resistor will avoid possible instability (see Technical Correspondence, QST, Nov 1989, p 38, column 3).—Ed.

QRP calling frequency. This may not seem like much of a difference, but 3 kHz is really out of the money for most QRP stations who might be monitoring.

If you plan to do a lot of operating with this kit, you might want to purchase a replacement 14.056 MHz crystal from a source like JAN crystals. With a tweak or two of the trimmer, you'll be able to operate on 14.060 MHz.

For your station to work effectively, you'll need a technique to switch your antenna between a receiver and the Oner transmitter. Without such a switching technique, the constant oscillation of the Oner will interfere with your receiver. A DPDT switch will enable you to switch the antenna between the transmitter and receiver, and to turn off the power to the Oner. The wiring diagram shown in Figure 2 shows you how to do this.

Parts List

All of the parts that you will need (other than the film box and kit) are available from Radio Shack (the Radio Shack part numbers are given in the following parts list). The total cost of the radio is about $20:

Oner Transmitter Kit	From 624 Kits
35-mm Film Box	From Kodak
5.5 mm/2.1 mm dc female jack	274-1563
2 phono jacks	274-346
Key jack	274-251
DPDT toggle switch	275-614

Prepare the Box

An easy way to begin the project is to prepare the case. Cut three sides of the top of the case to make a flap, so that the radio can be opened and closed.

To strengthen the box, form two strips of cardboard (I used one of my QSL cards) into a **U** shape, and glue the cardboard into the film box in opposite directions with ordinary white glue. For example, one of the **U**s goes from side to side, and one goes from front to back. This has a lamination effect, and makes the box quite sturdy.

Next, cut two holes in the front of the box, and three holes in the rear as shown in Figure 3. Forget your electric drill for this project. The tool of choice is an X-Acto knife.

Label the case as shown in the photograph. It is much easier to label the case before you've mounted the components on the case. For labeling I used Helvetica 8 rub-on labels that I purchased at a local hobby shop, finished with transparent Scotch tape.

Install all of the jacks. Just finger tighten the nuts for now.

Assemble the Circuit Board

If this is your first kit, take a moment to prepare. Before you open your first parts package, you may want to purchase a plastic compartmentalized parts box, which can be very handy for sorting components. I

found some very nice boxes at a local housewares/kitchen supply store. Alternatively, Radio Shack has a suitable component box that costs a bit more (64-552).

If you're an experienced kit builder, skip this section, dump the parts into a soup bowl, and solder up the board. I've built several of these kits, and the last one took me 25 minutes.

For first-time kit builders, here are answers to some commonly asked questions:

❑ *Can the trimmer capacitors or ceramic disk capacitors go in the wrong way?*

No. Resistors can not be put in the wrong way either.

❑ *Can the electrolytic capacitors go in the wrong way?*

Yes. Electrolytic capacitors have a positive and a negative side. The negative lead is shorter and marked with a stripe and a "minus" mark. The positive lead is longer; it may have a small "+" sign or may be unmarked.

❑ *Can the transistors go in the wrong way?*

Yes. When you install the transistors, be certain to match up the flat side of the transistor with the flat side in the layout diagram.

❑ *How are the toroids wound?*

The documentation comes with an excellent picture of the toroids. You count turns from the *inside* of the toroid. For example, 6 turns on the RF choke will look like 6 turns from the inside of the toroid, but only 5½ turns on the outside.

❑ *How do you solder the coated toroid wires?*

Theoretically, the magnet wire uses a coating which melts off during soldering. I found, however, that the coating does not melt off completely, and the resulting solder joint does not make a good connection in all circumstances. It's safer to carefully scrape away the coating with an X-Acto blade prior to soldering.

❑ *Can the crystal be put in the wrong way?*

No.

Armed with the answers to these questions, you're ready to populate the little circuit board with electronic components. Identify each of the components and solder them in place. Be sure to keep the leads as short as possible.

Wire the Circuit Board to the Case

The final step is to wire the circuit board to the various components on the box: transmit/receive switch, key jack, antenna jack, receiver antenna jack and 12 V dc jack. Refer to the attached wiring diagram to make the connections. You'll find the job less confusing if you use black wire for the ground connections, red for 12-V connections, and green for all other connections.

If you find it difficult working in the

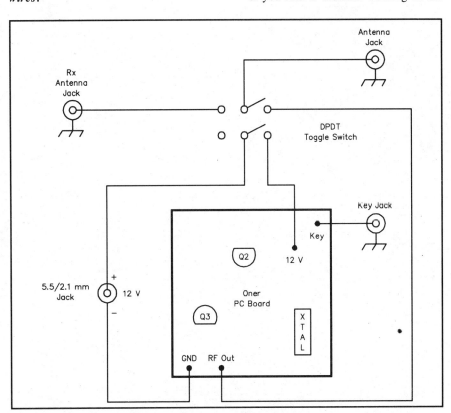

Figure 2—Wiring the Oner to your connectors and the antenna switch.

Figure 3—An inside view of the Kodak-box transmitter. The Oner fits nicely and the jacks are easy to mount.

confined space, you may choose to get out your X-Acto knife and slit open the back of the case along the vertical sides. This will give you more working room. When you're finished, tape the box shut.

Operating Results

Under normal conditions, I've had good luck with 1-W transmitters into a Cushcraft A-3 tribander beam antenna mounted at only 30 feet. I've also experimented with QRPp (extremely low power), and worked ZS6KO with 20 mW, which is one-fiftieth the power of the Oner transmitter!

With this QRP experience, I was eager to get my little transmitter on the air. When the radio was finished, I telephoned my friend Ernie, KN4MN, who helps me troubleshoot all of my projects. Ernie lives about two miles away, and he gave me a signal report of S-9 with his 4-element Yagi pointed in my direction. Ernie reported the CW signal was very clean. He also said that he could hear my oscillator running continuously about 1 kHz down from my main signal—even when I wasn't transmitting. The oscillator was much fainter (he gave it an S-4 report).

My first QSO was with LU4VZ, and I received a 529 report. Next, I worked KW1C and received a solid 599 from Fort Kent, Maine.

Later that evening, I went down to the low end of 20 meters with my Yaesu FT-1000 running 200 W. After a bit of searching, I recruited the loudest New Zealand station I could hear, ZL1BDG. Frank said he'd be happy to change frequencies and listen for my Kodak film box at 14.063 MHz. I called him with the Oner...and got a prompt reply! My signal report was 539 and, thanks to Frank's patience and excellent CW skills, we had a pleasant conversation over an 8000-mile path!

Next Steps

You might want to consider building other Oner projects. Kanga US imports a terrific Oner QSK unit which uses a relay to switch the antenna between the transmitter and receiver. The QSK also includes a sidetone oscillator. It's a logical follow-on project to the Oner transmitter. For more skilled kit builders, Kanga also imports a Oner *receiver* that works in conjunction with a Oner VFO. ◻**QST.**

Contact List

624 Kits
171 Springlake Dr
Spartanburg, SC 29302
tel 803-573-6677

Kanga US
3521 Spring Lake Drive
Findlay, OH 45840
tel 419-423-5643

JAN Crystals
2341 Crystal Drive
PO Box 60017
Fort Myers, FL 33906-6017
tel 800-JAN-XTAL

From QEX, March 1993, p 3:

Birth of a 7-MHz Transceiver

By Zack Lau, KH6CP/1
ARRL Laboratory Engineer
email: zlau@arrl.org (Internet)

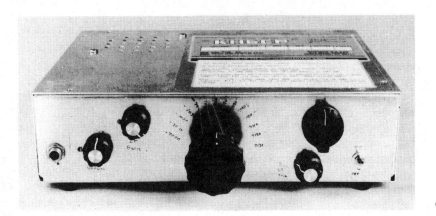

Tired of canned printed-circuit-board projects that don't leave any room for innovation? This project shows one of many possible ways to build projects that can be easily modified to take advantage of the latest technology as it becomes available. The project is a 40-meter QRP CW transceiver. While you can just build the circuits shown if you like, our discussion of the project will focus on the *why* more than the *how*. It's at least as useful to understand why a designer made the choices he did as it is to understand how the circuit works.

The design goal of this project can be stated simply: a clean QRP CW transceiver with a minimum of glitches and decent performance. As we discuss the design, keep in mind that it is almost always possible to improve the performance of an individual circuit, but making the cost and complexity of the circuit fit the need, and integrating the circuit into the design as a whole are the essence of good design. These issues drive many of the design choices discussed here.

Fig A shows the block diagram of the transceiver. Since it is a transceiver, some of the circuits are used in both transmit and receive modes. While this choice complicates the initial design, it dramatically lowers the total parts count.

The Receiver

Choice of mixing frequencies is what often makes or breaks an HF receiver. Choose the wrong ones and you will have to struggle to get something that even sounds halfway decent. A particularly *bad* choice is to have the IF and local oscillator approximately equal, such as using a 3.59-MHz IF and a 3.41-MHz LO. Not only can it be difficult to keep the local oscillator out of the IF, but there are spurious responses that can't be filtered out easily. If necessary, one can substitute high-Q tuned circuits for the broadband transformers to filter out unwanted signals. Don't forget, though, that the purpose of having an IF in the first place is to make things easy. It makes little sense to choose one that makes it a real pain to get circuits to work!

For most amateurs, the choice of IF is determined by what crystal filter they can get their hands on. For this 40-meter unit, I found that using 12-MHz crystals resulted in a Cohn filter design that neatly matched 50 ohms. I also considered other frequencies, but ruled them out for the following reasons: With 10-MHz crystals, the image is at 13 MHz, which is a little close if you use a top-coupled filter with its characteristically poor high-side rejection, although picking off your receiver input signal after the transmitter's low-pass filter is somewhat of a help. On the other hand, with 16-MHz crystals, you need a 9-MHz VFO. With VFO stability degrading as you go up in frequency, 9 MHz may be a little too high, though there is a commercial rig, the ICOM IC-502, that used an incredibly high VFO frequency of 36 MHz. That's probably too high, as evidenced by '502s with significant drift problems.

A disadvantage of the 12-MHz VFO frequency is that the oscillator tunes "backwards"—the highest VFO frequency corresponds to the lowest operating frequency. This pretty much rules out using capacitors with built-in reduction drives, as they usually have stops that prevent you from having a capacitor that is at minimum capacitance when you have rotated the shaft fully clockwise. And the capacitors I've seen don't appear to be rugged enough to be modified easily.

Mixing, RF Switching and Filtering

As with any receiver design, one major decision was what to use as the first receive mixer. I opted for the moderately high-performance approach of using a Mini-Circuits SBL-1 doubly balanced mixer. I also decided to take advantage of its bilateral operability, using it on transmit as well. The Siliconix Si8901 quad JFET mixer can also be used bilaterally, but these devices are difficult to obtain. The Plessey SL6440 is a good, strong mixer, too, but it is still quite difficult to get unless you want to buy a kilobuck worth of parts! Like most active mixers, it is also unilateral.

Using the mixer for both transmit and receive requires that it be switched between the active signal paths. Rather than use sometimes hard to find or expensive PIN diodes for mixer switching, I chose to use 1N4007 rectifier diodes. Unlike the 1N4001, the 1N4007 has the required intrinsic layer (signified by the *I* in PIN). 1N4007s are also used to switch the band-pass filter, which is also used bilaterally so that only one filter has to be aligned.

One of the difficulties in getting maximum performance out of an SBL-1 is terminating it properly. The most straightforward way of doing this is with a broad-band amplifier with a good input SWR (as indicated by low return loss) across a frequency span that includes as many of the mixing products as possible. It is possible to get better performance if you use a diplexer—but a diplexer, which is a network of two or more filters, has to be properly aligned to work. A swept return-loss measurement setup is often needed to adjust a diplexer properly, due to the LO and intermediate frequencies typically used in MF and HF systems. A significant advantage of

the SBL-1 is its wide IF-output specification—unlike some active mixer designs that will not accommodate a VHF IF because they have too much stray capacitance. Conceivably, the SBL-1 could even be used with a UHF IF. Getting suitable oscillators for those frequencies can be a problem, though.

While perhaps not important to the casual builder, the problems with using a broadband-amplifier termination for the mixer are those of excessive gain and degraded intercept point. The first might seem pretty strange, as you would think you want as much gain ahead of the filter as possible to override the noise figure of the filter plus the following stages. But crystal filters often have very weird distortion properties—I've reduced the level of two-tone test signals by 10 dB and seen the distortion products drop by only 10 dB, rather than the 30-dB drop expected. So, for the ultimate in dynamic range, you often want to *limit* the gain ahead of the crystal filters. And in fact, the poor return loss of the crystal filter at the IF isn't as important as the termination it presents at the image frequency.

The problem of the degraded intercept point is more straightforward. The broadband amplifier has to handle all the signals at the output of the mixer. At minimum, the intercept point should be degraded by at least 3 dB, since the unwanted image is just as strong as the desired sig-

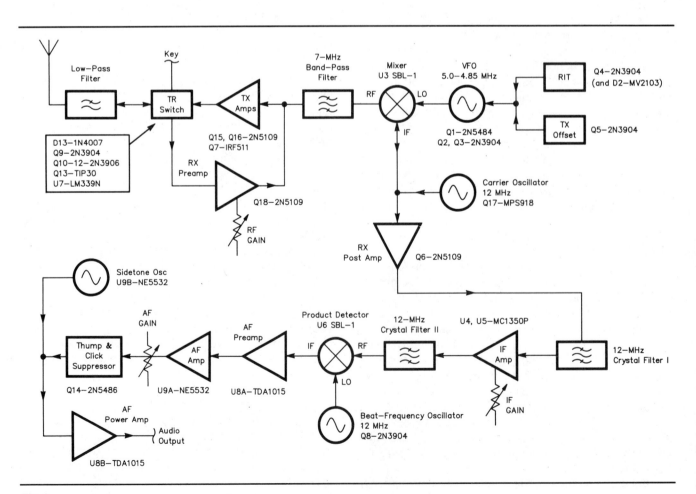

Fig A

nal. The other signals, such as the higher-order mixing products and the local oscillator feedthrough make things even worse.

Terminating the mixer with a diplexer can reduce the sorts of problems encountered with a broadband amplifier termination. A question that comes up when designing diplexers is how good do they have to be. A paper by Paul Drexler in the *1987 Mid-Atlantic States*

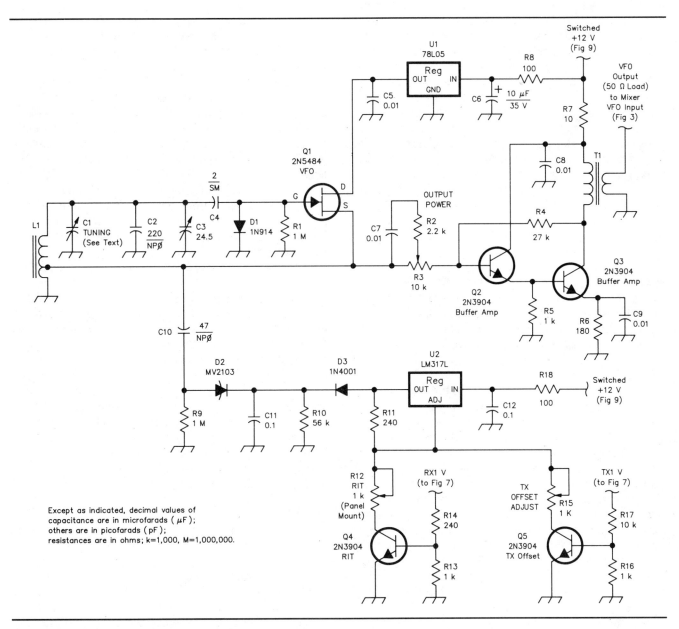

Fig 1—Schematic diagram of the VFO circuit.

C1—23.1 pF, air dielectric, variable. (Millen 21020) (Main tuning control that should have a reduction drive).
C3—2.4 to 24.5 pF air dielectric trimmer. Johnson 189-509 type.
D1, D5, D6, D7, D8, D9, D10—1N4148 or 1N914 switching diode. (Some of these are shown in other figures.)
D2—MV2103 varactor tuning diode.
D3—1N4001 rectifier diode used for temperature compensation. Do

not substitute.
L1—29 turns #26 enameled wire on T-50-7 iron-powder toroid. Tap 9 turns up from ground.
Q1—2N5484 JFET. 2N5485 or 2N5486 will work with increased drift. The MPF 102 may also work.
Q2, Q3, Q4, Q5, Q8, Q9—2N3904, PN2222, 2N2222. BJT. (Some of these are shown in other figures.)
T1—Broadband transformer, 5:1 turns ratio. 10 turns of #30

enameled wire on an FB-2402-43 balun core (primary). Secondary has 2 turns of #30 enameled wire over primary. #26 or #28 enameled wire may be used if the larger FT-37-43 toroid core is used.
U1—78L05 5-volt regulator. A 78M05 or 7805 regulator will work but is physically much larger.
U2—LM317L adjustable voltage regulator. A LM317M or LM317T will work but is physically much larger.

VHF Conference seems to indicate that there is a difference of several decibels in output intercept between using a 20-dB resistive pad (40-dB return loss or better) and a diplexer with 20 dB of return loss or better, with the advantage to the pad. Clearly, return loss is critical in this scheme. Of course, getting 40 or 50 dB of return loss out of a wide-band filter network is awfully difficult in the HF and VHF spectrum, so perhaps there is room for better approaches. By the way, for those accustomed to thinking in terms of SWR, going from a 20-dB to 40-dB return loss is lowering the SWR from 1.222 to 1.020.

There is a totally different approach that one can take to terminating mixers. If you know what you are doing and have the test equipment available, excellent results are often possible with nonresistive terminations. Edward Meade Jr, apparently did just that about 20 years ago, getting a +15-dBm output intercept and 5 dB of conversion loss out of a mixer quite similar to today's SBL-1 at VHF. His material is still in today's *Handbook,* in case you want to know what can be done with a properly designed low-pass-filter termination, as well as how to do it. Since his approach requires a relatively low IF, it might be something to consider at HF if you use a single-conversion 455-kHz IF with sufficiently sharp front-end filters to get rid of the really close image response. His approach actually makes more sense than the textbooks' gospel of broadband termination—just try and design a diplexer that works into the UHF spectrum with parts available to amateurs in the 1970s! Even today, while you can use chip components to terminate images in the SHF spectrum, you will likely find that the output transformer of the mixer has nowhere near the required amount of bandwidth, and your carefully crafted SHF circuit does you no good. Theory is fine for ideal parts, but compromises are often needed when dealing with stuff you can actually get your hands on.

In the end, I chose to go with a broadband termination. The receiver post amp (Q6, Fig 2) is designed to present this termination to the mixer. A resistive pad is needed at the output of this stage to prevent the poor out-of-passband impedance of the 12-MHz crystal filter from affecting the mixer through the amplifier. (A difficulty with this simple feedback amplifier design is that the isolation between the input and output isn't very good.) I prefer to use metal-film resistors, as older carbon-composition resistors often have oxidized leads that require more work to solder properly, and there is little difference in RF performance. Using an exotic high-power JFET in this stage would produce better isolation, but such devices aren't easily available to most amateurs. (The Motorola MRF-136 TMOS device looks like an interesting transistor to try, featuring very high intercepts and a low noise figure.) An adventurous experimenter might want to try using feedback amplifiers with directional couplers, but I haven't seen a ready-to-go design.

While mixer performance is important, so is the performance of the circuit in front of the mixer. I decided to implement an RF gain stage (Q18, see Fig 8) with a true RF gain control. Varying the amount of Q18's emitter resistance that gets bypassed by capacitor C85 varies the gain of the stage. A disadvantage to this approach is that the input impedance of the amplifier increases as the gain drops. Also, you need a decent potentiometer: an inductive wire-wound pot won't work. But these disadvantages are offset by the advantage that the dc bias remains the same, so that signal handling isn't degraded when you need it most. Testing shows this isn't *entirely* true, as the two-tone dynamic range does degrade as the MDS increases from −130 to −120 dBm as the RF gain control is varied. But the dynamic range does increase as expected in going from −141 to −130 dBm. The RF gain stage also works to further isolate the input of the transmit amplifier chain from its output, improving transmitter stability. Removing the stage may cause difficulties in obtaining a stable transmitter. The selectivity ahead of the RF amplifier—a single tuned circuit and a low-pass filter—isn't great, but it is similar to that of many rigs. An additional band-pass filter could be placed between the single tuned circuit and the RF amplifier for even better performance.

Designing broadband amplifiers like that of Q18 requires solving a couple of circuits simultaneously. The most basic circuit is the dc biasing circuit—you usually want a certain collector or drain current that doesn't vary too much with temperature or component tolerances. Next, you want a flat gain characteristic while maintaining input and output impedances close to your design goal, typically 50 ohms. Increasing the emitter degeneration resistor decreases gain and increases the input impedance, while increasing the shunt resistor from the output to the input has the opposite effect—increasing gain and decreasing the input impedance. Finally, you want the amplifier to be stable regardless of load. Usually, the first two requirements are easily combined, while the third is often tacked onto the final result.

The VFO

Given the problems in obtaining a stable VFO, why not use a synthesizer? They usually offer improved stability, but only at the cost of increased complexity. It appears possible to combine direct digital synthesis (DDS) with a phase-locked loop (PLL) to eliminate the major problems of both—the phase-locked loop can remove the spurs generated by the DDS, and the DDS can help to reduce the lockup time/phase noise trade-off of PLLs. But this ends up with a circuit as complicated as the rest of the transceiver! Of course, one can reduce the amount of control circuitry by using a computer, as shown in the 1988 to 1990 ARRL *Handbooks.* In the end, I decided to keep it simple and use a VFO.

The VFO used in this radio, shown in Fig 1, is a JFET Hartley circuit, Q1, followed by a two-stage bipolar buffer circuit, Q2 and Q3, that drives the mixer. Since there is a bit of variation in the power output from one JFET transistor to another, I decided to allow the gain of the buffer to be adjusted with R3. (Of course, you could use a selected JFET and skip the adjustment circuit.) A JFET with a lower drain-to-source resistance or higher I_{DSS}

rating usually provides more power output, though usually at the expense of frequency stability. Improved performance, perhaps another 6 dB of IMD dynamic range, could be obtained by waveshaping the local oscillator to provide a good square wave. Since the IMD occurs primarily at the switching transitions, shortening the length of those transitions improves performance. While not the ultimate in stability, this circuit does provide good phase noise performance. Yes, you can still have a phase noise problem even without digital circuits! (See *QRP Quarterly* July-October 1992, "Experimenter's Corner: A High Performance DC Receiver," by Denton Bramwell, K7OWJ.)

One of the trade-offs that has to be made when using tuning diodes is to choose between phase noise performance and tuning range. By using lower voltages on the diode, you can get much more range out of the diode, but the Q decreases, and therefore the phase noise gets worse. For casual applications this isn't important, but you lose much of the benefit of improved mixer dynamic range if your receiver is unable to eliminate strong signals because the selectivity is smeared by poor phase noise performance.

Use of a 78L05 three-terminal, 5-volt regulator prevents the oscillator frequency from varying with changes in the supply voltage. Don't forget to bypass the input terminal of this regulator properly with a 0.33 μF or larger capacitor; I have seen this type of regulator oscillate if not properly bypassed. One I saw took off at a few MHz and amplitude modulated the oscillator it was connected to!

The VFO inductor uses a Type 7 Micrometals iron-powder coil. While not as easy to get as the common

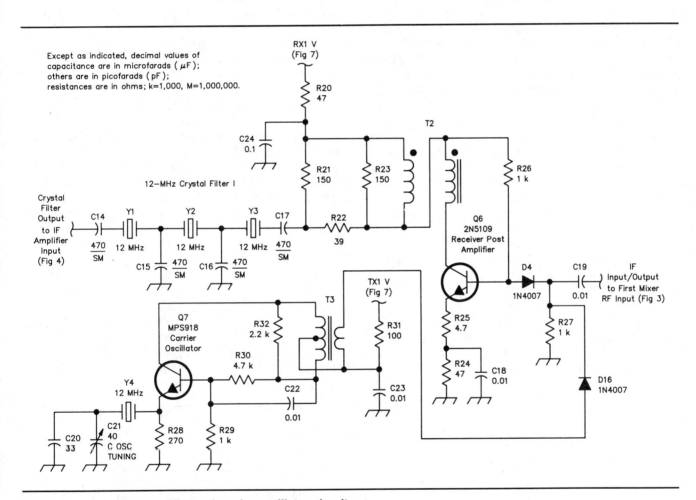

Fig 2—Receiver post amplifier and carrier oscillator circuits.

C20—Exact value depends on the crystal used. It might even be omitted if Y4 is appropriately low in frequency compared to Y1.

D4, D11, D12, D13, D16—1N4007 rectifier diode used as a PIN switching diode. More expensive PIN diodes such as the 1N5767 may be used. (Some of these are shown in other figures.)

Q6, Q15, Q16, Q18—2N5109 BJT. (Some of these are shown in other figures.)

Q7—MPS 918. A 2N5179 or 2N5109 will also work.

R32—May not be necessary. Added to prevent amplitude modulation present on one of the oscillators built.

T2, T6, T7—Broadband transformer. 10 bifilar turns #28 enamel wire on FT-37-43 toroid core. (Some of these are shown in other figures.)

T3—Broadband transformer. 10:1 turns ratio; 20 turns of #26 or #28 enameled wire on an FT-37-43 core (primary). Tap is 13 turns from the collector. Secondary has 2 turns of #26 or #28 enameled wire over the primary.

Type 6 core, it has a slightly lower temperature coefficient (30 versus 35 ppm/°C). It doesn't hurt to get the most stable parts possible, given that we want a VFO stable to within at least 10 ppm, if not better. You may wish to anneal the core by boiling it in water and letting the water and coil cool slowly, but I've not done measurements to see how effective this is.

One of the critical circuits I almost forgot to include is a receiver incremental tuning (RIT) control, which is the first thing I would have noticed if I used it on the air! RIT is really important if you are attempting to work someone using a DC receiver/transmitter combination that has no frequency offset capability. They can only work stations that can operate split frequency. RIT is implemented by U2, an adjustable three-terminal voltage regulator IC (see Fig 1). The voltage applied to D2, the varactor tuning diode, is controlled by R12 when receiving and by R15 when transmitting. I haven't seen this particular method of obtaining transmit and receive offsets used previously. It allows you to add transmit incremental tuning (XIT) fairly easily, though the biggest problem is likely to be finding the panel space! A compromise may be to use a single control and a DPDT switch to choose either XIT or RIT. Since a dedicated 8- to 10-volt regulator is needed in order to get enough range from a tuning diode, I decided to just switch the resistors that determine the output voltage. This allows the use of cheap NPN switching transistors (Q4 and Q5). There should be no interaction between the two variable resistors, and none has been noted. This method also has the advantage that it is usually possible to set up the RIT with just a voltmeter, although a frequency counter would eliminate any error caused by the transmitter pulling the VFO. This error, while sometimes severe if the transmitter operates on the same frequency as the VFO, is usually negligible in a properly designed heterodyne system. D3 and R10 are suggested by a Motorola application note as temperature compensation for the MV2101 series of varactor diodes, though I've not verified their results. An LM2931 low-dropout regulator was tried at U2 with mixed results: the high output capacitance required for stability hinders its transient response. Thus the circuit I tried doesn't change voltages quickly enough for QSK use. Wasting current with a small-valued resistor load would speed things up, but conserving current drain is usually a design criterion.

The BFO and CFO

You may be wondering why I don't just use the cheaper method of using the same oscillator for the BFO and carrier oscillator, swinging the VFO to obtain the proper offset. Yes, it's cheaper, and it works cheaper, too, as the offset you get depends on what frequency you are on. That's not too bad if you only cover 20 or 40 kHz of the band, but it certainly can be noticeable if you want the VFO to cover the entire band.

I added 47- and 100-Ω swamping resistors to the beat frequency oscillator (Q8 in Fig 5) after I discovered that the circuit had a tendency to take off on the third overtone of the crystal. This happened because of the poor load provided by the mixer, as demonstrated by the fact that such techniques as rolling off the gain of the oscillator with a capacitor from collector to ground had little effect. Not only isn't crystal overtone operation desired in this case, but I've found that using overtones the crystal manufacturer didn't expect you to use can lead to unreliable results, caused by spurious responses close to the desired frequency. As an example, I looked at the 5th overtone of an 18-MHz crystal and found two responses 300 kHz apart showing only about a dB of difference in series attenuation in a 50-Ω system. Careful crystal manufacturers make sure that the spurious responses are at least 3 or 4 dB down.

Crystal Filters

Since I know how much people hate to wind transformers, I designed these crystal filters to work well with 50-Ω input and output impedances. As a result, the only transformer needed to match the filters to the rest of the circuitry is the one that couples to the high-impedance MC1350 IF amplifier output (T4 of Fig 4). A second crystal filter is used just before the product detector. Since a

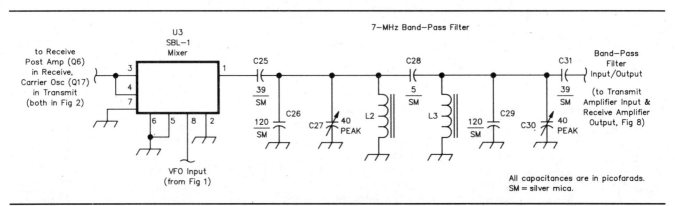

Fig 3—Mixer and band-pass filter.

L2, L3—22 turns of #20 enameled wire on a T-68-6 iron-powder toroid. (2.7 μH, Q=340 at 7.1 MHz)

U3, U6—SBL-1 doubly balanced mixer. (U6 is shown in Fig 6.)

product detector acts like a direct conversion receiver, it detects the audio image noise amplified by the IF amplifiers unless you filter out the noise.

AGC, Product Detector and Audio

You may wish to add your favorite AGC circuit, keeping in mind that the CW-bandwidth crystal filter adds a slight delay that may or not improve the AGC response. This delay *can* be helpful, as it can give time for your circuit to decide exactly what to do.

The product detector is another SBL-1 diode mixer, U6 in Fig 5. Use of the SBL-1 avoids local oscillator leakage resulting from poorly matched diodes, a common problem with home-brew diode mixers. If you do add AGC, the mixer's LO suppression of about 70 dB should be sufficient to prevent the carrier injection from upsetting the AGC, though be sure to avoid poor layout. Of course, balancing a mixer over a narrow range of frequencies isn't difficult, if you have the test equipment to make the adjustments. If you do have trouble with a feedthrough from a home brew mixer, you might consider using a 6-dB hybrid combiner/splitter to separately feed the AGC and product detector from the IF amplifier. This should give you another 40 dB of LO suppression, making even a mixer with lousy balance usable.

The TDA1015 audio chip used in this design (see Fig 6) puts out quite a bit of power; 4 watts is plenty for a quiet room. But this two-stage amplifier also has quite a bit of gain, and it will oscillate if you aren't careful with your circuit layout. You probably can substitute an LM380 and increase the gain of U9A to compensate. The LM386 is a possibility too, but, while I can't say it's bothered me, people have complained about the LM386 being "hissy" so I won't recommend it.

Like "The QRP Three Bander" I presented in the October 1989 *QST,* this rig uses an audio gate made with a JFET switch, Q14, to cut down on pops and clicks. This switch is controlled by the T-R sequencer, so we'll discuss it when we get to that part of the circuit.

A simple sidetone oscillator, shown in Fig 9, is made from an op amp section. It's not a particularly clean sounding tone, so you may wish to substitute your own favorite circuit.

The Transmitter

When trying to listen on one band while transmitting

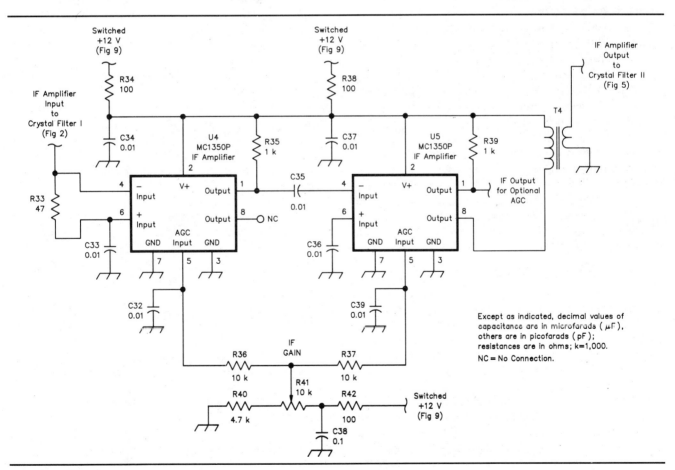

Fig 4—IF amplifiers.

T4—Broadband transformer. 19:4 turns ratio; 19 turns of #26 or #28 enameled wire on an FT-37-43 core (primary). Secondary has 4 turns of #26 or #28 enameled wire over the primary.

U4, U5—LM1350P IF amplifier.

on another, transmitter stability often makes a big difference in how successful you are. Even a low-level instability makes a huge signal in a nearby receiver. While solutions to stability problems are not trivial, it *is* possible to make a transmitter stable enough that you can listen to it with a receiver in the shack and have it sound clean. Of course, unwanted coupling paths and ground loops can have you chasing "problems" that don't really exist.

This transmitter uses a broadband amplifier driving a MOSFET transmitter output circuit developed by Mike Masterson, KA2HZA. Not only does the MOSFET run at high efficiency, but it's cheap and rugged as well! His design was reworked for use at the 5-watt-output QRP level. Those looking for a little more power might look at Mike's original article, "Three Fine Mice—MOuSeFET CW Transmitters," which appeared in the December 1986 *QST* and is reprinted in the ARRL book, *QRP Classics*. His circuit provides the component values for getting approximately 16 watts out. I spent a little time combining the transmit broadband amplifier, the receive preamplifier, and the switching circuit so that fewer parts are needed. In addition, a little less current is required, since some of the bias current for the transmit amplifier is also used to turn on the T-R switching diode.

Transceiver Switching

As many home brewers have discovered, merely having a transmitter and a receiver circuit doesn't make a transceiver. In fact, most will say that quite a bit of work is needed to get a radio that works well, with the difficulty coming in the circuitry that switches the unit between transmit and receive modes. To make things relatively straightforward and understandable, I used an LM339 quad voltage comparator to build a sequencer (Fig 7), a device that not only switches voltages sequentially, but switches them in reverse order when switching the other way. These voltages make it a lot easier to design a transmitter that doesn't oscillate when switching between transmit and receive and a receiver that has a minimum of unwanted noises. There are two diodes in the circuit, D6 and D7, that might not seem entirely necessary at first glance. D6 is used to raise the threshold voltage of the T-R switch, Q9. If the threshold is too low, you run into the situation where the transistor switches of some electronic keyers won't key the rig properly. Surprisingly, some commercial rigs have this problem. D7 is in series with a 68-kΩ timing resistor. This network equalizes the key-up and key-down timing—I thought it might improve the rig to have the times approximately equal.

A more flexible—and simpler—substitute for the LM339 sequencer is to use an LM3914 bar graph chip with an R-C generated ramp voltage on its input. In the bar graph mode, as opposed to the dot mode, you can ignore the first LED and use the other 9 sequenced outputs—enough for almost any transceiver or transverter application. The circuitry is also a bit simpler, the only real disadvantage being the higher cost of the chip. You'll probably also need at least one inverter, but this is just another PNP transistor and resistor. In the case of the LM339 circuit, you can do inversion by merely interchanging the comparator inputs.

A Darlington PNP pair, Q12 and Q13, switch the transmitter driver amplifier on and off with wave shaping. Not only does this reduce the current that has to be sinked by the comparator output, it also reduces the timing capacitances to more reasonable values. While you can buy 2.2-µF nonpolarized capacitors, they tend to be hard to find and more expensive than smaller metal-film capacitors. Ordinary electrolytics probably won't work because the voltage across them reverses.

To get rid of those annoying pops and clicks resulting from a receiver being energized before the transmitter is truly off, the sequencer disables the audio line via Q14 (see Fig 6) during the transition between modes. The timing capacitor connected from the gate of Q14 to ground is normally chosen to be the smallest that will cut off the annoying noises, though you certainly could increase it to suit personal preference. Not everyone appreciates hearing background noise between CW "dits." Should you wish to use this circuit, keep in mind that the circuit feeding the JFET source must always maintain a dc potential of several volts. If it drops below a certain threshold, annoying noises will be generated. Critical parameters of FETs—unlike those of bipolars—often vary considerably, so experimentation will be needed to find the threshold of your transistors, if you need to cut things that close. It's often necessary to use a pair of clipping diodes in the feedback loop of the op amp (U9A) to ensure that the JFET source voltage never drops below the threshold.

Finally, for a really polished result, you might consider designing your radio to be well behaved enough to be cycled on and off, no matter what it happens to be doing at the time. Or at a minimum, allow it to be turned on and off without making annoying noises. The circuit presented here needs more work in this regard, as the audio does make an annoying click as the supply voltage dies. It's a lot easier to solve this problem if the power supply is designed as a part of the rig—you want to disable the speaker before the voltage drops appreciably. Then again, you may just choose to live with the problem. We have seen some awfully complex projects make some equally awful noises when we turned them off!

An interesting design issue has to do with power supply bypassing. I elected to R-C bypass almost everything, even though it might not be necessary with a good power supply. Not only does this isolate noise, but it tends to simplify troubleshooting. A stage that has failed often draws abnormal current. This will easily be detected by the excessive voltage drop—or no drop at all—across the series decoupling resistor. R-C decoupling does run up the part count, of course. On the other hand, if you are doing a printed-circuit layout, it makes layout easier: the resistors bridge traces, sometimes eliminating the need for jumper wires.

Construction and Testing

At a minimum, you will need a voltmeter and an RF

probe to build this project. For a project as complicated as this, I recommend you build and test each stage, one at a time. I'd probably start with the VFO, as it's the most difficult stage to align. Then again, someone looking for the easiest circuit to start with may wish to build the sequencer first. By tacking a 33- to 470-µF electrolytic capacitor across C69 and connecting some indicator lights to the outputs of the circuit, you can watch the behavior and see if it works properly.

If you have a calculator, you can do some playing around to see why breaking down a big project such as this into manageable chunks for testing is so important. Plug in a typical accuracy rate, say 0.95, and multiply this number by itself $n-1$ times, where n is the number of parts you used. For instance, a circuit with 10 parts means you do the multiplication nine times to multiply the 10 numbers together. Alternately, those with scientific calculators can do this with one step, using the exponent function. I get approximately 0.599 on my calculator. This isn't terribly good—this implies that 40% of the time the circuit won't work on the first try! It's even worse with 100

parts, as the expected chance of failure jumps to 99.99 %! (Obviously, those automated electronic assembly plants have accuracy rates much better than 95%.)

While I don't use it too often, it's often helpful to use one of the various "superglues" available. I've had pretty good luck with the thick viscosity stuff available from a local hobby shop. There are several different varieties available, and it seems important to choose the right one. While a recent discussion in *Model Airplane News* indicates these adhesives contain no cyanide, when heated they do give off a gas that seriously irritates the eyes.

Similarly, if you choose to use a thread-locking compound instead of lock washers, you should probably get the low-strength material designed to be removed, unless you have no intention of separating the parts again! Even if there is a solvent, it won't be too useful, as how can you get at the stuff between the threads? And keep in mind that the stuff is nonconductive—don't use it with fasteners you expect to provide good electrical contact!

While a "custom" chassis was used in the prototype, finding a suitable substitute shouldn't be difficult for

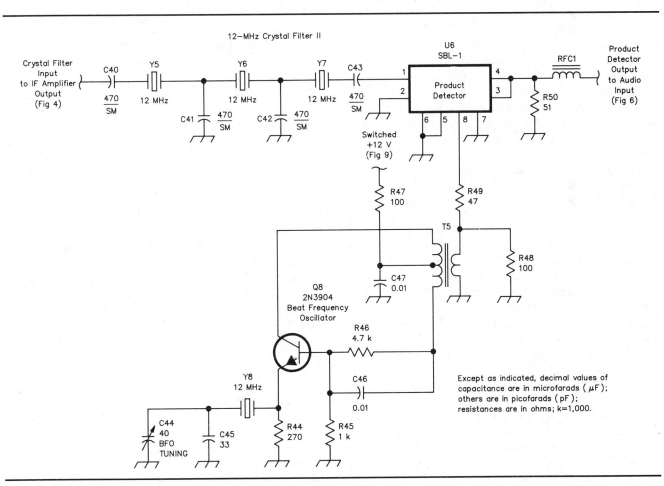

Fig 5—Second crystal filter, product detector and beat frequency oscillator.

RFC1—20 turns #28 enameled wire on an FT-23-75 ferrite core. An exact turns count isn't important—just fill the core with a single layer of wire.

T5—Broadband transformer. 5:1 turns ratio; 20 turns of #26 or #28 enameled wire on an FT-37-43 core (primary). Tap is 13 turns from the collector. Secondary has 4 turns of #26 or #28 enameled wire over the primary.

anyone who calls himself an experimenter. It's just an L-shaped piece of aluminum (bottom and back panels). Actually, you could probably even use steel, since the chassis doesn't have to carry RF currents. (It's not unusual for a steel chassis to sit around for a long time in the junkbox, simply because steel is harder than aluminum and much more difficult to work with, though cobalt drill bits do a fine job with steel. Some of the older rigs, such as the Drake TR-4, used copper-plated steel to provide good RF conductivity.) The circuits are built on pieces of 1/16-inch-thick circuit board roughly 2.7 by 3.7 inches in size. I tapped four #4-40 mounting holes in the corners of each piece to easily attach the boards to the chassis with 1/4-inch #4-40 screws. (I find holes threaded in glass epoxy circuit board to be adequate for attaching the boards. Don't attempt this with phenolic board—the corners will crack off.) Although I used double-sided board because it was available, single-sided board might be preferred. (Theoretically, having the copper and aluminum next to each other invites corrosion, but I haven't noted a problem. Nonetheless, this might be something to consider if you are going to use this building technique where corrosion is a problem, such as locations having high humidity or salt spray.)

Using 3/8-inch-long screws at the corners of the chassis instead of 1/4-inch screws allows rubber bumper pads to be affixed to the chassis with the screws used to hold down the circuit boards. I find the screw-attached bumper pads to be more reliable than the self-stick type.

Other mounting schemes I have tried include soldering nickel-plated brass nuts to the circuit board and using PEM nuts, but merely tapping the glass epoxy board has proven to be the most cost effective. (PEM nuts may be obtained from Small Parts Inc, a supplier that caters to the experimenter needing small quantities of metal stock and hardware. Unfortunately, they carry only steel and stainless steel PEM nuts rather than aluminum ones that might be preferred by amateurs.)

For those intent on making the ultimate chassis, one way to go is to make it out of aluminum bar and sheet stock. Having only flat panels certainly makes fabrication easier, and it allows you to use 6061-T6 stock, which machines quite well, for the panels. In other words, you can drill nice, clean holes without too much work, though the result isn't quite as clean as holes drilled in cast aluminum. (You may want to think twice about using aluminum alloys such as 3003. While they are easily formed, their softness sometimes makes them difficult to deburr, particularly if you get lazy and don't use sharp drill bits.) Don't try to bend 6061-T6, even if you have a sheet metal brake, as this alloy will crack, being too brittle for forming.

A difficulty with tempered stock such as 6061-T6 is that holes are more difficult to punch through the material. But there are ways of making the task easier. First, don't forget to use some sort of oil or cutting fluid to reduce friction. This makes a big difference. Also, remember that punching metal deforms it—less pressure is required if the stressed metal in the cutout has someplace to go. The easiest way to ensure that it does have

a place to go is to drill a set of strain relief holes on the inside of the circle to be punched. I suppose you could also make progressively larger holes, but this seems to be a lot more work. To ensure that the final hole is truly in the right place, you can either make centering lines or use the big, final-size punch to make some indentations that help line things up. I find that the thin rings of material that result from using progressively larger punches are easier to remove from the punch than a solid blank. Finally, you can increase the torque by using a cheater bar or simply a piece of steel pipe that extends the length of your wrench. I don't want to get letters reporting what you have broken by overdoing it, though, so use caution!

As the cover photograph indicates, I used small-diameter Teflon-dielectric coax (RG-188 or similar) instead of cheaper RG-174, with its polyethylene dielectric that melts easily. Since the coax lengths involved are so short compared to a wavelength, it's unlikely that the exact impedance of the coax is important, so use what you have available. (If you do come across 25-ohm coax, though, save it for winding broadband matching transformers.) By the way, contrary to popular belief, you do not need lots of expensive test equipment to figure out the impedance of coax. In many cases, you can get pretty close by comparing it against known 50-ohm coax of the same dielectric type and guessing. After all, there really aren't that many impedances (25, 50, 52, 70, 75, 93 and 125 ohms, the 25 and 125 being awfully rare—don't ask me where to get it!) Of course, you *will* need test equipment if you don't know that the impedance goes up as ratio of the diameter of the outer conductor to that of the inner conductor goes up. What I *would* skip is coax with an aluminum shield. While some people insist that it can be soldered, why bother if you can get tinned or copper-shielded coax? Then again, if you find that your shiny coax braid won't take solder no matter how clean it is, perhaps you bought coax with an aluminum shield by mistake. Oh, well...

For audio cables, the preferred transmission line is twisted pair, rather than coax. Twisting the wires alternates the sense of the field pickup in the wire, causing the 60-Hz hum to cancel itself out. This is much more cost-effective than buying the special metals needed to get low-frequency magnetic shielding. (Even the ARRL Lab's expensive screen room does a poor job of low frequency shielding—I've picked up all sorts of noise on VLF inside it.)

Also, you might pay attention to where you place the RF amplifier. You want to put it close to the RF gain control; short leads for this potentiometer are essential for the amplifier to work properly.

Perhaps the biggest challenge in building a VFO-tuned rig is mounting the tuning capacitor. Often, you want it to be shielded, although I found it wasn't necessary for this radio. The challenge is to mount it securely without putting a torque on its shaft and creating backlash. (Backlash occurs when the energy you put into turning the capacitor shaft deforms the capacitor instead of moving its plates the way you want them to go. Backlash is the culprit when you start tuning in one direction and the radio tunes a bit in the opposite direction first and then hurries to catch up, or when you let go of the knob and the radio tunes back the other way a little!) One help to avoiding backlash is to *not* insist on nice right angles in boxes and mounting brackets. Making boxes from copper-clad circuit-board material facilitates this—you just solder their pieces together in whatever alignment is needed to prevent the capacitor and drive mechanism from binding.

Shielding is essential when you use an air-core VFO inductor—toroids, which are largely self-shielding, aren't quite so fussy. But air-core inductors don't have ferrite slugs to degrade stability, and very stable oscillators can be built using them.

Setting up a VFO is almost always a problem because toroids aren't precise enough components. Expect to have to add or remove a few turns in the process of get-

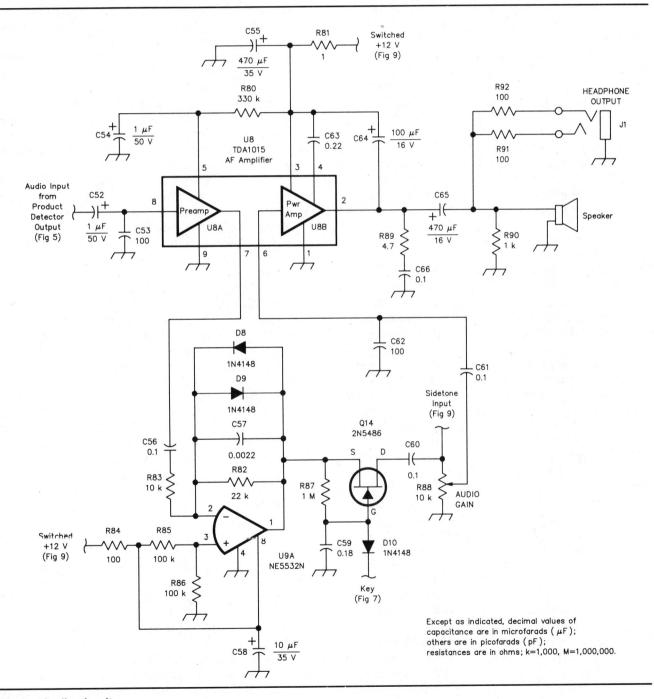

Fig 6— Audio circuits.

Q14—2N5486 JFET. 2N5484 or 2N5485 will work with slightly higher loss in the audio path.

U8—TDA1015 audio amplifier.
U9—NE5532N dual audio operational amplifier.

ting the VFO to cover the frequency range you want. A little fine tuning can be obtained by compressing the turns of the toroid coil to increase the inductance. A quick test with 12 turns of #28 wire on a T-25-6 core showed the apparent inductance going from 0.40 to 0.49 μH, with the Q dropping from 156 to 154 when the turns were compressed. The stray capacitance also changes, which is why I said the *apparent* rather than the actual inductance, but this distinction is rarely important for the cut-and-try experimenter. It's a bit more important for those trying to model circuits on computers. If you really want to figure out the stray capacitance, measure the inductance at several frequencies and calculate, keeping in mind that the permeability of some ferromagnetic materials is frequency sensitive.

Ground-plane construction is superior to printed circuits when "cutting and trying"—you can easily damage a printed circuit board by repeatedly unsoldering parts. Incidentally, the biggest cause of foil lifting from printed circuit boards is excessive temperature. If you have a temperature-controlled iron, set it to no more than 750 degrees. With ordinary irons, you will have to practice to see what the ideal warm-up time happens to be for your iron. What you should *never* do is let the iron sit around for half an hour and then use it to heat up a tiny circuit board pad.

One of the advantages to home brewing is that you get to optimize the circuit to meet your needs. Such personalization is easily done with the VFO. There are different ideas on how best to set up your tuning mechanism. Perhaps the simplest is just to cover a small portion of the band, say from 7.030 to 7.050. This range covers most of the QRP activity, for instance, and is the cheapest to implement. If you want to cover all of the CW band, the usual approach is to install a reduction drive to slow down the tuning rate to 50 kHz/turn or less. This invites mechanical complexity, so the "all thumbs" builder should probably avoid this rather than end up with a backlash-ridden drive. The compromise approach is to use two knobs, one for coarse tuning and the other for fine tuning. This actually makes a lot of sense for many amateurs. For instance, when you move frequency to dodge interference it's normally a few kHz from your current operating frequency, something easily done with a vernier control. On the other hand, someone trying to spot specific frequencies may get frustrated by a two-control system, unless a frequency counter is used.

While you could haul out the equations, here are some simplified rules for getting the tuning range you want. First, use an ordinary tuning capacitor, avoiding those with the unusually shaped plates. For small tuning ranges, such as a single amateur band, those special capacitors work worse, as they are designed to cover wide frequency ranges (such as 2 or 3 to 1). In general, the more capacitance you use to get the circuit tuned to resonance, the less range your tuning capacitor will have. Conversely, the more inductance you use the more range your tuning capacitor will have. So, if you try out your VFO and you want to cover a slightly larger chunk of the band, add a few turns to L1 and reduce the capacitance across the inductor.

The question always comes up as to what type of capacitors to use for building VFOs. The best capacitors to use are air variable ones, but they are often too expensive and bulky to be used where you just need a fixed capacitance. For fixed capacitors, NP0 capacitors seem to be a good choice, and can often be found in purchased capacitor assortments. I recommend you buy at least one of those assortments, especially if you can find one with lots of temperature compensating capacitors. These either have dots of paint on the top, or markings like *N220*. These tough-to-find parts are invaluable for getting your circuit temperature stable, though it's a time-consuming process that you may not feel is necessary. Most of these capacitors have negative coefficients, since they are made to compensate inductors, which commonly have positive temperature coefficients. You can also use polystyrene capacitors, but I avoid them, since they are so easily destroyed by errant soldering irons and solvents. (The errant soldering iron may be the biggest disadvantage to ground-plane construction. A drilled circuit board does work as a good shield to keep the parts and the hot iron separated.) Silver-mica capacitors can also be used, but they generally aren't as predictable as NP0 capacitors. Of course, if you get all your parts at bargain-basement prices, do keep in mind that some of the parts you buy may simply be of poor quality or mislabeled. (There are sometimes good reasons why something is unbelievably cheap.) I suspect the temperature-compensating capacitors are cheap because of the difficulty in selling them—imagine the space you need to carry all the different values and temperature coefficients, not to mention the time it takes for someone to need a particular value and coefficient.

I've also noticed that some of the beautiful-looking monolithic capacitors—the ones with the shiny epoxy coating—aren't particularly rugged when it comes to removing them from circuits. Their internal terminations seem to become unsoldered. While they are cheap enough to just throw away, you certainly don't want a broken or worse, intermittent unit in your circuit.

If you do choose to temperature compensate a VFO, keep in mind that the soldering iron affects the warm-up drift of the VFO. While I don't have any good numbers on how long you should wait for things to cool off, the way I do it is to make measurements before and after work, giving the circuit many hours to cool off. Also, keep in mind that the warm-up drift, the drift from turn-on to settling down, may differ considerably from the drift after things have "stabilized." It is possible for the circuit to be quite stable for the first few minutes, and then start to creep upwards in frequency, seemingly forever. This is not what you want! Also, the drift is sometimes temperature dependent—it will work fine at 70 degrees, for instance, and be pretty lousy when you show it off during Field Day when it's 90 degrees in the shade. The way to avoid such problems is to get the most stable parts you can, rather than trying to correct a highly temperature-sensitive coil with equally sensitive temperature-compensating capacitors.

I've avoided the use of a potentiometer for my main tuning knob. While they do work, I use that knob so much that wearing it out is quite likely. Worn out volume controls are quite common in "old style" non-digital radios and TV sets—and those really don't get constant use like a tuning control on an HF amateur transceiver. Trimmer potentiometers often have ratings of 100 cycles or less.

When laying out VFO parts, it's helpful to remember that high-Q tuned circuits often have high circulating currents. What you want to do is to minimize the path that these currents take, both to prevent radiation and to prevent unwanted signals from getting in and disturbing things. What this means is that you usually want to strap as much as your capacitance as possible directly across the inductor leads. This is best done by mounting the largest capacitor in the best spot and mounting the smaller ones further away. This also applies to other circuits, such as band-pass filters. If you do a decent job, you can

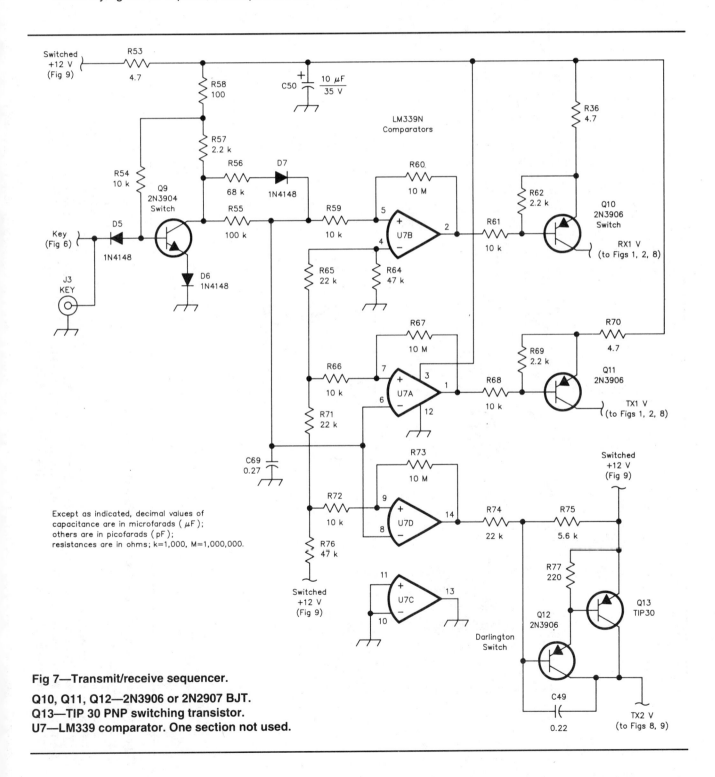

Fig 7—Transmit/receive sequencer.

Q10, Q11, Q12—2N3906 or 2N2907 BJT.
Q13—TIP 30 PNP switching transistor.
U7—LM339 comparator. One section not used.

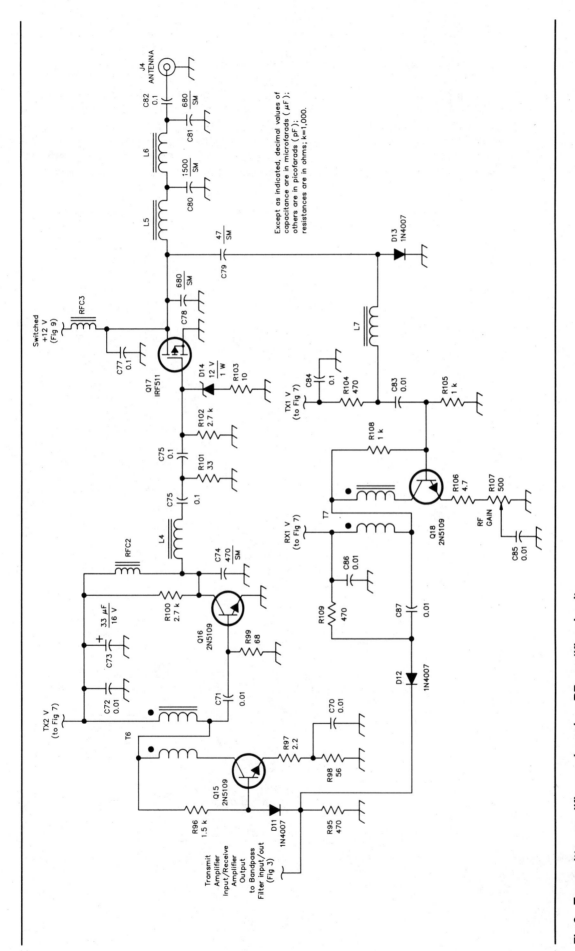

Fig 8—Transmitter amplifiers and receiver RF amplifier circuits.

D14—1N4742. 12-volt, 1-watt zener diode.

L4—12 turns #28 enameled wire on a T-44-6 toroid core.

L5—12 turns #26 enameled wire on a T-30-6 toroid core. (0.68 µH).

L6—15 turns #26 enameled wire on a T-37-6 toroid core. (0.88 µH)

L7—42 turns #28 enameled wire on a T-50-2 toroid core. (10.6 µH).

Q17—IRF510, IRF511. The IRF510, available from Radio Shack, is slightly more efficient.

RFC2—8 turns of #28 enameled wire on an FT-37-61 ferrite core.

RFC3—12 turns of #24 enameled wire on an FT-37-43 ferrite core.

often minimize the shielding needed to isolate the individual circuits from each other. Building this shielding is a time-consuming task, and shielding often makes circuit modification more difficult.

The 7-MHz band-pass filter shown in Fig 3 is pretty easy to align—if you build the transmitter you should be able to set it up by tuning for "maximum smoke" in the middle of the passband (tune your power meter for a maximum reading). It should then be tuned up for receive as well. In the process of developing a simple design I discovered that tapped inductors often have more loss than those with link coupling. But who wants to deal with all those leads, anyway? Hence the design with simple coils and capacitive coupling, even though capacitors are more expensive than wire.

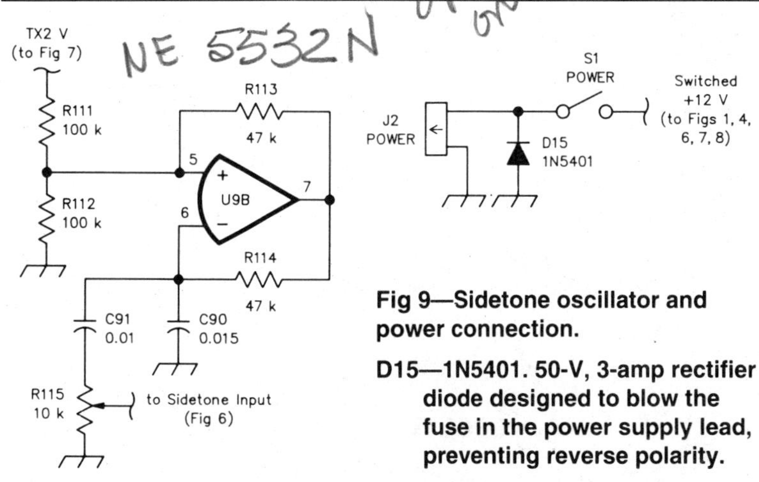

The tricky circuits to align are the two oscillator trimmers. What you want to do is to set up the beat frequency oscillator so that when a signal is in the middle of the crystal filter passband, it comes out on your favorite CW tone's frequency. Then, the carrier insertion oscillator is set up so that you also hear that exact tone. If you have an attenuator or don't mind building one, one way to set things up is to feed the carrier oscillator into the receiver through the attenuator and then adjust it for maximum audio output. Then the beat frequency oscillator is adjusted for the proper pitch or frequency. You might have to go back and forth a few times to get everything really set right.

For those experimenters who are looking to test their crystal filters without a whole lot of expense, there is a way to do it if you have a way of measuring frequencies accurately. One of the oscillators can be used as a signal source. Add 20 dB or so attenuation to avoid damaging the crystal filter and add some inductance in series with the oscillator's crystal to generate lower frequencies. To measure the power output, make a logarithmic detector using one of the FM receiver chips that features a signal strength indicator. (The October 1988 issue of *QEX* shows an example using the Motorola MC3356P receiver chip.) These chips are temperature-sensitive, so your measurements may vary between winter and summer if you work in an unheated basement. A frequency counter easily measures the frequency, if you have one. With a bit more work, a modern general-coverage receiver could also be used.

To keep the VFO stable despite changes in supply voltage, a 78L05 regulator is used. Bypassing is recommended by the manufacturer on the input for stability, while the bypass capacitor on the output suppresses the

Fig 9—Sidetone oscillator and power connection.

D15—1N5401. 50-V, 3-amp rectifier diode designed to blow the fuse in the power supply lead, preventing reverse polarity.

noise generated by the regulator. Zener-diode regulators tend to be pretty noisy unless well bypassed, so one wasn't used here. (A 6.8-volt Zener is actually used as a noise generator in the *ARRL Handbook's* noise bridge.)

An interesting problem is what sort of dc power connector to use with QRP equipment. Phono, or RCA, connectors have serious problems, being easy to short out if you aren't careful. ARRL's Field Services Department has published a 12-volt-connector recommendation that appeared in the newsletter sent to affiliated clubs. A difficulty with this standard is that it is *almost* the same as that on the popular Heathkit HW-9, the difference being that the positive and negative leads are reversed! I've had a report of significant damage to an HW-9 from reverse polarity. I strap 3-A diodes across the power leads to prevent problems like this. In any case, if you are building portable equipment, miniature Molex connectors may make more sense than the recommended one.

You need to match the crystal frequencies, ideally within 50 Hz. Normally, a lot of 10 crystals should be sufficient to get the needed 6 matched crystals. One way to measure the crystals is to put them in an oscillator circuit, such as either the carrier insertion oscillator or beat frequency oscillator, then measure the output frequency. It should be possible to match the crystals using a partially built transceiver. You can use the receiver to listen to the relative frequencies of the carrier insertion oscillator. To avoid the "both sides of zero beat" problem, you probably want to make sure the crystals are matched at both a high and a low pitched tone. The problem is that a crystal 1 kHz above the BFO sounds just like one 1 kHz below the BFO—you could get a crystal that is off by twice the audio tone frequency used. Running a quick check with another audio tone eliminates this ambiguity. □□

4. Receivers

From QST, September 1992, p 35:

A 40-Meter Regenerative Receiver You Can Build

Modern transceivers' bells and whistles only accompany the song *this* radio still *sings*.

By David Newkirk, WJ1Z
Senior Assistant Technical Editor

So slick is current radio technology that we sometimes imagine our prehistoric radio forebears surmounting near-impossible odds in managing to work as far as three blocks away without direct digital synthesis, dual IF filtering, 1.5 kW and a heap of aluminum atop hundreds of pounds of steel. Based on painstakingly deciphered ham cave paintings, this article reports that trailing-edge receiving technology actually hauled in the world quite well—with just enough challenge to keep its operators awake, and radio magical.

Eighty years ago this month, Edwin Howard Armstrong developed the circuit that moved radio reception out of the Dark Ages and into the Renaissance. His invention, later named the *regenerative* detector, didn't just rectify radio signals to audio as did the passive diode detectors of the day. It used RF feedback to *amplify* incoming signals by a factor of hundreds before detection.

No less astoundingly, the regenerative detector could simultaneously *oscillate*—produce a continuous-wave radio signal itself.[1] This gained it the name *autodyne*—

"self force." Thus generating its own stable, controllable heterodyning signal, the regenerative detector could amplify incoming Morse CW signals *and* convert them to audio as musical dots and dashes—all within *one tube*. Suddenly, spark and CW transmitters could communicate much farther—simply because a better receiver existed to hear them.

Up-and-coming radio amateurs eagerly adopted the regenerative receiver as soon as finances and the availability of vacuum tubes permitted. Armstrong himself announced the regenerative receiver's ultimate successor, the *superheterodyne*, in 1919. But a basic superhet was considerably more complex than even a lavishly built regenerative set, and good regens[2] were already hearing right down to the band noise. Highly selective intermediate-frequency filtering, something we now list among the superhet's obvious advantages over the regen, would not appear until single-signal superheterodyne reception emerged from the ARRL Lab in 1932. So it was that between World War I and the introduction of affordable, reasonably selective superhets in the 1930s, the autodyne served as hamdom's receiving mainstay.

Single-signal superheterodyne reception—rejecting the "audio image" in Morse CW reception so signals no longer came in at two dial locations for a given receiving pitch—meant the beginning of the end for the regen's reign. In quite a few amateur stations, though, especially those of beginners and hams short on cash, the regenerative receiver continued to cast its

magic spell right up until ham radio's second closedown during World War II. Postwar, the regen faded even in its role as a beginners' introductory receiver. By the early 1960s, it had all but vanished.

Radio History You Can Build

Regenerative receivers were in on receiving the first US ham signals heard across the Atlantic. Regenerative receivers were there for the first two-way transatlantic amateur contact. And a regenerative receiver—a 0-V-1—did the "inhaling" for the first Worked All Continents awardee. But regens didn't just make firsts and win awards. From ragchewing to QRP to traffic to DXing, they did yeoman work day in and day out for a generation of hams.

In no way can a regenerative receiver beat a good superhet, or even a solidly executed direct-conversion receiver, in terms of the basic radio performance we take for granted today. But ham radio isn't just about using the latest tools no matter what. It's also about experimenting, and *experiencing radio history with radio hardware you can build yourself.* That's where this article comes in. I think regens are fun, and I'd like you to learn about them for yourself by building one.

So Build One

Fig 1 shows the regenerative receiver circuit I'd like you to try. Coworkers who listen to my rendition (see the photos) can't believe their ears, and usually respond with something like "It sounds like a *real radio!*" or "You could actually *work* someone with

Four tubes and a few handfuls of parts can bring radio history back to life in the form of a 40-meter regenerative receiver. Each of the two glass *envelopes* houses two tubes—a triode and a pentode. In the regen's heyday, this radio might have been called a *1-V-2* because it consists of a tuned RF stage (*1*), detector (*V*) and two audio stages (*2*). From left to right, the controls are **RF INPUT**, **REGENERATION**, **SPREAD TUNING**, **MAIN TUNING** and **AF GAIN**. Fig 1 shows the circuit. Those **MUTE** and **SIDETONE** jacks don't do anything yet.

Ah, the Parts!

At press time, you could buy *all* of the parts for this receiver by mail—and I mean newly manufactured or "new old stock" parts, not used or surplus stuff. Here's an overview of sources for parts that may seem hard-to-get:

Air-dielectric variable capacitors suitable for use at C3 and/or C4	Antique Electronic Supply, Ocean State
High-voltage electrolytic capacitors	Antique Electronic Supply, Digi-Key, Mouser, Ocean State
RF chokes	Digi-Key, Mouser
Variable capacitors suitable for use at C1	Antique Electronic Supply, Digi-Key, Mouser, Ocean State
500-ohm controls	Digi-Key, Mouser, Ocean State
500-volt NPØ ceramic capacitors	Digi-Key, Mouser
500-volt (or greater) disc-ceramic capacitors suitable for bypass use	Digi-Key, Mouser, Ocean State
6GH8 and equivalent tubes	Antique Electronic Supply, Ocean State
9-pin miniature (not Compactron) tube sockets	Antique Electronic Supply, Ocean State (PC-board mount)

This list is by no means all-inclusive. Check *QST* advertisements for additional suppliers of new and new-old-stock components. Fair Radio Sales and Surplus Sales of Nebraska carry a variety of used and surplus components in many of these categories. (Chapter 35 of the 1992 *ARRL Handbook* carries their addresses, as well as those of all but one firm mentioned in the table, in its coverage of component sources. Antique Electronic Supply can be reached at 6221 S Maple Ave, Tempe, AZ 85283, tel 602-820-5411.)

But you don't have to buy parts for this receiver by mail or over a store counter. Ham flea markets are great places to pick up capacitors, tubes, tube sockets and chokes. Hams you know may have some of these parts in their junk boxes. Asking around on the air may net you more offers of freebies than you can handle.

The parts are out there. All you have to do is go out and get them.—*WJ1Z*

---

this!'' Yeah. One other HQ ham has already successfully duplicated it.[3] And I've had enjoyable QSOs using the version shown in the photos. So a regenerative receiver *is* a real radio—as anyone who's ever depended on one already knows.

The autodyne your dad or grandad remembers using may have contained fewer parts—and a stage or two less—than my Fig 1 circuit. But my hookup is pretty much a direct descendant of George Grammer's Rationalized Autodyne[4] with an additional stage of audio. And the Rationalized was the Cadillac of its day. You can cut back to one audio stage to simplify things, but don't hack off the RF amplifier in the name of nostalgic oversimplification. Without it, your receiver will radiate too much of its

own signal on the air to be neighborly (or legal) in 1992. It may also be more finicky than you can bear!

Construction Hints

Build as much mechanical stability into your receiver as you can. *You're building an oscillator.* If your receiver's wiring is floppy or mechanically resonant, or if touching its controls warps its enclosure enough to cause the detector's wiring or components to move, its tuning, and thus the pitch of received Morse and SSB signals, will shift. If you wax nostalgic and build with the fruit crates and coffee cans many hams had to put up with during the Great Depression, okay, but your regenerative receiver will perform likewise. I recommend using a cast aluminum box—one approximately 5 × 7 × 2 or 3 inches in size should hold everything in Fig 1 nicely. One of the box's sides can be your panel, as in the version I built. If the glow of tube heaters alone does not impart sufficient spiritual warmth as you ply the airwaves with your version, consider mounting its neon regulator lamp in a front-panel grommet.

Keep your receiver's tuned circuit wiring short—don't put your variable capacitors way up on a panel, with half-foot wires connecting them to the tubes. Minimize coupling between the detector tuned circuit and the RF stage grid components. Use shielded wire for intertube audio lines as appropriate.

Build the receiver and power supply in separate enclosures. Vacuum-tube grids, especially V2A's in this circuit, operate at very high impedances and can easily pick up hum from nearby power transformers. Radio Shack's largest blue-plastic project box should hold all of Fig 4's components if you plan carefully.

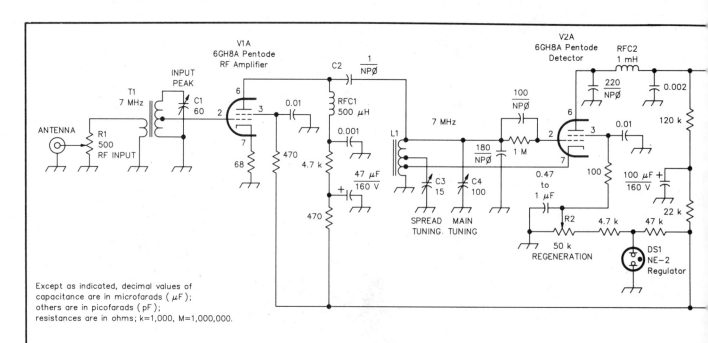

Except as indicated, decimal values of capacitance are in microfarads (μF); others are in picofarads (pF); resistances are in ohms; k=1,000, M=1,000,000.

Rediscovering Regen Fact and Legend

Experiencing the regen's radio magic requires you to mesh with its limitations. And the regen's many quirks and rough edges spawned a jargon nearly every ham could speak during its heyday. We can learn much about these receivers—and the circuit I present in Fig 1—by tuning in on that litany:

"They're unselective." Generally, yes, compared to modern radios. Oscillating, a regenerative detector converts to audio anything within audio-frequency distance of the radio signal it generates. Capacitive high-frequency rolloff in the Fig 1 circuit limits the resulting audio's high end to somewhere between 5 and 10 kHz. Without it, only the frequency response of your ears and headphones would set the limit.

Old-time hams enjoyed better regen selectivity than this because their magnetic headphones significantly restricted audio frequency response. As early as 1915, Armstrong himself described how tuned AF amplification could improve the regenerator's selectivity.[5] Despite its advantages, however, AF peaking was apparently not in widespread amateur use by the time single-signal reception arrived.

With an oscillating regenerative detector, you hear "both sides of zero beat." There's no rejection of the audio image or "opposite sideband." The regen's *RF* selectivity is greatest right around *critical regeneration*, the feedback level at which oscillation just starts. This doesn't mean much in CW and SSB because an oscillating detector's RF selectivity is much broader than CW and SSB signals. Just below oscillation, however, a *non*-oscillating detector can actually be *too* selective for comfortable spark and AM phone reception! A regener-

ative detector is generally capable of higher selectivity and gain when receiving weak signals than when it's receiving stronger ones.

"They're prone to hand capacitance." *Hand* or *body capacitance* is what's happening when you move your hand near your radio and its receiving pitch shifts like a Theremin. It was common in poorly shielded and doubtfully grounded regenerative receivers, especially those without RF-amplifier stages. *This* receiver won't unwantedly react to your presence if you shield it properly. Completely enclosing it in an all-metal box is good enough. You don't have to shield its tubes. Likewise, grounding hasn't been critical with the antenna arrangements (dipole and random wire) I've tried.

"They radiate signals of their own." Without shielding and an RF stage, yes. This receiver's shielding and RF stage keep it out of trouble. (That's why I can't in good conscience suggest in 1992 *QST* that you build and use a "two-tube blooper" of yesteryear. Oscillating or not, an RF-stageless regenerative detector can radiate RF pretty strongly—enough to be heard miles away.) The RF stage also reduces the chance that the receiver will hear strong, local AM broadcasters across its dial—another characteristic sometimes encountered in oversimple regens.

"They go into oscillation 'with a soft plop.'" Armstrong's detector, and apparently many regenerative receivers that used triode detectors, did this. But good screen-grid-detector regens don't. And they slide smoothly in and out of oscillation at *the same* setting of their regeneration controls. (Some regenerative detectors, especially some of the solid-state hookups I've tried, exhibit some feedback-control hysteresis. The Fig 1 circuit doesn't.)

"They suffer from tunable hum." Tunable hum is ac hum that varies in strength with tuning and/or the setting of the REGENERATION control. It occurs when the receiver receives its own radiated signal as modulated by line ac in diode junctions —the diodes in its own power supply, or

Fig 1—A four-tube regenerative receiver for radio fun at 40 meters. All of the circuit's nonelectrolytic fixed-value capacitors are rated 500 V or greater, except for the 0.05-µF bypasses in the 6GH8A heater wiring, which can be 50 V or greater, and the 0.47- to 1-µF bypass on R2's wiper, which can be 100 V or greater. Use the most temperature-stable capacitors you can find for the units labeled NP0. They materially affect the receiver's tuning stability. All of the circuit's fixed-value resistors are ½ watt—carbon-film, composition, whatever. Fig 2 shows audio-output options. This drawing simplifies the pentodes' internal elements for clarity. Fig 3 shows the tubes' pinout in detail. The circuit's plate and screen circuitry requires 100 to 150 volts dc at approximately 20 milliamperes. Fig 4 shows a suitable 135-V dc power supply. You can use a 12.6-volt filament transformer to power the tubes' heaters (0.45 ampere), but I recommend using a 12- to 13.8-volt regulated dc supply to minimize hum.

C1—60-pF trimmer, dielectric unimportant. This capacitor need *not* be front-panel controllable. One setting suffices for the entire 40-meter band.

C2—If you can't find a 1-pF capacitor for C2 (NP0/C0G best, polystyrene/silver-mica next best, general-purpose ceramic least best), twist two 1-inch pieces of insulated hookup wire together as a substitute.

C3, C4—Air-dielectric variable.

DS1—NE-2 neon glow lamp.

L1—Approximately 1.7 µH: 19 turns of #22 enameled wire on a T-68-6 toroidal powdered-iron core, tapped at 1 turn above ground (V2A cathode) and 5 turns above ground (C3, SPREAD TUNING). I placed C3's tap at 5 turns to provide a SPREAD TUNING range of about 10 kHz with a 15-pF capacitor at C3. Tapping C3 farther up from L1's grounded end increases the SPREAD TUNING range.

R1—500-Ω control, taper unimportant.

R2—50-kΩ control. A linear-taper control (Radio Shack's 271-1716, for instance) will provide smoother control than an audio-taper one.

R3—1-MΩ control. Use an audio-taper control if you can find one. If you can't, a linear control (Radio Shack's 271-211, for instance) will work; that's what I used.

T1—Secondary (approximately 10 µH): 14 turns of #20 enameled wire, tapped at 7 turns, on an FT-50-61 ferrite toroid. Primary: 2 turns of insulated hookup wire over secondary.

V1, V2—6GH8 or 6GH8A triode-pentode tube. Types 6U8, 6KD8, 6U8A/6KD8, 6EA8, 6678 and 7731 are also suitable.

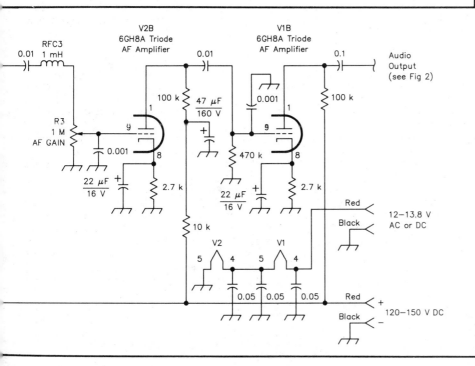

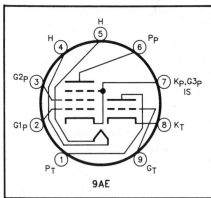

9AE

Fig 3—Pin-by-pin connections, viewed from the tube/socket *bottom*, for the tubes listed in the Fig 1 caption. The *9AE* is the manufacturing industry's designator for this particular *basing* diagram. Here's what the element codes mean:

G_T = triode control grid
$G1_P$ = pentode control grid
$G2_P$ = pentode screen grid
$G3_P$ = pentode suppressor grid
H = heater
IS = internal electrostatic shield
K_P = pentode cathode
K_T = triode cathode
P_P = pentode plate
P_T = triode plate

I built the receiver prototype into a 2¼ × 12 × 2½ (HWD) aluminum box because that's what I had on hand. A cast aluminum box would be a much better choice for the reasons mentioned in the text. This version succeeds mechanically and electrically even though its weird form factor and Flying Mod construction make for an overcompact layout I don't recommend you duplicate! *(photos by Kirk Kleinschmidt, NT0Z)*

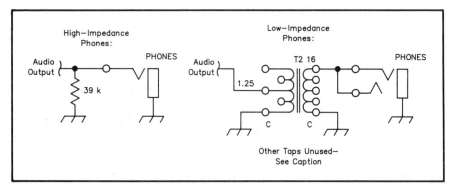

Fig 2—Audio-output options for the regenerative receiver. High-impedance headphones require only the addition of a pull-down resistor (to charge the receiver's output-coupling capacitor so your headphones don't have to). Low-impedance headphones require the addition of a jack and T2, a Radio Shack 32-1031 "70-Volt Line" transformer. T2's primary taps are labeled in output watts; its secondary taps, in load ohms. My receiver sounded best with the receiver output (see Fig 1) connected to T2's **1.25**-watt primary tap and my stereo headphones connected to the secondary's 16-Ω tap. I recommend that you experiment to see which tap combination works best for your headphones. For both T2 windings, **c** means *common*.

in poor house-wiring or conduit joints. This receiver's RF amplifier and shielding keep its detector from radiating, and therefore from receiving, its own signal.

"They're full of dead spots." Dead spots are parts of a regenerative receiver's tuning range where it won't oscillate even with its **REGENERATION** control turned all the way up. This was common with RF-stageless detectors. It happens on frequencies where a random-length antenna exhibits a low impedance that loads the detector to a grinding halt. (A wire an odd multiple of a quarter wavelength long will do it.) This receiver's RF stage keeps the antenna from pulling energy out of the detector grid tank—if you're careful to build the receiver so V1A's grid components are nowhere near V2A's grid components.

"They're prone to fringe howl." Most common in triode detectors with inductive plate loads, *fringe howl* occurs when a

regenerative detector interrupts its own RF oscillations by simultaneously oscillating at audio. In triode detectors, it tends to occur right around critical regeneration. (In screen-grid detectors, simultaneous audio and radio oscillation usually occurs well *above* critical regeneration.) Armstrong noted this effect,[6] evaluated it, determined its cause and effects, enhanced it with a separate supersonic interruption (*quench*) oscillator, and harnessed it as *superregeneration.* Superregenerative detectors helped hams colonize the VHF bands—but that's another story. If your screen-grid detector generates an earsplitting high-pitched whine when you increase its regeneration well past critical, it's superregenerating. (Cure: the doctor's response in the two-liner that begins, "Doc, it hurts when I do this.")

"Their tuning varies with feedback." Yes, this was often so. Hams spent con-

siderable time and effort fiddling with various detectors and regeneration-control methods to minimize this effect. I didn't do so with the circuit shown in Fig 1, though. So this receiver's **REGENERATION** control also tunes it a bit—by up to a few hundred hertz, depending on where you are in the **REGENERATION** control range.

"Their feedback varies with tuning." Yep. No big news, considering that the reactances of a tuned circuit's L and C vary with frequency. So, to stay near critical regeneration, you may—*gasp*—have to adjust your receiver's **REGENERATION** control as you tune! You'll have to do so anyway, because:

"They pull in." Yup. Fed a strong incoming signal close in frequency to where it's already oscillating, a regenerative detector tends to synchronize its frequency with that of the incoming signal. When this *pulling* happens, reduce the input signal and increase regeneration. The Fig 1 circuit's **RF INPUT** and **REGENERATION** controls let you maximize your regen's resistance to pulling. (Adjusting the **RF INPUT** control shifts signal pitches just a teense because V1A doesn't afford perfect isolation.) Sometimes, in extreme cases during CW reception, you may need to tune for a higher receiving pitch to stop the pulling. Despite your best efforts, strong signals even a ham band or two away may pull your oscillating detector a few hundred hertz. Cure: Put up with it or give up on it—just like in the good old days! On AM signals, you can *use* pulling to achieve a poor man's sort of synchronous AM detection by adjusting the detector to lock in on

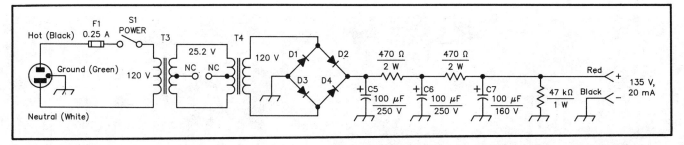

Fig 4—The tubes' plates and screens require 100 to 150 volts at about 20 milliamperes, and this circuit can supply it. The transformers are Radio Shack 273-1366s (120 V input; 25.2 volts/0.45 ampere output). Digi-Key carries high-voltage electrolytics C5 through C7. Diodes D1-4 are 1A, 600 PIV (1N4005). The 470-Ω smoothing resistors can be any value from 470 through 560 Ω. *NC* means *no connection*. Read the "High Voltage Safety" sidebar before building this circuit.

AM-signal carriers. (Wait'll you hear how hi-fi the BBC's shortwave can be!)

"They block." Quite. *Blocking* is when a very strong signal—say, from your own transmitter—makes the detector stop oscillating. When it happens, you stop listening.

Now you know what you're in for. Or do you? The next thing to do is turn on the magic box and see what's what.

Using It

Hook up your antenna, headphones and power wires, but don't turn on the power yet. Turn **RF INPUT**, **SPREAD TUNING** and **AF GAIN** to midrange. Turn **REGENERATION** all the way down, and **MAIN TUNING** to maximum capacitance. Adjust C1, **INPUT PEAK**, to something like 40 or 50 pF (just guess). Turn on your heater supply and let the tubes warm for at least half a minute. Turn on your plate/screen supply.

"Thank you for not smoking" is an appropriate thing to be able to say to a new vacuum-tube project upon powering it up. Assuming that you can say this to your receiver, put on your headphones. Slowly turn up **REGENERATION**. At some point, you should hear a soft *thwush* and the hiss of band noise as your detector goes into oscillation. Adjust **MAIN TUNING** until you start hearing 40-meter ham signals and stop at the center of the band. Adjust C1 for maximum signal strength.

When you hear a signal you want to listen to closely, leave **MAIN TUNING** alone and fine-tune with **SPREAD TUNING**. Reread "Rediscovering Regen Fact and Legend" to get a feel for how to adjust the radio's controls for strong- and weak-signal conditions. In general, you'll need to turn **REGENERATION** up and **RF INPUT** down for strong CW and SSB signals. You'll probably be able to use much more RF input during the day than at night.

When receiving AM signals, you can try two approaches. You can jockey the **REGENERATION** and **RF INPUT** controls carefully for best reception just short of oscillation. (Remember, less RF input will let you adjust **REGENERATION** for higher selectivity.) Or you can adjust these controls so the detector just oscillates, and then tune with **SPREAD TUNING** to allow the detector to lock onto the signal carrier. Expect to hear some squeals and growls as the signal fades and the detector loses lock.

It's okay to be amazed.

A Source of Splendid Pleasure

No other text I've seen captures the regen's magic better than this passage from the November 1929 edition of ARRL's *The Radio Amateur's Handbook*:

And now, when the receiver has been built, adjusted and placed in satisfactory working condition it will be permissible to sit back and take a long breath. For the receiver is one of the two essential parts of an amateur station. If the receiver has been correctly built and if the location of the station is satisfactory it will receive as far as any transmitter can send. If it has open tuning scales; if it has lots of sensitivity and amplification; and if it is smooth and quiet in operation, it will be a very great comfort and a source of splendid pleasure.

Notes

[1] Here I use the term *continuous wave* in its classical, radio physics sense instead of in its more common role as a synonym for *Morse code.* Continuous waves are *undamped* waves; spark transmitters produced *damped* waves. For a drawing that shows the difference, see Fig 2 in H. Hyder, "The Final Days of Ham Spark," *QST*, Mar 1992, pp 29-32.

[2] I know that regenerative receivers were almost certainly *not* called *regens* in their heyday. I went fishing for a synonym short enough for heavy use and that's what the line dragged in. Accent the first syllable and give it a long *e.*

[3] Some readers may worry that running a receiving-tube article in 1992 *QST* may irrevocably throttle The Very Technological Progress of Amateur Radio As We Know It Today. I disagree because I've never seen a vintage car rally cause a general lemminglike stampede back to starter cranks, running boards and 6 miles per gallon. In fact, I'm even working on talking the Editor into letting me publish a tube *transmitter* to match this receiver! So if you'd like that to see the light of day (or not), tell me so on a postcard to ARRL HQ. Whatever you do, keep in mind that Amateur Radio As We Know It Today will cease to exist at midnight tonight.

[4] G. Grammer, "Rationalizing the Autodyne," *QST*, Jan 1933, pp 11-16, 23.

[5] E. Armstrong, "Some Recent Developments in the Audion Receiver," *Proceedings of the Institute of Radio Engineers*, Vol 3, No. 3 (Sep 1915), pp 215-247.

[6] See Note 5.

References

C. Albrecht, W. Shelton, H. Schrecker, R. Kempton, preparers, *Essential Characteristics* (Owensboro, KY: General Electric Co, 1973).

R. Hull, "Selectivity in Radiotelegraph Reception," *QST*, Jan 1932, pp 9-15.

J. Lamb, "What's Wrong With Our C.W. Receivers?," *QST*, Jun 1932, pp 9-16, 90; and "Short-Wave Receiver Selectivity to Match Present Conditions," *QST*, Aug 1932, pp 9-20, 90.

F. Langford-Smith, ed, *Radiotron Designer's Handbook* (Sydney, Australia: Wireless Press, 1953; reprinted in 1968 by RCA Electronic Components, Harrison, NJ).

T. Lewis, *Empire of the Air* (New York: HarperCollins, 1991).

Receiving Tube Manual (1975: RCA Corporation, Deptford, NJ).

H. Robinson, "Regenerative Detectors," *QST*, Feb 1933, pp 26-30 and 90.

F. Terman, *Radio Engineering*, 1st ed (New York: McGraw-Hill, 1932), pp 309-316.

From QST, June 1992, p 27:

The "Ugly Weekender" II:
Adding a Junk-Box Receiver

To many low-power enthusiasts, operating a 100% home-brewed station maximizes the joy of QRP. Here's a simple way to expand a popular QRP transmitter design into a complete direct-conversion transceiver.

By Roger D. Hayward, KA7EXM
c/o 7700 SW Danielle Dr
Beaverton, OR 97005

The original Ugly Weekender article[1] described a simple 40-meter QRP CW transmitter. It offered electronic TR switching and chirp-free operation, and its output power of 1.5 watts has proven to be quite adequate for the casual backpacking trip, Field Day, or study break. The original article didn't cover an obvious requirement, however: a companion receiver.

Making one alteration to the VFO circuit and adding the receiver described in this article turns the Ugly Weekender into a fully functional transceiver. The Ugly Weekender receiver is built with many common parts, most of which are probably already in your junk box. Constructing the receiver shouldn't take more than an evening or two.

The Receiver Circuit

A copy of the Ugly Weekender article (see Note 1) is essential in constructing the receiver. In its original form, the Ugly Weekender consists of a four-stage, 7-MHz CW transmitter designed for ease of duplication. The receiver circuit (Fig 1) connects to the existing Ugly Weekender VFO and keying circuits. The added circuitry consists of a product detector, audio amplifier, muting circuit, sidetone generator and a crystal calibrator that can help you keep your Ugly Weekender on frequency.

The Ugly Weekender receiver is a classic direct-conversion design. The transmitter's 7-MHz VFO (applied via **Local Oscillator Input**) is used to "beat" incoming signals (at **RX RF Input**) to audio in the product detector consisting of diodes D8-D11 and transformers T4 and T5.[2] The transmitter VFO circuit includes a jack (J4, **AUX OUT**) that provides VFO energy for this purpose. Antenna RF for the Ugly Weekender receiver is available at the transmitter's jack J4, **TO RECEIVER**, associated with the transmitter output network.

The product detector output is increased to high-impedance-headphone level by a four-transistor amplifier chain (Q8-Q10 and Q12). Careful attention was given to suppressing power-supply hum. The active decoupling circuit (Q11 and associated components) helps eliminate this problem. More details are provided in "An Optimized QRP Transceiver" by Roy Lewallen, W7EL.[3] All transistors in the receiver circuit are 2N3904s, or equivalent.

The original Ugly Weekender receiver was designed to drive only a high-impedance load. I recently added an LM386 IC audio power amplifier to drive a favorite pair of portable hi-fi headphones. Fig 2 shows the additional gain stage.

The Ugly Weekender transmitter's **B** terminal provides +12 V during key-down periods. This signal is applied to Q15 in the receiver. Q15, an emitter follower, switches power-supply current to the sidetone oscil-lator (Q16-Q17) and the mute switch (Q13). The sidetone oscillator is a multivibrator. Q13 shuts the receiver audio off by pulling the base of Q12 to ground.

Semi-break-in delay is accomplished by R45, R46, and C43, near the base of Q13. R45 provides a discharge path for C43 after key-down is complete. Although the JFET switching scheme described by W7EL for the Optimized Transceiver would provide cleaner, click-free muting, the Q13 circuitry is adequate.

The sidetone is injected into the Ugly Weekender's audio output by a separate amplifier, Q14. Sidetone volume is fixed; increasing the value of R47 lowers the volume of the sidetone.

Crystal Calibrator

The final Ugly Weekender Transceiver design includes a crystal oscillator (Q18). Over time, I discovered that the coarse and fine VFO tuning knobs can easily get bumped out of adjustment when transporting the unit. Use of a band- or subband-edge crystal is suggested. S2, **CALIBRATE**, turns the oscillator on and off.

The calibrator signal is capacitively coupled into the receiver RF chain by running a wire across to the mixer circuitry. The mixer end of this wire is left unconnected. (Fig 1 shows the capacitance obtained by this arrangement as C35.) If the signal from the crystal calibrator is too strong for your ears, move the wire a little farther from the mixer to lower the

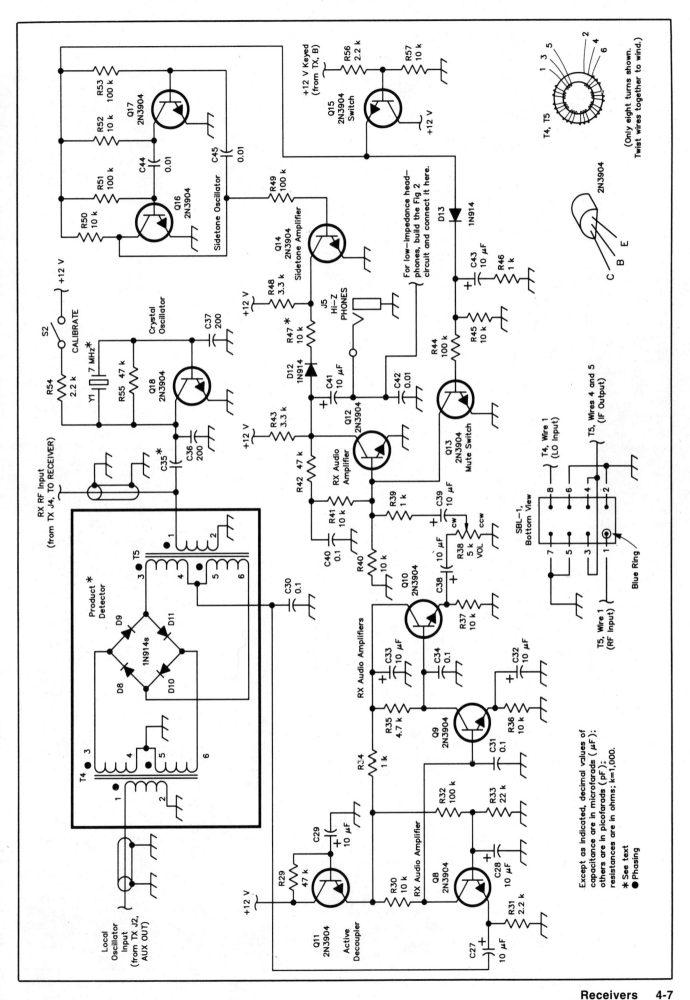

Fig 1—The Ugly Weekender receiver uses easy-to-get parts and goes together in an evening or two. The receiver's unpolarized capacitors are disc ceramics; its polarized capacitors are aluminum or tantalum electrolytics rated at 16 to 35 V dc. Its resistors are 5- or 10%-tolerance, ¼-watt, carbon-film or -composition units. The inset shows how to wire a Mini Circuits SBL-1 mixer in place of T4, T5 and D8-D11 (see Note 2); the SBL-1 replaces the boxed components in the main drawing. Component designators not listed below are for the purpose of PC-board part placement (see the ''Ugly Weekender PC Boards?'' sidebar). This circuit is designed to drive high-impedance headphones; Fig 2 shows an add-on amplifier capable of driving low-impedance phones or a speaker.

D8-D13—Silicon switching diode, 1N914, 1N4148, 1N4152 or equivalent (D8-D11: see Note 3).

R38—5 kΩ, audio-taper control.

Q11-18—2N3904 or equivalent.

T4, T5—10 trifilar turns #28 enameled wire on a toroidal ferrite core, FT-37-43 (0.37-inch OD, Mix 43 ferrite) or equivalent. See Note 2.

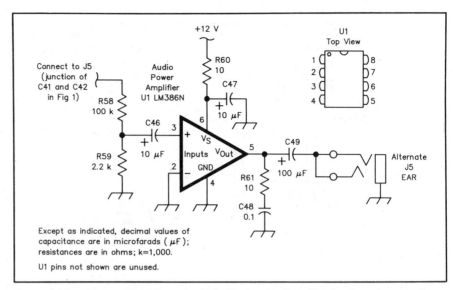

Fig 2—Adding this amplifier allows the Ugly Weekender II to drive low-impedance audio loads. The component information in the Fig 1 caption also applies to this circuit. U1 is an LM386 audio power amplifier IC.

coupling effect. One advantage of the ugly construction technique is that this value may be adjusted at any time, even in harsher portable environments. If the carrier needs to be louder, just open the rig and move the wire. If necessary, the end of the wire may be wrapped around the center conductor of the **RX RF Input** coax to provide sufficient coupling.

Modifying the Existing Transmitter

The Ugly Weekender VFO must be altered slightly in order for the VFO to be shared by the receiver. As originally designed, the VFO shifts approximately 25 kHz higher than its operating value during receiving periods. Altering the VFO to shift only a few hundred hertz is accomplished by shunting D2 (in the original Ugly Weekender VFO/buffer schematic) with a capacitor. I used a 200-pF, silver-mica unit, which yields a shift of about 600 Hz. (More capacitance equates to less shift.) This shift becomes the correct pitch at which to tune in received signals for transmitter zero beat.[4]

Construction Hints

The original mechanical layout of the transmitter was not changed. The BNC connector at J4 was replaced with a less-expensive phono type, and appropriate connectors were added to the VFO/buffer circuitry to provide the necessary signals to the receiver. All signal lines required by the receiver were routed behind the chassis.

As the title photo shows, I bolted an additional LMB SL-139 chassis box onto the lid of the original amplifier module. A scrap piece of copper-clad PC-board material was bolted onto the base of the box. Starting with the mixer, I wired the circuit from left to right, just as shown in

the schematic. Fig 3 details the receiver interior.

When building any circuit on copper-clad board, you may tend to get a little carried away before realizing where the circuit is going. I've found that approaching every circuit transistor by transistor works well. Give a little thought to your layout, and where the next stage will be constructed. This will keep you from working your way into a corner. It may work out better to solder some components together before setting them onto the copper ground plane.

All components are soldered to each other in point-to-point fashion. Any component with a grounded lead can be soldered directly to the copper ground plane. *Important:* The ground plane must be provided with a *real* supply ground line. Don't rely on the chassis and board-to-chassis fasteners to provide this path.

High-value resistors can act as standoffs when additional mechanical support is required. At 12 V, any resistor value above 220 kΩ acts more like an insulator than a resistor. Additional standoffs can be added anywhere within the receiver chain, although few are required for this circuit. I managed to build the entire receiver stage without a single additional standoff. Although the completed receiver won't win any neatness awards, its structural integrity has yet to fail!

Operating the Ugly Weekender II

After completing the receiver, it's time to get on the air. Before transmitting, be sure you know where the VFO is tuned. Turn on the crystal oscillator and tune the coarse adjustment (C1) until the crystal's frequency is reached. It may be convenient to calibrate the main tuning knob (C2, **VFO TUNE**) before portable operation is attempted. The title photo shows an example of this. I set **VFO TUNE** to the double dots. Then I tune with C1 to zero-beat the

transceiver's calibration oscillator (about 7024 kHz with the crystal I used).

Check the VFO shift modification by turning on the **SPOT** switch and zero-beating any incoming signal (the calibrator, for instance). Turning off the **SPOT** switch should make the signal of interest audible at the transmit offset (600 to 800 Hz, depending on the value you shunted across D2 in your Ugly Weekender).

For *Real* QRP Fun, Go Portable!

Constructing the Ugly Weekender transmitter is a quick way to get on the air from your home. With not much more than a handful of components and a slab of copper-clad circuit board, you're on the air. Adding this receiver circuit will allow you to take the Ugly Weekender into the sticks on your next outdoor adventure!

Many operators find QRP operating frustrating. One way to overcome this feeling is to add one more dimension to operating QRP: Go portable! I've found that the real fun comes when your QTH is somewhere far away from your home station, where that 100-W HF rig may be begging for some attention. Many portable locations work very well: the beach, the mountains, a snow cave, a boat, etc. These locations not only enhance the joy of QRP operating, but they can also increase your effective signal strength. In a boat, especially on salt water, you have a very good ground plane that helps your signal carry. If you're on a mountaintop, your increased height above average terrain can (under certain conditions) increase your effective radiated power. Sometimes, the view from a portable QTH is so overwhelming that you forget to get on the air!—*KA7EXM*

Fig 3—Interior view of the receiver, with the front panel at the top. Product-detector transformers T4 and T5 appear at the left, just below the audio VOLume control, R38. A rubber band holds Y1, the marker crystal, snug against its retaining bracket. A small daughterboard, right, carries the LM386 amplifier circuitry. The U1 stage could have been built on the main board, but keeping the LM386 amplifier's ground foil separate from that of the rest of the receiver helps avoid audio feedback problems. A single wire connects the LM386 board foil to chassis at the EAR jack (alternate J5, Fig 2). *(photos by Kirk Kleinschmidt, NT0Z)*

Unlike the single-signal superheterodynes commonly used by hams, this simple direct-conversion receiver causes every signal to be heard "twice" as you tune through it. Only one (the lower-frequency) of the two **VFO TUNE** settings that receive a given signal at the transmit-offset pitch correctly tunes the Ugly Weekender's transmitter to incoming signals. The **SPOT** switch allows you to tune correctly every time by defeating the transmit offset. Just turn on **SPOT**, tune the desired signal to zero beat (as close to 0 Hz as your ears can detect), and turn off **SPOT**. You might even consider bandscanning with **SPOT** already turned on. Then, when you hear a station you want to contact, tune it to zero beat, turn off **SPOT**, and you're ready to call.

Contest operation calls for a faster spotting procedure. The title photo shows part of the solution: an arrow (just above the **VFO TUNE** knob). To spot with the tuning arrow, keep the **SPOT** switch turned off. Starting at a frequency above the desired signal's, turn **VFO TUNE** *in the direction the arrow points*—that is, to decrease frequency—until the station you want to work comes in at the transceiver's CW-offset pitch. If you tune for this pitch from the low side of zero beat while moving *against* the arrow, your transmitted signal will be off by twice the frequency of the VFO shift— between 1 and 2 kHz! Without the arrow, you may find yourself yelling "Superhet!" to other members of your Field Day team.

Operating the Ugly Weekender transceiver has been very enjoyable. The excitement in operating this radio has been the greatest when operating in a portable environment, where the typical appliance couldn't be carried, or powered. From the Oregon Cascades, the radio's 1.5 watts has proven to be more than enough power to contact stations up and down the entire West Coast.

Summary

The original Ugly Weekender transmitter can be converted into a transceiver with not much more than a handful of components from your junk box. I encourage you to add this receiver to your Ugly Weekender and operate it portable sometime soon!

Acknowledgments

Thanks to Roy Lewallen, W7EL, for his teaching and encouragement. I have had the honor to operate his Optimized QRP Transceiver, the radio on which this design is based. Thanks also to my father, Wes Hayward, W7ZOI, for providing the design and the encouragement to write this article.

Notes
[1]R. Hayward and W. Hayward, "The 'Ugly Weekender,'" *QST*, Aug 1981, pp 18-21. The Ugly Weekender also appears on pages 30-33 to 30-36 of the 1992 *ARRL Handbook*.
[2]A Mini-Circuits SBL-1 may be used in place of this hand-assembled mixer. There is little performance difference between the two. The diode ring mixer is still the best product detector for low intermodulation distortion and immunity to amplitude-modulated broadcast signals.
[3]R. Lewallen, "An Optimized QRP Transceiver," *QST*, Aug 1980, pp 14-19; also see Feedback, *QST*, Nov 1980, p 53. The Optimized QRP Transceiver also appears on pages 30-37 to 30-40 of the 1992 *ARRL Handbook*, and in the second printing of *QRP Classics* (available from the ARRL Bookshelf as #3169). The Ugly Weekender is heavily based on Roy's design.
[4]The mechanics of CW offset are described in G. Collins and D. Newkirk, "Transceiver Features That Help You Beat Interference," *QST*, Mar 1991, pp 16-21.

Licensed since 1979, Roger Hayward holds an Advanced Class license and is active in VHF mountaintopping, HF operating and applying DSP techniques in ham radio. He obtained a Bachelor's of Science in Electrical and Computer Engineering from Oregon State University, Corvallis, Oregon, in 1987, and will receive his Master's degree in Electrical Engineering from OSU this month. His area of study involves digital signal processing and communications systems; his MS thesis involves improved simulation techniques for sampled-data systems. Roger is a development engineer for Mentor Graphics.

Ugly Weekender PC Boards?

In order to simplify construction, no PC boards were used in the original Ugly Weekender. Instead, a point-to-point wiring technique now known as *ugly construction* was described.*

This construction technique utilized in the original transmitter has proven to be as reliable as PC-board construction. In the past 10 years, the radio has logged many miles in my backpack during various outdoor excursions and Field Day events. No failures have ever occurred. Because of this proven reliability and ease of construction, the Ugly Weekender receiver was also built with ugly-construction techniques.

If you are involved in a club, and wish to replicate this circuit in quantity, it may be better to build the receiver on a printed circuit card. Or you may simply prefer PC-board to ugly construction. PC boards are available for the Ugly Weekender receiver and VFO.† However, I encourage everyone to try ugly construction before simply purchasing an etched circuit board. Ugly construction costs less, works as well (and sometimes better!) and lets you get started in building *now.—KA7EXM*

*You can learn more about this technique, also called *ground-plane* construction, in B. Hale, "Build It Yourself from *QST*," *Part 2, QST*, May 1992, pp 35-39.—Ed.

†Etched, plated and drilled PC boards are available from FAR Circuits, 18N640 Field Ct, Dundee, IL 60118-9269. Prices: Ugly Weekender VFO/buffer, $4; Ugly Weekender receiver, $6; Ugly Weekender transmitter, $5; all three boards as a set, $11. Add $1.50 shipping and handling to each order. Check or money order only; credit cards are not accepted. Part-placement diagrams are included with each order.

PC-board templates and part overlays for the Ugly Weekender VFO/buffer and receiver boards are available free of charge from the ARRL Technical Department Secretary. With your request for the UGLY WEEKENDER PC BOARD TEMPLATE PACKAGE, send a #10 SASE.

From QST, January 1993, p 32:

High-Performance, Single-Signal Direct-Conversion Receivers

The direct-conversion receiver described in August 1992 *QST* featured high dynamic range, low-distortion audio and a super SSB filter shape factor. What more could you ask for? How about adding an image-reject mixer to that basic design for great opposite-sideband rejection?

By Rick Campbell, KK7B
Department of Electrical Engineering
Michigan Technological University
Houghton, MI 49931

Direct-conversion receivers are capable of outstanding performance. The The high-performance receiver described in August 1992 *QST*[1] has now been used from 25 kHz to 6 GHz with excellent results. Nicknamed "R1," that receiver works well and sounds good because it combines several desirable traits:

- high third-order, two-tone dynamic range;
- moderate noise figure;
- low distortion from antenna to speaker leads; and
- 60 dB of output signal-to-noise ratio.

The significant flaw in R1 is that it has no opposite-sideband rejection. This flaw can cause real problems when you try to use the receiver for serious listening. On the crowded HF bands, the opposite sideband is almost always occupied by an interfering signal or two. On VHF and microwaves, the noise in the opposite sideband reduces the signal-to-noise ratio by up to 3 dB.[2]

There are two ways to get rid of the opposite sideband: (1) a narrow filter before the downconverter; or (2) an image-reject mixer. A fixed-frequency direct-conversion receiver preceded by a narrow filter and tunable converter is a conventional superhet. The image-reject mixer is less familiar.

Fig 1 is the block diagram of an image-reject mixer, along with the mathematical relationships between the local oscillator (LO) and signals above and below the LO frequency. Readers comfortable with trigonometric identities may verify that signals above the LO frequency cancel at the output, while signals below the LO frequency add. Less ambitious readers may simply recognize the block diagram of a phasing SSB exciter (from any radio handbook published in the last 30 years), with the arrows turned around.

Old timers will remember the phasing-type SSB rigs of the 1950s and '60s. Those memories may be a bit less than fond. Maintaining amplitude balance to less than 0.1 dB and phase error of less than 1° in a band-switched, vacuum-tube-and-paper-capacitor transmitter was truly a nightmare. The rigs often sounded bad on the air. Many operators just gave up trying to adjust their rigs after a while and transmitted poor signals until they could afford a filter-type SSB radio.

The situation is reversed today. The required phase and amplitude tolerances are easy to obtain with modern components, and a properly designed phasing exciter has fewer adjustments (and fewer spurs) than a filter rig!

Although image-reject mixers and phasing SSB receivers are scarce in the North American Amateur Radio literature, they are very common in professional circles and in other parts of the world. *SPRAT*, the journal of the G-QRP club, published in England, has presented *three* HF phasing receivers in the past year. Commercially, the Drake R8 shortwave receiver uses an image-reject mixer to downconvert from a VHF first IF to a 50-kHz second IF, and the Kenwood TS-950SDX uses a digital signal processing (DSP) phasing exciter and detector.

R1 Becomes R2

With a wealth of excellent technical material at hand, in particular the outstanding papers by Oppelt,[3,4] I did not have to start

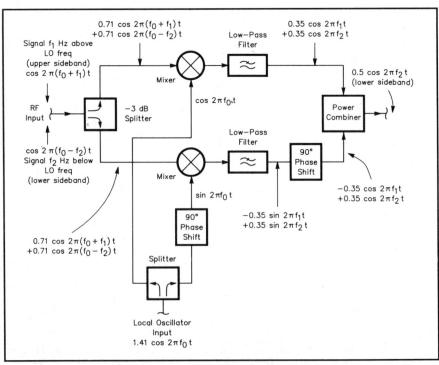

Fig 1—Block diagram of an image-reject mixer. The sines and cosines represent the local oscillator signal and signals above and below the LO frequency. Signals above the LO frequency cancel at the output, while signals below the LO frequency add.

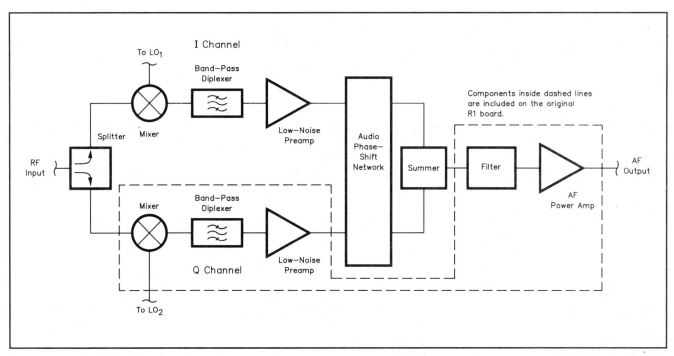

Fig 2—Block diagram of the R2 single-signal direct-conversion receiver. The sections inside the dashed lines are included on the original R1 board. Added are an RF splitter, second mixer diplexer and low-noise preamp, an audio phase-shift network and a summer.

from scratch to design a single-signal direct-conversion receiver. My goal was to add single-signal capability to the R1 board without degrading its otherwise outstanding performance.

Fig 2 is the block diagram of the R1 receiver board, with the necessary blocks added to suppress one sideband. The resulting receiver is called "R2." The additional parts on the R2 board are an RF splitter, a second mixer, diplexer and audio preamp, and an audio phase-shift network and summer using a pair of quad op amps. For maximum flexibility, the 90° phase-shift network for the LO is off the board. The complete schematic is shown in Fig 3. All of the parts fit comfortably on a 3½ × 5-inch double-sided PC board.[5]

Circuit Details

The first component the input signal sees is the RF input splitter. I used a Toko TK2518 because it's cheap ($2), small, and available from Digi-Key.[6] It is rated from 20 MHz to 600 MHz, but I tried one on 40 meters and it works. A Mini-Circuits PSC2-1 splitter worked fine as well, but it is a lot more expensive ($12) and will have to be mounted off the board. For operation below 20 MHz, a home-brew alternative to commercial splitters is shown in Fig 4. I am using the one in Fig 4 on 40 meters.

The RF level at each mixer is 3 dB below the RF-input signal level. That translates to an improvement in the input third-order intercept point. Since there is also a 3-dB (maximum) improvement in signal-to-noise ratio, the R2 board has intrinsically better dynamic range than the R1 board. I haven't built an R2 board with high-level mixers, but based on measurements of the high-level R1

board and the R2 board with SBL-1 mixers, it should have a two-tone, third-order IMD dynamic range of greater than 100 dB.

After the splitter, the input signals are multiplied with the 90°-out-of-phase LOs, filtered and amplified in a pair of identical channels. They are referred to as the I channel (for "In phase") and the Q channel (for "Quadrature," a fancy word for "90° out of phase"). Amplitude and phase-shift errors in the I and Q channels must be carefully controlled. If there is a difference in the conversion loss of the two mixers or the gain of an audio preamp, it can be compensated by adjusting the **AMPLITUDE BALANCE** potentiometer (R30).

If there is an amplitude difference that is a function of frequency, however, R30 can

only correct for it at a single audio frequency. Since the diplexer network between the mixer IF port and the audio preamp in each channel has an amplitude and phase characteristic that varies rapidly with frequency over the audio range, it is necessary to carefully select the components marked with asterisks in the schematic. Each component needs to be within 1% of the value of its counterpart in the other channel. The matched pairs may vary from the schematic value by up to 10% with no significant change in performance, *but they must be within 1% of each other.* I bought 10 of each of the marked parts and matched them with an RLC bridge. I obtained four sets matched to within 1%, and built R1 boards with the extras.

In an ideal world with ideal components,

Fig 3 (see next page)—The R1 receiver board circuit board holds all of the non-frequency-sensitive components. The local oscillator, LO phase-shift network and front-end filter are located off the board. The resistors in the audio phase-shift networks (R20-R28 and R35-R43) are 1%-tolerance metal-film units. Other resistors are 5%-tolerance carbon-film or composition units. Inductors are Toko 10RB series fixed inductors. Polarized capacitors are aluminum electrolytics rated at 16 V dc. The capacitors in the audio phase-shift networks (C21-C23 and C26-C28) are 1%-tolerance XICON polyester-film units available from Mouser (see text and Note 5). The capacitors in the diplexers (C1, C3-C5, C11, C13-C15) and 300-Hz high-pass filter (C43, C44) are Panasonic type ECQ-E(F) 100-V, 10%-tolerance miniature metalized polyester film units. C32-C37 in the low-pass filter are Panasonic V-series 50-V, 5%-tolerance metalized film capacitors; C31 is a 50-V Panasonic P-series polypropylene capacitor. C38, C46 and C48 are disc-ceramic capacitors. The other capacitors can be metalized polyester or ceramic-disc capacitors. See Note 5 for part sources.

C2, C12—0.001-μF chip capacitor. These parts are necessary only if the board is used at VHF or UHF.
R30—10-kΩ single-turn PC-board-mount control (Panasonic MAG14 or equivalent).
R53—500-Ω audio-taper control.
R57—10-kΩ single-turn PC-board-mount control (Panasonic MAG14 or equivalent).
U1—Toko TK-2518 power splitter (this part is called a balun transformer in the Digi-Key catalog). See text.
U2, U3—Mini-Circuits SBL-1 double balanced mixer. Other mixers may be substituted if higher dynamic range is needed or other frequency ranges are desired.

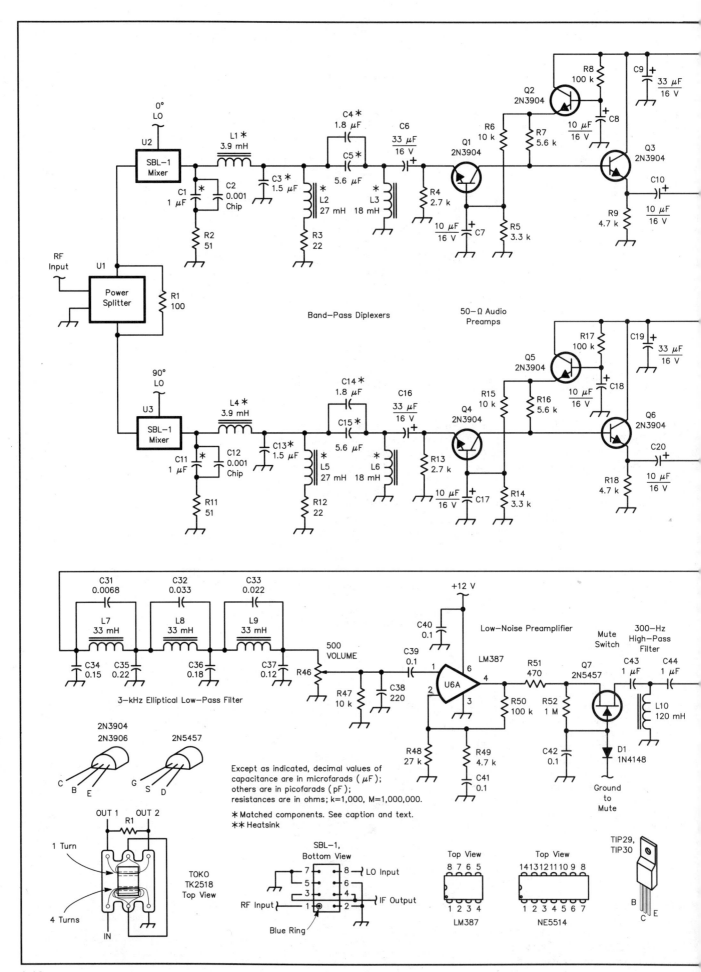

Band-Pass Diplexers

50–Ω Audio Preamps

3-kHz Elliptical Low-Pass Filter

Low-Noise Preamplifier

Except as indicated, decimal values of capacitance are in microfarads (μF); others are in picofarads (pF); resistances are in ohms; k=1,000, M=1,000,000.

*Matched components. See caption and text.
**Heatsink

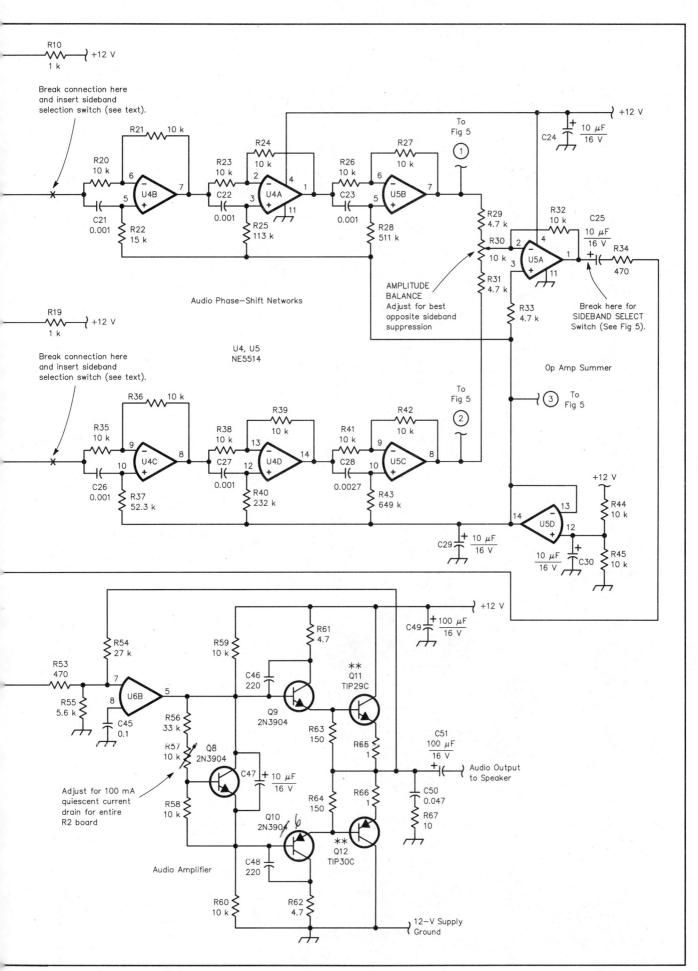

Break connection here
and insert sideband
selection switch (see text).

R10
1 k
+12 V

R21 10 k
R20 10 k
C21 0.001
R22 15 k
U4B 6 5 7

R24 10 k
R23 10 k
C22 0.001
R25 113 k
U4A 2 3 4 1 11

R26 10 k
R27 10 k
C23 0.001
R28 511 k
U5B 6 5 7

To Fig 5
1

Audio Phase-Shift Networks

R29 4.7 k
R30 10 k
R31 4.7 k

AMPLITUDE
BALANCE
Adjust for best
opposite sideband
suppression

U4, U5
NE5514

R32 10 k
U5A 2 3 4 1 11
R33 4.7 k

C24 10 µF / 16 V
+12 V

C25 10 µF / 16 V
R34 470

Break here for
SIDEBAND SELECT
Switch (See Fig 5).

Op Amp Summer

R19
1 k
+12 V

Break connection here
and insert sideband
selection switch (see text).

R36 10 k
R35 10 k
C26 0.001
R37 52.3 k
U4C 9 10 8

R38 10 k
R39 10 k
C27 0.001
R40 232 k
U4D 13 12 14

R41 10 k
R42 10 k
C28 0.0027
R43 649 k
U5C 9 10 8

To Fig 5
2

To Fig 5
3

U5D 14 13 12
C29 10 µF / 16 V
10 µF / 16 V C30
R44 10 k
R45 10 k
+12 V

+12 V
C49 100 µF / 16 V

R53 470
R55 5.6 k
C45 0.1
U6B 7 8 5

R54 27 k

R59 10 k
C46 220
Q9 2N3904
R63 150

R61 4.7
** Q11 TIP29C
R65 1

C51 100 µF / 16 V
Audio Output
to Speaker

R56 33 k
R57 10 k
Q8 2N3904
C47 10 µF / 16 V

R64 150
R66 1
C50 0.047
R67 10

Adjust for 100 mA
quiescent current
drain for entire
R2 board

R58 10 k
Q10 2N3904
C48 220
** Q12 TIP30C

Audio Amplifier

R60 10 k
R62 4.7

12-V Supply
Ground

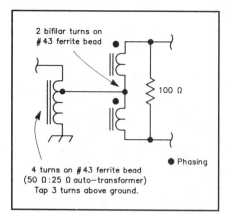

Fig 4—This home-brew in-phase splitter is an alternative to the commercial RF power splitter (U1) of Fig 3.

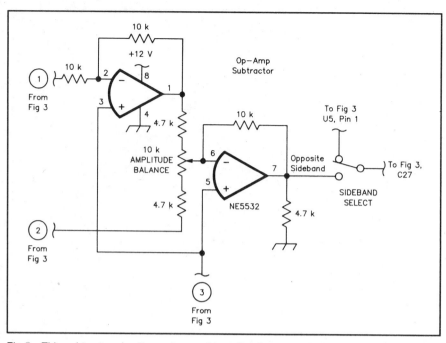

Fig 5—This subtractor circuit may be used to switch between sidebands or for simultaneous reception of both sidebands (see text).

it would be possible to have identical I and Q channels, a perfect 90° audio-phase-shift network, and thereby obtain infinite opposite-sideband suppression. Oppelt has done an excellent study of the errors introduced using real components (see Note 3). To paraphrase his many pages of analysis, it is trivial to build a receiver with 20 dB of opposite-sideband suppression, easy to get 30 dB, not too tough to obtain 40 dB, a real stretch to reach 50 dB, and quite likely impossible to hit 60 dB.

Since I wanted easy reproducibility and decent performance with off-the-shelf components, I settled on the "not-too-tough"

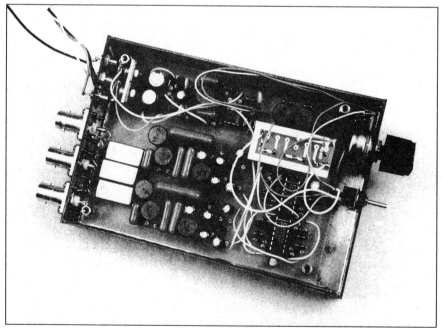

The 3.5 × 5-inch board R2 PC board layout follows the schematic of Fig 3 fairly closely. This version uses a Mini-Circuits PSC2-1 power splitter and a pair of SBL-1 mixers at the lower left-hand edge of the board. The mixers are followed by the diplexers and 50-ohm preamplifiers of the I and Q channels, followed by the audio phase-shift network (a pair of NE5514 quad op-amps) in the lower right corner. The three inductors and seven capacitors of the 1-kHz elliptical low-pass filter are arranged just above the op-amps, near the VOLUME control. A second filter, this one a 4-kHz Butterworth, is built on a separate PC board and glued (upside down) to the main R2 board. Filter bandwidth is switched from the front panel. The intermediate audio amplifier, 300-Hz high-pass filter, mute switch and audio power amplifier are on the top half of the board. All that is needed to make a complete receiver is a front-end filter, a VFO and 90° phase-shift network, and a speaker.

40 dB and designed my audio-phase-shift network accordingly. My phase-shift network is similar to the one used by Breed, but it uses the third-order coefficients calculated by Oppelt (see Note 4). In the audio phase-shift network, R20-R28, R35-R43, C21-C23 and C26-C28 must be within 1% of the schematic value. For the first prototype, I measured and selected six capacitors from a large bag obtained at a flea market, and then made up series combinations of 5% metal film resistors using a digital ohmmeter. For all the subsequent versions I have used off-the-shelf 1% resistors and capacitors (see Note 6). There is no performance difference.

The phase-shift network and combiner are capable of handling fairly large signals without distortion. The design goal was to have the preamplifier distort before the phase-shift network, since the performance of the preamplifier on the R1 board is well characterized. If distortion occurs between the RF splitter and op-amp summer, the distortion products will not have the proper phase relationship, and they will not be suppressed in the opposite sideband. The result will be that strong signals have worse opposite-sideband suppression than weak signals! This would be an unhappy circumstance indeed, but I have not encountered it at input signal levels well up into the millivolt range.

A DPDT sideband selection switch may be inserted at the points marked in Fig 3. I built one receiver that way, but I do not recommend that method of switching sidebands because the optimum setting of R30 is different for suppression of the upper or lower sideband. A better approach is to switch the 90°-shifted LO between the mixer LO ports.

The best approach is to add the op-amp subtractor circuit shown in Fig 5, with its own AMPLITUDE BALANCE pot. Then sideband selection is simply a matter of connecting the volume control to the appropriate sideband output with an SPDT SIDEBAND SELECT switch. An independent filter and audio output stage could be added if ISB reception is desired.

Many other audio-phase-shift networks may be used in place of the op-amp version

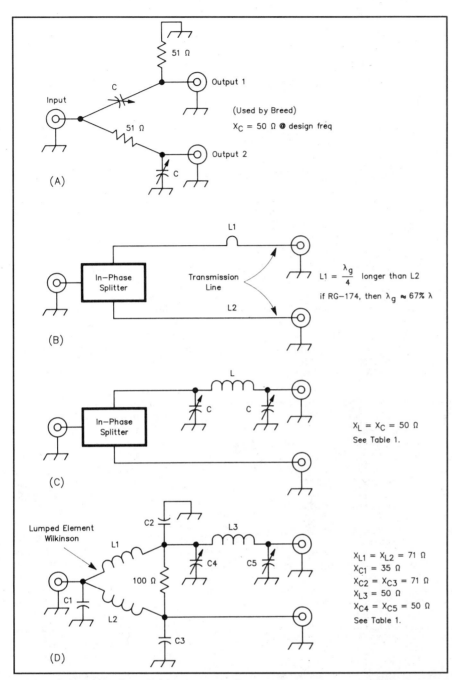

Fig 6—Four possibilities for a 90° LO phase-shift network. The simple RC network shown at A is fine for many MF/HF applications and has been used by the author on 40, 20 and 2 meters. The actual value of the capacitors depends on terminating impedances. Start with 450 pF on 7 MHz, 225 pF on 14 MHz and 22 pF on 144 MHz. See text. The circuit at B uses transmission lines and is practical at VHF and UHF. Examples: If L1 and L2 are made from RG-174, L1 is 69.1 inches longer than L2 at 28.5 MHz; 13.7 inches longer at 144.2 MHz and 8.86 inches longer at 222.1 MHz. The circuits at C and D will work better for more serious applications (see text). Component values for a variety of frequencies are shown in Table 1.

Close-up of the LO phase-shift network from Fig 6A. This version is built for 40 meters.

shown here. The I and Q channel signals may be digitized at the points marked X in the schematic, and all of the phase shifting, combining and filtering operations performed in DSP hardware and software. That will probably be the preferred receiver architecture for any band and any mode in the 21st century.

All of the circuitry after the op-amp summer is identical to the R1 receiver described in August '92 QST. Fig 3 shows component values for a 3-kHz elliptical low-pass filter. Information on other filters is given in the August '92 article. As with the R1 board, audio hiss may be objectionable during headphone listening. If you're bothered by hiss, add the RC networks described in the August '92 article to U6.

Receiver Construction

I built the first prototype using cut-up pieces of R1 boards interconnected over an unetched PC board ground plane. I followed good RF grounding techniques and hoped for the best with my audio grounds. It worked fine. On the single-board layout, I was much more careful with the audio grounds, and still didn't have any problems. The only instability I have found is audio feedback via magnetic coupling between a speaker lead (either one!) and the inductors in the diplexer stages. This is easy to cure by simply moving the speaker wires a few inches away from the inductors, but it can be a real puzzle if you don't expect it.

I built two more prototypes on single-sided PC boards to work out the bugs, and then produced a double-sided R2 board with plated-through holes (see Note 1). The R2 board has a number of jumpers to make it easier to try different filters and sideband-selection methods.

The R2 board is almost as easy to use as the R1 board. As explained in the August 1992 R1 article, a band-pass filter on the RF input is good practice, although a simple low-pass filter to suppress signals near the odd harmonics of the LO will suffice. On 40 meters, a narrow band-pass filter to attenuate broadcast stations may be necessary. Above 10 MHz, a preamp will be needed in quiet locations. The preamp will also help isolate the LO from the antenna. The R2 board may be used on any frequency from 1 to 500 MHz with the SBL-1 mixers shown in the schematic. Other mixers can be substituted for higher or lower frequencies.

If you do all the trig identities, follow the phase shifts through the schematic, and carefully connect everything, Murphy guarantees that you will end up with the wrong sideband. It is much easier to simply hook it up and then switch the LO connections if it's wrong. If you can convince Murphy that you really don't care, you have a 50% chance of getting it right the first time!

Local Oscillator

The R2 board with SBL-1 mixers needs two +7 dBm (nominal) LO signals, 90° out of phase. I have used all of the LO phase-shift techniques shown in Fig 6, and there are

Table 1

LO Phase-Shift Network Component Values

For the network in Fig 6C			For the network in Fig 6D					
Frequency (MHz)	C (pF)	L (μH)	Frequency (MHz)	L1, L2 (μH)	C1 (pF)	C2,C3 (pF)	C4,C5 (pF)	L3 (μH)
3.525	903	2.26	3.525	3.21	1290	645	903	2.26
7.05	452	1.13	7.05	1.62	645	323	452	1.13
14.05	227	0.566	14.05	0.809	325	162	227	0.566
21.05	151	0.378	21.05	0.541	216	108	151	0.378
28.5	112	0.279	28.5	0.399	160	80	112	0.279
50.1	63.5	0.159	50.1	0.227	91	45	63.5	0.159
144.2	22.1	0.0552	144.2	0.0789	31.6	15.8	22.1	0.0552
222.1	14.3	0.0358	222.1	0.0512	20.5	10.2	14.3	0.0358

many others I have not tried. Since there may be a few degrees of phase error in the splitters and mixers, it is necessary to tweak the LO phase-shift network for best opposite-sideband suppression. Some phase-shift networks are easier to tweak than others—it is easier to adjust a trimmer capacitor than cut ⅛-inch pieces off RG-174 phasing lines!

The simple LO phase-shift network in Fig 6A has been used on 40, 20 and 2 meters by tacking in different capacitors and adjusting them for best opposite-sideband suppression. It works fine, but has two peculiarities:

• When adjusted for a 90° phase difference with loads connected to outputs 1 and 2, the output levels will be different.

• The phase at each output depends on the load impedance.

The LO-port impedance and conversion loss of the SBL-1 mixers are functions of drive level, so there is a complicated interaction between the adjustments of the network

in Fig 6A and the **AMPLITUDE BALANCE** potentiometer (R30). In practice, you just tweak them both and forget the theory, but strange things can happen with the network in Fig 6A in the system.

Anything that changes the LO drive level at the input or the impedances connected to the outputs of the network will require readjustment of both the phase-shift network capacitors and the **AMPLITUDE BALANCE** control. One operator noted greatly reduced opposite-sideband suppression when he increased the supply voltage from 12 to 14!

The network in Fig 6A is easy to build and works well within the limitations described above. For more serious applications (especially if sideband selection or operation from a variety of supply voltages is anticipated), I recommend using one of the LO phase-shift networks shown in Fig 6C, Fig 6D and Table 1.

It is difficult to recommend an LO for a receiver board that may be used anywhere from VLF to microwaves! For HF use, *The ARRL Handbook*, *QRP Classics* and *Solid State Design* contain many suitable examples. For VLF and LF, old signal generators work fine, and they have incredible bandspread. At VHF and up, the literature is a bit sparse, but an HF VFO followed by a simple transverter works well. At higher frequencies, a VXO and multiplier chain may be used.

The cost of direct digital synthesis (DDS) is falling rapidly, and many of the DDS chips offer two outputs 90° out of phase. The phase-noise performance of low-cost DDS chips is not good enough for a high-performance direct-conversion receiver, but that will change in the future. Fig 7 is the block diagram of an all-mode receiver using a DDS chip for the LO and a DSP chip for the signal processing.

Tuning

There are two trimmer potentiometers on the R2 board and a single LO phase-shift adjustment off the board. It's not quite "no tune," but it's easier than even a simple superhet! R57 sets the quiescent current of the audio-output stage. It can be set for a total R2 board current of about 100 mA—it's not critical.

The **AMPLITUDE BALANCE** pot (R30) and the LO phase-shift adjustment can be set by

---

Crunch Time: We Test R2 in the ARRL November Sweepstakes

"That good, huh? Maybe I'll hook it up to my 40-meter beam and give it the acid test this weekend in CW Sweepstakes." Rick Campbell had just finished telling me how well his 40-meter R2 prototype (the one in the photos) stacks up against commercial radios. Playing the skeptic, I told Rick I'd connect the transceiver to a good antenna and try to use it on a weekend when the band was sure to be full of rock-crushing signals.

Saturday afternoon rolls around. Hmm...better hook up Rick's radio and listen to a few signals. Maybe I can even work a few people with that dinky (2-inch-square) 1-W transmitter. Out come the clip leads...let's see, we need 12 V, a keyer, headphones and an antenna...wow! this thing really does put out a watt...there's Mike, W9RE, warming up for Sweepstakes...he's *loud* but there's just a trace of his signal on the other side of zero-beat...this receiver *works*.

The contest starts. I call W9RE. He comes right back and gets my entire exchange without missing a beat. Must be a fluke. Next, W2RQ...then KW8N..and so it goes—42 contacts logged in the first hour. This might be fun! During the weekend I manage to squeeze in nine hours of operation, an hour here and an hour there amid raking about a billion leaves and other domestic activities. On Sunday night, the log shows 313 QSOs in 60 ARRL sections—all on 40 meters with Rick's 1-W transceiver.

The R2 receiver is impressive. I have a very low tolerance for poor receiver performance: I'd rather spend a sunny November afternoon picking up leaves one by one than working Sweepstakes with a lousy receiver. Fortunately, R2 sounds great—no IMD or blocking problems show up. CW signals please the ear. Compared to R2, signals on a commercial transceiver with 500-Hz filters sound harsh. Some audio hiss is noticeable during headphone listening, but that can be tamed with a couple of RC networks as explained in Rick's August 1992 *QST* article.

This receiver has no AGC, which I thought would be a problem after years of listening to radios that do a great job of flattening out signals on the band. After a while, my ears and brain figured out how to deal with a receiver without AGC, and I found myself adjusting the **VOLUME** control for only the weakest and strongest signals.

Although the CW filter in this version has a rather broad 700-Hz bandwidth, I had no problem tuning the band and separating stations from each other. Even with a band full of big signals, I only heard the opposite sideband on the strongest stations. Even then, it was just "oh, there's the other sideband." It was not a bother except when I cranked up the power supply voltage from 12 to 14 (this phenomenon is explained in the text).

Bottom line: This home-brew receiver holds its own, even under demanding conditions. Some radios are fun to build but less fun to use ("it doesn't work quite right, but after all it's only a home-brew rig," or "what do you expect for the money?"). I like projects you can build and enjoy without apologies. This is one of those projects.—*Mark Wilson, AA2Z*

ear by tuning in a strong carrier on the wrong sideband and then alternately tweaking the two controls for a null.

I tune for best opposite-sideband suppression by setting a signal generator on the audio image ("wrong side of zero beat") and then alternately adjusting the phase shift and amplitude balance (R30) while watching the output on an audio-frequency level meter. I optimize the circuit at a frequency near the middle of the audio range, and then tune around to make sure the opposite-sideband suppression is good from 300 to 3000 Hz. I then adjust a step attenuator for the same signal level on the desired and undesired sideband and record the respective attenuator settings. The difference in step attenuator settings is the opposite-sideband suppression. Once the phase shift and amplitude balance are adjusted, they may be locked in place with nail polish. After a year and thousands of miles on the road, the first prototype shows no signs of needing alignment.

R2 Performance and Impressions

The R2 prototype with a 3-kHz elliptical filter was assembled and tested on the bench. There were no surprises—it was an R1 board with slightly better dynamic range, slightly better noise figure, and 41 dB of opposite-sideband suppression. The real shock came when I connected a 40-meter antenna and VFO. CW signals simply disappeared as I tuned through zero beat. Murphy had it connected for USB, and there was no way I could copy any LSB up in the phone band. It

sounded too good—something was wrong with the picture.

I connected my old transceiver with its 2.4-kHz IF filter, and sure enough, CW signals were audible on the wrong sideband. I switched the antenna over to a Collins 75S-3C with its F455FB21 mechanical filter, and they were still there. After listening to the other radios, I returned to the R2. It sounded even better than before. Why?

I have been pondering this for about a year, and I've thought of several explanations. The first is that the commercial radios both have AGC, so the receiver gain is reduced on the desired sideband and increased on the undesired sideband—in other words, the AGC is trying to remove the IF selectivity from the system. I defeated the AGC on both radios and listened again. I could still hear low-frequency CW signals on the wrong sideband that were not audible on the R2. I made a few measurements and discovered that low-pitch CW signals (up to several hundred hertz) on the wrong side of zero beat are suppressed considerably less than 40 dB on both radios. The old Collins dipped below 40 dB at about 400 Hz, and the other radio went below 40 dB a little higher in frequency. The bottom line is that the R2 sounds better than I expected, because it has better selectivity than the radios I'm used to.

I demonstrated a 40-meter R2 at the QRP Hospitality Suite in Dayton this year. Several experienced HF CW operators were amazed when we could not find any CW signals that were strong enough to detect on

the wrong sideband.

Comparison with a Superhet

Receiver fans will point out that the schematic in Fig 3 is as complicated as a superhet. If the image-reject direct-conversion receiver has so many parts, why not just "do it right" and build a superhet?

First, this is a high-performance direct-conversion design, with no attempt to reduce the parts count. It could be greatly simplified with only a small reduction in performance. Even in simplified form, it could still outperform most of the simple superhets I've encountered—especially those based on the ubiquitous NE602. The NE602 is not a bad part, but its limited dynamic range should confine its use to low-cost, low-current-drain, minimum-parts-count applications.

Direct-conversion receivers have a number of significant advantages over superhets. Because there is only one LO, there are no internally generated birdies. There are no image frequencies to filter out, and no spurious receiver tuning ranges at strange combinations of LO harmonics and the intermediate frequency. A low-pass front-end filter to reject signals near odd multiples of the LO frequency will ensure a spurious-free receiver.

Since direct-conversion receivers do all of their signal processing at audio, the input frequency is unrestricted. An R1 board with an SRA-3 mixer and an old signal generator for an LO works well below 25 kHz. At the other end of the spectrum, I have an R1 board

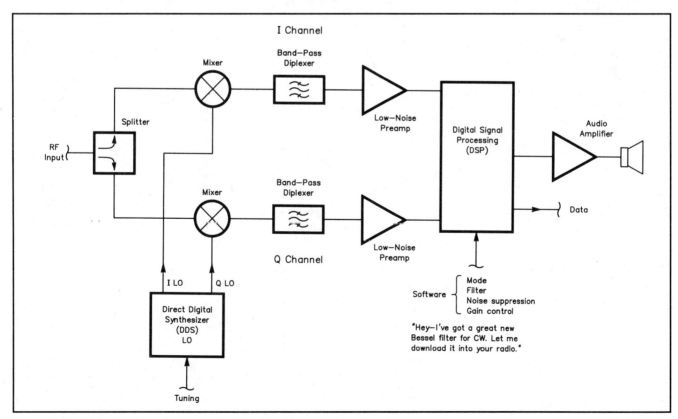

Fig 7—The R2 board can serve as a basic building block for a receiver of the future. Just add a direct-digital synthesizer for the LO and digital signal processing for the audio processing.

Fig 8—A simple modular 40-meter CW QRP transceiver built around an R2 board. R2 is built in the box on the lower left; the LO phase-shift network from Fig 6A is in the small box connected to rear of R2 with BNC connectors. A 7-MHz VFO is in the larger box on the right. Resting atop R2 is a 1-W CW transmitter with low-pass filter and break-in circuitry. The transmitter and VFO were borrowed from other published projects (see text). This transceiver acquitted itself well in the 1992 ARRL Sweepstakes—see the sidebar. *(photos by Kirk Kleinschmidt, NTØZ)*

with a printed rat-race mixer working at 5760 MHz.

A direct-conversion receiver can be combined with a VFO-controlled CW transmitter to build a transceiver that is simpler than a superhet transceiver. The only spurs are harmonics, which are reduced by the transmitter low-pass filter.

Direct-conversion receivers also have some disadvantages. The need for isolation between the antenna and LO makes direct conversion a poor choice for hand-held radios with integral whip antennas. At HF, a full-size outdoor antenna works best.

I do not recommend the direct-conversion, image-reject approach for a band-switched radio. It is easy to obtain good performance over a single amateur band, but the RF phase-shift network and amplitude balance must be tweaked when changing bands.

Finally, 41 dB is about the practical limit for opposite-sideband suppression in an easily reproduced analog design. While this is as good as some HF and most VHF SSB rigs, the fact remains that the basic superhet design is *capable* of better performance.

R2 Applications

The modular 40-meter QRP CW transceiver shown in Fig 8 features full break-in keying, 1 W output, a slow tuning rate, switched SSB and CW bandwidths, 93 dB two-tone, third-order IMD dynamic range, low-distortion audio, and true single-signal reception. The transmitter, VFO and break-

in circuitry were borrowed from "The Ugly Weekender" and the "Optimized QRP Transceiver" in *The 1992 ARRL Handbook.*[8] The receiver is an R2 board with the RC LO phase-shift network from Fig 6A. It is a joy to operate.

The R2 board is small enough to build a high-performance portable HF CW transceiver in a smaller package than the popular commercial versions. For portable use, the receiver's audio power transistors can be removed to reduce the current drain, as discussed in August *QST.*

At Microwave Update '92, I demonstrated another interesting R2 application: a no-tune microwave transceiver, using a Down East Microwave no-tune 1296-MHz transverter with an R2 board and premixed VFO as a tunable 2-meter IF. The transmit IF uses an SSB/CW exciter board, which I'll describe in a future issue of *QST.* The use of image-reject techniques makes it possible to build single conversion microwave radios with any desired IF. I'll explore this concept more fully in a future *QST* article.

Conclusions

The image-reject, direct-conversion receiver is a viable approach to SSB and CW reception for many applications. When combined with high-performance, direct-conversion receiver techniques, it can provide basic receiver performance that surpasses many superhets. Image-reject techniques are in wide commercial use, and both Drake and Kenwood have recently introduced high-

performance products that combine image-reject and superhet techniques. In the future, high-performance receivers will be built by combining a high dynamic range I and Q channel front end with a digital signal processor. Future Old Timers will sit around reminiscing about multiple-conversion superhets!

Acknowledgments

Dr Ward Helms, W7SXM, at the University of Washington, and Dr Ben Logan, WB2NBD, at Bell Labs taught me to look for unconventional solutions to problems. Without their influence I would be less inclined to pursue strange ideas like microwave transverters with no tuning and SSB receivers with no IFs.

Notes

[1]R. Campbell, "High-Performance Direct-Conversion Receivers," *QST*, Aug 1992, pp 19-28.

[2]R. Campbell, "Low Noise Receiver Analysis," in *Proceedings of Microwave Update '91*, published by the ARRL. Available from your local dealer or the ARRL Publications Catalog elsewhere in this issue (order no. 3703).

[3]R. Oppelt, "The Generation and Demodulation of SSB Signals Using the Phasing Method Part 1: Basic Theory," *VHF Communications*, vol 19, ed 2, summer 1987, pp 66-72.

[4]R. Oppelt, "The Generation and Demodulation of SSB Signals Using the Phasing Method Part 2: Signal Processing for a SSB/DSB/AM Transceiver Without Using Crystal Filters," *VHF Communications*, vol 19, ed 3, fall 1987, pp 130-140.

[5]Etched, plated and drilled PC boards (double-sided, with plated-through holes) for the R2 board are available from Applied Radio Science, PO Box 225, Houghton, MI 49931 for $20 postpaid (send an SASE for a catalog with current kit information). For individuals wishing to make their own PC boards, an etching template/part-overlay package for a single-sided version of the R2 PC board is available from the ARRL for an SASE. Address your request for the CAMPBELL R2 BOARD TEMPLATE to Technical Department Secretary, ARRL, 225 Main St, Newington, CT 06111.

[6]One source for SBL-1 mixers is Oak Hills Research, 20879 Madison St, Big Rapids, MI 49307, tel 616-796-0920). XICON 1% polyester film capacitors used in the audio phase-shift network are available from Mouser Electronics, 2401 Hwy 287 N, Mansfield, TX 76063, tel 800-346-6873, 817-483-4422, fax 817-483-0931. All other parts are available from Digi-Key, PO Box 677, Thief River Falls, MN 56701-0677, tel 800-344-4539, 218-681-6674, fax 218-681-3880.

[7]G. Breed, "A New Breed of Receiver," *QST*, Jan 1988, pp 16-23.

[8]R. Lewallen, "An Optimized QRP Transceiver," *QST*, Aug 1980, pp 14-19; also see Feedback, *QST*, Nov 1980, p 53. The Optimized QRP Transceiver also appears on pages 30-37 to 30-40 of *The 1993 ARRL Handbook*, and in the second printing of *QRP Classics* (available from the ARRL Bookshelf as #3169). R. Hayward and W. Hayward, "The 'Ugly Weekender,'" *QST*, Aug 1981, pp 18-21. The Ugly Weekender also appears on pages 30-33 to 30-36 of *The 1993 ARRL Handbook*. Etched, plated and drilled PC boards for the VFO/buffer are available from FAR Circuits, 18N640 Field Ct, Dundee, IL 60118-9269. Price is $4; add $1.50 for shipping and handling to each order. Use the board's **AUX OUT** output for the correct drive level for the SBL-1 mixer.

From QST, August 1992, p 19:

High-Performance Direct-Conversion Receivers

High dynamic range, low-distortion audio,
1.6:1 SSB filter shape factor...the latest
$4000 transceiver from Japan?
No—a diminutive
PC-board
direct-conversion
receiver from KK7B!

By Rick Campbell, KK7B

**Department of Electrical Engineering
Michigan Technological University
Houghton, MI 49931**

In this article I'll describe two high-performance direct-conversion receivers that are part of a series of SSB and CW receivers I've been experimenting with. Each receiver is engineered for a very specific purpose and is designed from the ground up to perform one task as well as possible. *Classic 40* is a high-dynamic-range, high-fidelity direct-conversion receiver for the 40-meter band. *Sisu* is a simple, compact, high-performance add-on receiver for use with VFO-controlled QRP transmitters. Classic 40 and Sisu share a common building block—a compact 2.5 × 3.5-inch PC board that contains most of the circuitry. (I call this the R1 receiver board.)

These designs are considerably less complicated than commercial multiband, multimode receivers, yet they achieve performance levels equal to the best laboratory equipment. There are no bells and whistles here—the goal is the best possible *basic receiver performance*. The only constraint is reproducibility. PC boards and parts are available, so you will have no trouble building a receiver for your station.[1]

A few engineering methods applied to these receivers are somewhat uncommon to amateur projects. Every circuit was analyzed and optimized using textbook engineering and the computer circuit-modeling program *PSPICE1*.[2] Circuitry was borrowed from the amateur and professional literature, dissected to the component level, entered into the computer, and studied to discover the effects of component tolerances, audio distortion, dying batteries and a host of other real-world problems. Individual stages were then breadboarded and bench tested to confirm the computer predictions. In many cases, previously published designs were found to be at least as good as anything new that I could generate. In the few cases where I was able to make significant improvements, the best of the previously published designs was built to serve as a benchmark.

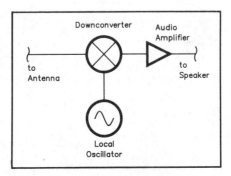

Fig 1—Block diagram of a direct-conversion receiver.

Although these designs are "optimum" in some sense of the word, each one represents only one of many possible "optimized" receivers for the same application. My intent in publishing this information is not to close the book on SSB/CW receiver design, but to add a few chapters. I hope that these designs inspire further modifications and improvements. When amateurs begin concentrating on good basic receiver performance, manufacturers will follow, and in a few years I may find a new commercial transceiver that sounds as good as my home-brew receivers.

The Classic 40

This receiver is built to show how good a direct-conversion receiver can be. Ever since direct-conversion receivers became popular in the late 1960s, authors have raved about the clean direct-conversion sound, "like a window on the band." Yet direct-conversion receivers have also earned a reputation for a set of particularly obnoxious problems: hum, microphonics, limited dynamic range, AM broadcast detection, and insufficient audio gain and output level for comfortable listening with a speaker. Several commercial direct-conversion transceivers have suffered from all of the above ills.

The currently popular NE602-LM386 receivers, in particular the Neophyte[3] and its English cousin the Sudden,[4,5,6] have

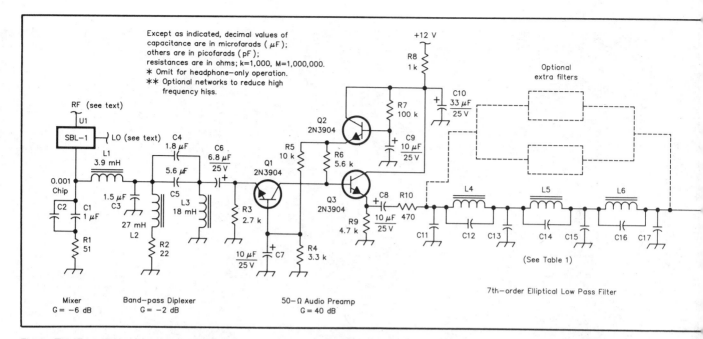

Fig 2—The R1 receiver board is the basic building block for the Classic 40 and Sisu receivers. All parts except the mixer (U1) are available from Digi-Key; kits are available (see note 1). Resistors are 5%-tolerance carbon-film or -composition units. Inductors are Toko 10RB series fixed inductors. Polarized capacitors are aluminum electrolytics rated at 25 V dc. The capacitors in the diplexer (C1, C3-C5) and 300-Hz high-pass filter (C23, C24) are Panasonic type ECQ-E(F) 100-V, 10%-tolerance miniature metalized polyester film capacitors. The capacitors in the low-pass filter (C11-C17) are Panasonic V-series 50-V, 5%-tolerance metalized film capacitors, except C12 in the 3000-Hz elliptical filter, which is a 0.0068-μF, 50-V Panasonic P-series polypropylene capacitor. C19, C21, C25, C28 and C29 are NP0 disc-ceramic capacitors. C18, C20, C22, C26 and C32 can be metalized polyester or disc-ceramic capacitors.

C2—0.001-μF chip capacitor. This part is necessary only if the board is used at VHF or UHF.

R11—500-Ω audio-taper control.
R24—10-kΩ single-turn PC-board-mount control (Panasonic MAG14 or equivalent).

U1—Mini-Circuits SBL-1 double balanced mixer. A TAK-3H mixer may be substituted if higher dynamic range is needed (see text).

done much to prove that an adequate receiver can be built for very little money with very few components in a very small box. Unfortunately, the NE602 crumbles with a 40-meter dipole connected to the input, and the NE602-LM386 pair has noticeable distortion when driving a small speaker with multiple CW signals.

It is unfair to judge the capabilities of direct-conversion receivers by listening only to designs optimized for simplicity and low cost. A much better indication of the potential for high-performance direct-conversion receivers is the excellent design by Lewallen, An Optimized QRP Transceiver.[7] Lewallen optimized for small size as well as high performance, which limited his engineering options and the reproducibility of his design. Lewallen's discussion of high-performance direct-conversion receiver design is mandatory reading.

In preparation for designing and building a high-dynamic-range, high-fidelity direct-conversion receiver, I built and tested a score of circuits. I tried product detectors using a single diode, a dual-gate MOSFET, a pair of back-to-back diodes, an LM1496, an XR2208, single balanced diode mixers and double balanced diode mixers. I built a direct-conversion 2-meter receiver on a superstrip (not recommended) and an NE602 20-meter receiver in a matchbox (real cute).

I didn't build all those circuits in a

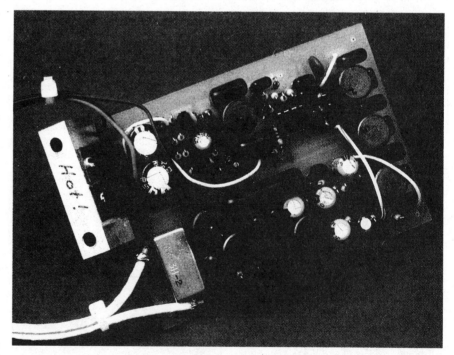

The 2.5 × 3.5-inch board R1 PC board is the heart of the Classic 40 and Sisu receivers. The board layout follows the schematic of Fig 2 fairly closely. This version uses a Mini-Circuits TAK-3H high-level mixer (in the lower-left corner of the board). The mixer is followed by the diplexer and 50-ohm preamplifier, built along the lower half of the board. The three inductors and seven capacitors of the 7th-order elliptical low-pass filter are arranged along the right-hand edge of the board. The intermediate audio amplifier, 300-Hz high-pass filter, mute switch and audio power amplifier are on the top half of the board. All that is needed to make a complete high-performance direct-conversion receiver is an RF input circuit, a VFO, a 500-ohm volume control and a speaker.

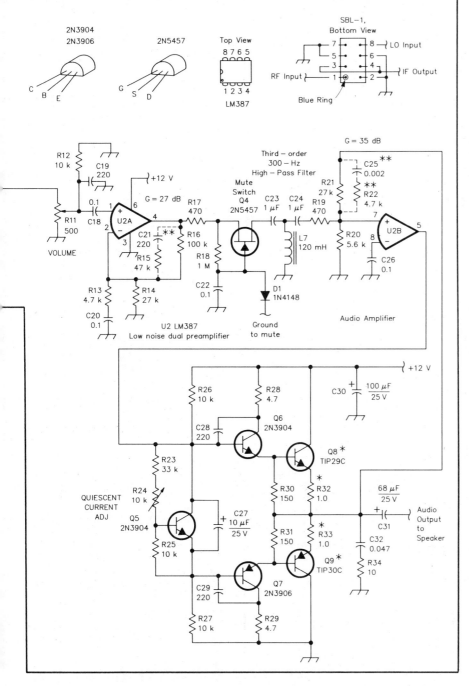

Table 1
7th-Order Elliptical Low-Pass Filter Values

Component (see Fig 2)	Passband 1000 Hz	3000 Hz
L4, L5, L6	100 mH	33 mH
C11	0.39	0.15
C12	0.022	0.0068
C13	0.68	0.22
C14	0.1	0.033
C15	0.56	0.18
C16	0.068	0.022
C17	0.39	0.12

Note: Capacitance values are in microfarads. L4-L6 are Toko 10RB series fixed inductors and C11-C17 are 5%-tolerance metalized-film capacitors. See text.

and the audio amplifier. Fig 2 is a schematic of the receiver. Not shown are the LO and RF input circuits (discussed later). I will not discuss LOs—if there is anything about high-frequency VFOs and VXOs that hasn't already been published in the amateur literature, I don't know what it is. My VFO designs are shamelessly lifted from the numerous articles by two generations of Haywards, Lewallen and DeMaw. Maybe I can improve on them, but I haven't done it yet.

Downconverter

A product detector in a conventional superhet receiver has an easy job: downconvert the output of a narrow-bandwidth IF strip to audio. The signals at the input to the product detector have been scrubbed clean by a narrow-bandwidth crystal filter, and in most cases, a gain control of some type is used to keep all of the signals at the input to the product detector at about the same level. Since the narrow filters in a superhet precede the product detector, everything at the input is downconverted to audio, amplified a little, and sent to the speaker. A casual product detector design that works well in a superhet may provide disappointing performance as a direct-conversion receiver front end.

The first step in improving direct-conversion receivers is to throw away all the superhet product detector designs and start treating the downconverter stage as a low-noise, high-dynamic-range receiver front end. All of the rules for high-dynamic-range receiver design still apply, whether the IF is at 9 MHz or 0.3-3 kHz.

The fundamental difference between a superhet product detector and a direct-conversion receiver front end is that there are literally thousands of signals, from nanovolt to millivolt levels, simultaneously present in the direct-conversion mixer. A typical 40-meter direct-conversion receiver with a 500-kHz-bandwidth filter preceding the mixer downconverts the entire 500-kHz-wide band to low frequencies from dc to several hundred kHz, and upconverts the 500-kHz-wide band to fre-

month. During the period when I was building receivers I started shaving, got my first real kiss, got my first job, joined the Navy, got married, stopped shaving, played a lot of music, climbed some big volcanoes, had children, started shaving again and went to school for a long, long time. One of the things I should have learned in school is that anything worth doing deserves a little forethought. In other words, "engage brain before plugging in soldering iron." My junk box is full of direct-conversion receivers loosely categorized as the good, the bad and the ugly. The bad designs I can blame on someone else, but the good ones are none of my doing either. They are all ugly.

None of the circuits I have copied over the years would do what I wanted—take a CW pileup on the low end of 40 meters and fill my living room with it, with no distortion, clipping or hum. The dynamic range represented by the signals in my 40-meter dipole is greater than the dynamic range of a compact disk audio recording, but the audio output of a typical 40-meter receiver sounds like an AM pocket radio. I wanted a 40-meter CW receiver with the clarity and signal-to-noise ratio of a CD player. To get it I had to start from scratch.

The block diagram of a direct-conversion receiver shown in Fig 1 is deceptively simple. There are only three blocks: the downconverter, the local oscillator (LO)

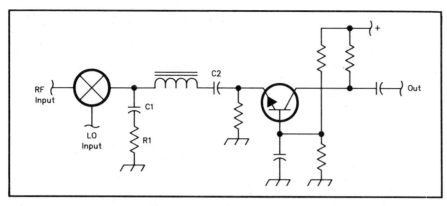

Fig 3—Several authors have attempted to properly terminate the mixer in the desired audio range by using a 50-ohm-input, grounded-base audio preamplifier as shown here.

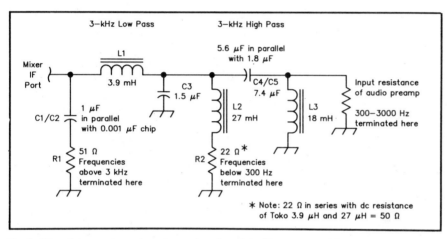

Fig 4—The diplexer shown here is used at the mixer IF port to provide a 50-ohm termination from dc to 300 Hz and 3000 Hz to daylight, and to pass 300 to 3000 Hz through to a matched low-noise amplifier.

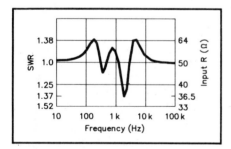

Fig 5—Input SWR and resistances of the band-pass diplexer of Fig 4 connected to Lewallen's matched audio preamp. The worst-case SWR, from dc to 500 MHz, is 1.4.

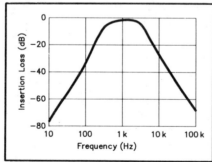

Fig 6—The mid-band insertion loss of the band-pass diplexer of Fig 4 is about 2 dB.

quencies near 14 MHz. All of these signals are present at the input to the audio circuitry following the mixer. Basic receiver performance is largely determined by our treatment of the signals we *don't* want to hear that are present at the mixer IF port.

A requirement for high dynamic range in a receiver front end is proper termination of the mixer IF port. Several authors, notably Lewallen and Hayward, have attempted to properly terminate the mixer

in the desired audio range by using a 50-ohm-input, grounded-base audio preamplifier, as shown in Fig 3. High frequencies are terminated using a series-connected low-value capacitor (C1) and a 50-ohm resistor (R1) to ground at the mixer IF port. The dc-blocking capacitor (C2) between the IF port and the grounded-base amplifier guarantees that low frequencies are poorly terminated. This is a significant departure from standard engineering prac-

tice in an otherwise conservative design. The strongest unwanted signal of all in a direct-conversion receiver is its own leaked and radiated LO signal, complete with low-frequency sidebands picked up from interactions with the outside world. A dioding-ring mixer is a nearly ideal coherent phase and amplitude detector. The subaudible frequencies at the IF port may reach millivolt levels in a direct-conversion receiver with a poorly shielded VFO. Diode ring mixer application notes stress that all frequencies present at the IF port must be properly terminated for predictable performance.

One recent receiver, A New Breed of Receiver, designed and built by Gary Breed,[8] properly terminates the downconverter from dc to daylight by connecting a 50-ohm resistor directly from the IF port of the mixer to ground. Breed reports a complete absence of hum and microphonics in his receiver. Another receiver described in a recent British *Radio Communication* magazine uses a 50-ohm resistor straight into the inverting input (virtual ground) of a low-noise op amp.[9] These techniques have two drawbacks: The resistor is a source of thermal noise, and the wide-bandwidth IF output of the double balanced mixer goes directly into the low-noise op amp. For high dynamic range, we need to restrict the bandwidth before the first audio amplifier, avoid resistors in the signal path, and still provide a wide-bandwidth 50-ohm termination of the mixer IF port.

The solution is simple but elegant—include a diplexer at the downconverter IF port that 1) provides a 50-ohm termination from dc to 300 Hz and 3000 Hz to daylight; and 2) passes 300 to 3000 Hz through to a matched low-noise amplifier. The design of the diplexer, shown in Fig 4, was not trivial and involved a number of trials using modern network theory and *PSPICE1* models before a final design was obtained. The Qs in the network are all kept low, so that components with 5% tolerance may be used.

Since the terminating impedance is fixed at 50 ohms, it is impractical to design the network using just surplus 88-mH toroids. Excellent lines of fixed, self-shielding inductors are made by Toko (available from Digi-Key) and HiQ (available from Mouser). They are much smaller than telephone toroids and offer a wide range of inductances at reasonable cost. The Toko inductors used in the network shown here have finite Q, with series resistances of tens of ohms.

The series resistances were included in both the network theory and computer models in order to synthesize a network that would work with non-ideal parts. Fig 5 shows the input SWR and resistances of the band-pass diplexer connected to Lewallen's matched audio preamp. The worst case SWR, from dc to 500 MHz, is 1.4.

Fig 6 shows the passband insertion loss of the band-pass diplexer, primarily due to the losses in the inductors. The mid-band insertion loss is 2 dB. The noise figure of Lewallen's preamp, driven by a 50-ohm source, is 5.1 dB,[10] so the noise figure of the diplexer-preamp combination is about 7 dB.

The best published direct-conversion receiver tested on the bench was from Lewallen's Optimized QRP Transceiver. Significant improvements in selectivity, close-in dynamic range and hum suppression were obtained by adding the diplexer network shown in Fig 4 between the mixer and Lewallen's matched low-noise amplifier. It is not at all clear whether the improvements are primarily due to proper mixer termination or better selectivity, since the band-pass diplexer offers both. I'll let you know when I figure it out!

Most modern engineering texts frown on the use of inductors in audio filter networks. Isn't it possible to build a diplexer using active filters with op amps, or even digital filters? The problem is dynamic range. Literally all the signals in the world are present at the input of the network shown in Fig 4. The dynamic range of a Toko inductor is limited on the low end by picoamp noise currents in the warm, lossy wire, to milliamps on the high end, where the ferrite core saturates. The dynamic range of the inductor is thus about 180 dB. No available op amp or practical digital filter even comes close. This is one application where an old fashioned RLC network clearly outperforms the latest active network.

Audio Amplifier

The audio amplifier chain has three stages: a low-noise preamplifier to properly terminate the downconverter and set the receiver noise figure; an intermediate stage to provide needed gain; and a low-distortion power amplifier stage to drive a speaker. A low-pass filter between the preamplifier and intermediate amplifier sets the upper edge of the audio passband, and a 300-Hz high-pass filter between the intermediate amplifier and power amplifier stages removes the last traces of hum from the audio output.

50-Ohm Input Preamplifier

A significant effort was made to design a low-noise audio preamplifier with a 50-ohm matched input. A noise figure of less than 1 dB was obtained at the expense of a step-up transformer and poor match at the input. My final design is nearly identical to the grounded-base amplifiers published 10 years ago by Lewallen and Hayward. I have retained the active decoupler used by Lewallen, and added an emitter follower to the output to drive the following low-pass filter. This amplifier has a gain of 40 dB, a noise figure around 5 dB, and is well matched to 50 ohms.

The preamplifier must handle the entire range of signal levels at the output of the diplexer, since it is in the circuit before the volume control. It was designed to handle signal levels from 10 nanovolts to 10 millivolts without distortion. The distortion-free dynamic range of the audio preamplifier stage is a good complement to the dynamic range of the SBL-1 double balanced mixer—the preamplifier adds little noise to the signal, and begins to distort at about the same input level as the mixer.

Low-Pass Filters

The low-impedance output of the audio preamplifier drives a low-pass filter designed for 500-ohm terminations on both ends. The PC-board artwork accommodates a number of designs, from a simple 3rd-order Butterworth to a 7th-order elliptical. The 3000-Hz SSB 7th-order elliptical filter designed by Niewiadomski[11] and the scaled 1000-Hz CW version shown in Fig 2 (C11-C17 and L4-L6) and Table 1 are excellent choices for use in crowded bands. The 6- to 60-dB shape factors of receivers with these filters in place are competitive with the best crystal filters. The use of off-the-shelf 5%-tolerance components in the SSB filter results in a fair amount of unpredictable passband ripple.

Since the Classic 40 was designed for high-fidelity sound, I opted to use a 5th-order Butterworth filter with 4-kHz bandwidth instead of the 7th-order elliptical filter. See Fig 7. The Butterworth design is more tolerant of component variations. Fig 8 is a plot of the measured passband of two different receivers with 7th-order elliptical SSB filters, and the Classic 40 with a 5th-order Butterworth filter. The elliptical designs really cut through the QRM, but the Classic 40 with the Butterworth filter sounds great.

Signal levels are high enough at the input to the low-pass filter, and impedance levels low enough, that it is possible to build additional filters on separate boards and select them with a switch, as shown with the dotted lines in Fig 2. The preamp output impedance is close to 50 ohms, so a series resistor is used to establish the filter driving impedance. The required 500-ohm output termination is provided by the **VOLUME** control. Fig 9 shows the *PSPICE1* calculated responses of the 1000 Hz and 3000 Hz 7th-order elliptical low-pass filters, and the measured response of the complete receiver with the 1000-Hz filter in place. The measured −6 dB bandwidth of the receiver with the 1000-Hz low-pass filter is 580 Hz, and the −60 dB bandwidth is 1210 Hz, for a shape factor of 2.1:1. The passband is flat, with rounded corners, no ripple and no ringing.

Lewallen and others have pointed out that elliptical filters are not the best choice for time-domain signals, particularly high-speed CW. The receiver with a 1000-Hz elliptical low-pass filter sounds very good

at 25 words per minute. Maybe if I change it to a Bessel filter I'll be able to copy 50!

The output of the low-pass filter is the ideal place to pick off a signal for digital signal processing (DSP) experiments and applications. The entire receiver is linear to this point (no AGC or other forms of distortion), so the usual drawbacks to audio filtering do not apply.

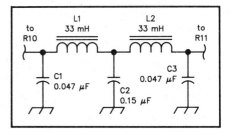

Fig 7—If you enjoy high-fidelity listening, you can replace the 7th-order elliptical low-pass filter shown in Fig 2 (L4-L6, C11-C17) with this 5th-order Butterworth filter (bandwidth = 4 kHz). The elliptical filter cuts through the QRM better, but the Butterworth filter sounds great. L1 and L2 are Toko 10RB-series fixed inductors and C1-C3 are 50-V Panasonic V-series 5%-tolerance metalized-film capacitors.

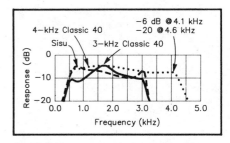

Fig 8—This graph shows the measured passband response of three different receivers: a Classic 40 with a 3-kHz elliptical filter; a Classic 40 with a 4-kHz Butterworth filter; and a Sisu receiver with a 3-kHz elliptical filter.

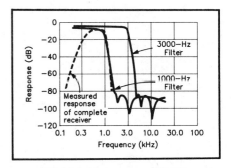

Fig 9—This graph shows the *PSPICE1* calculated responses of the 1000-Hz and 3000-Hz elliptical low-pass filters, and the measured response of a complete receiver with 1000-Hz filter in place. The measured −6 dB bandwidth is 580 Hz, and the −60 dB bandwidth is 1210 Hz, for a shape factor of 2.1:1. Using the calculated response of the 3-kHz filter, the shape factor is 1.6:1 for the SSB filter.

Intermediate Audio Amplifier

The wiper of the **VOLUME** control is connected to the input of the intermediate amplifier, one section of an LM387 low-noise stereo preamplifier.

The requirements for an audio amplifier for SSB are not too severe, since the speech signal occupies the entire bandwidth, and the in-band intermod products present in the transmitted signal are seldom more than 30 dB down. CW is an entirely different story. A pileup on the low end of the 40-meter CW band may result in 30 or 40 independent signals all transmitting at once within a 1-kHz band. The strong signals are often 30 or 40 dB stronger than the desired signal. In a typical amateur receiver, the audio and IF intermod products from the strong signals are stronger than the weak signals. Many amateurs are not aware of this problem, however, because once a strong signal appears in the passband, the AGC turns down the gain, and all the weak signals are lost in the noise anyway. Experienced CW contest operators often turn off the AGC (if possible!) when the band is crowded, and are all too familiar with the audio distortion that ultimately limits the ability to recover weak CW sig-

Classic 40 is enclosed in a solid-oak wraparound case with a polished-brass front panel and a piece of unetched PC-board material for the back panel. The front panel is 4 × 5½ inches, and the box is 5½ inches deep. The VFO is completely enclosed in a soldered-shut PC board case, but the receiver board is unshielded inside the wooden box. A simple two-resonator band-pass filter is built on the back panel. This unit is an early prototype: The audio amplifier power-output stage and 5th-order Butterworth filter are on separate PC boards. *(studio photos by Kirk Kleinschmidt, NT0Z)*

nals in a crowded band.

The intermediate audio amplifier and power-output stage were designed for good intermod and total-harmonic-distortion performance. These designs were copied from high-fidelity audio references[12,13] and modified for the restricted bandwidths necessary for communications. The LM387 was chosen for its low noise and single supply operation.

The audio output stage uses the second section of the LM387 as a gain element driving a Darlington complementary symmetry pair. The only drawbacks to this circuit are the unavoidable high parts count and the high (about 100 mA) quiescent current in the class AB output transistors. For portable operation with low-impedance headphones, Q8, Q9, R32 and R33 can be omitted, at a great saving in current drain. For operation with high-impedance headphones, the output of the LM387 can be connected directly to the dc blocking capacitor, and all of the external transistors may be eliminated. Total current drain will then be 10 or 15 mA.

The potentiometer R24 sets the quiescent current for the output transistors. I've had good results adjusting R24 for 100 mA total board current. If you omit the final transistors and associated parts and use low-current-drain headphone-only operation, R24 has little effect and can be replaced with a jumper.

Between the intermediate and power stages are an FET switch (Q4) and a 300-Hz high-pass filter (C23, L7, C24). The FET switch mutes the receiver during transmit, and the high-pass filter removes the last traces of 60-Hz hum. The time constant of the FET switch is set by R18 and C22, and may be modified for any convenient recovery time. In one version of the Classic 40, the time constant was set to many seconds, to simulate the warm up of a classic tube receiver! The FET switch is a ground-to-mute circuit, so the mute terminal may simply be ignored if muting is not needed.

The total gain of the three audio stages is 102 dB. The loss of the mixer and all the LC filtering is about 22 dB, for a net gain of about 80 dB. This is enough for comfortable speaker or headphone listening on 80 and 40 meters at night. Experimenters may increase the gain by changing the feedback resistors in the LM387 stages, but be careful—100 dB is already quite a bit of audio gain on a single small board.

Notice that the negative lead of the power supply must be connected at the collector of the PNP output transistor (Q9). The quiescent current drawn by the output transistors is 100 mA, and this much current flowing through a 1 microohm resistance will have a voltage drop of 0.1 microvolt—10 times greater than the weakest signals in the audio preamp stage. Grounding rules are entirely different for audio and RF circuitry.

The circuit built on the single-sided PC-board layout offered in the template package described in note 1 is stable, as long as the supply leads are connected at the indicated points and a low-pass filter is used between the preamp and intermediate amp stages. The circuit will oscillate at a frequency well above the audio range if the low-pass filter is omitted, and it may oscillate at a low audio frequency if the power supply leads are connected to the input side of the board. As long as the negative supply lead is connected at the audio output stage, it is acceptable to have other ground connections to the board—for example mounting screws to a metal box and the shields of the RF and LO coax. The important thing is to make sure that the current for the audio power transistors does not flow through the ground traces near the preamplifier input. Magnetic coupling from the speaker, speaker wires or power supply wires to the input inductors may cause audio-frequency oscillation. This can be cured by moving the speaker or wires.

There is no low-pass filtering after the **VOLUME** control. This is not a problem when using a speaker, but the high-frequency hiss is noticeable on headphones, especially when using a narrow CW filter. The high-frequency noise is also easy to observe on an oscilloscope or wide-bandwidth audio voltmeter, and may introduce errors into noise figure and minimum-detectable-signal measurements. The optional networks indicated in Fig 2 (R15, C21 and R22, C25) may be added across the LM387 feedback resistors to reduce the high-frequency hiss.

Automatic Gain Control

A human operator can copy one CW signal when several are present in the passband, even when the desired signal is considerably weaker than the interfering signals. An AGC system measures the total power in the passband and adjusts the system gain to keep the total power constant. When more than one signal is present, the output level of the desired signal will fluctuate as the signal environment changes. This limits the effectiveness of audio filtering and digital signal processing schemes in a receiver with AGC. It also reduces the intelligibility of signals presented to the ear and brain.

Historically, AGC has been needed in receivers with AM detectors, because the dynamic range of simple half-wave diode detectors is very limited.[14] In a multimode superhet receiver, the output of the IF strip is switched between several demodulators, and it is convenient to leave the AGC on for all modes. Once the receiver has AGC, it is possible to greatly relax the dynamic range requirements of all the stages after the first IF filter. Over the past several decades, the design of IF amplifiers, product detectors and audio amplifiers has become so relaxed that AGC is now necessary to maintain any semblance of linearity in most receivers. Only the most expensive models permit the AGC to be turned off.

There is no question that AGC is a convenience for some types of casual operation, and even a necessity for some more demanding applications like mobile SSB and traffic nets. Two quotes from the 1966 *ARRL Handbook* are still true 25 years later: "Automatic regulation of the gain of the receiver in inverse proportion to the signal strength is an operating convenience in phone reception" and "If the selectivity ahead of the AGC rectifier isn't good, strong adjacent-channel signals may develop AGC voltages that will reduce the receiver gain while listening to weak signals."

A receiver with AGC is constantly readjusting its gain to approximate the desired output level. It is always close, but never quite right, and always changing. Just as pro rally drivers require manual transmissions and professional photographers use manual focus cameras, serious radio amateurs need manual gain control. I offer no apologies for leaving AGC out of this receiver—it is considerably more difficult to design a receiver that works well without AGC than to include an AGC loop. A receiver with high dynamic range all the way from antenna connector to speaker leads sounds great, and opens up a world of possibilities for advanced analog and digital signal processing. In the near future, AGC, noise blanking, SSB and CW filtering and digital mode demodulation may all be performed by a single DSP chip set.

R1 Receiver PC Board

The downconverter, diplexer, 50-ohm preamplifier, low-pass filter, intermediate audio amplifier, 300-Hz high-pass filter, mute switch and audio power amplifier are all built on a single 2.5 × 3.5-inch PC board (see note 1). All that is needed to make a complete high-performance direct-conversion receiver is an RF input circuit, a VFO, a 500-ohm volume control, and a speaker.

There is little wasted space on the circuit board, but assembly is straightforward. Due to the tight layout, component substitutions may be difficult, but this should not be a major problem—all of the parts except for the mixer are available from Digi-Key.

Some care should be taken in selecting capacitors for the diplexer, low-pass filter and high-pass filter. The tolerances need to be tight to get the best performance from this receiver. In the low-pass filter (C11-C17), I used Panasonic V-series 50-V, 5%-tolerance metalized film capacitors. The V-series capacitors go only as low as 0.01 μF, so for C12 in the 3000-Hz elliptical filter I used a 0.0068-μF, 50-V Panasonic P-series polypropylene capacitor (2% tolerance). In the diplexer (C1, C3-C5) and 300-Hz high-pass filter (C23,

C24), I used Panasonic type ECQ-E(F) 100-V miniature metalized polyester film capacitors. Although these capacitors are specified at 10% tolerance, I measured many of them and they were within about 4% of rated value. The other nonpolarized capacitors are not critical and can be disc ceramic or metalized polyester film units.

It's important to use the Toko 10RB series fixed, self-shielding inductors specified, since their characteristics are designed into the circuit. An acceptable alternative is the HiQ series of inductors sold by Mouser. The HiQ parts have wire leads instead of pins, though, so it takes a little work to fit them on the R1 PC board.

C1 is a metalized polyester 1-μF capacitor that feeds the high frequencies to a 51-ohm resistor. If the R1 board is used at VHF or UHF, a chip capacitor of about 0.001 μF should be added in parallel with C1 to make sure all of the high-frequency energy at the input to the diplexer "sees" the 51-ohm resistor. The PC artwork has a spot on the foil side for the chip capacitor to be added.

The TIP29 and TIP30 audio-output transistors require a small heat sink. I've used scrap pieces of 1/8- or 1/4-inch aluminum plate to dissipate the heat.

The R1 board is very easy to use, as there are few interconnections and all are low impedances. The inductors in the audio stages will pick up hum from 60-Hz magnetic fields, so the board should not be mounted in the same box as an ac power transformer. On the bright side, the preamplifier active decoupler and the power supply rejection of the LM387 are so good that the R1 board is perfectly happy running on an inexpensive 12-V-dc plug-in wall transformer.

Local Oscillator

I have not included a VFO circuit here, but the amateur literature is full of good designs. For HF operation, any of the VFO circuits published by DeMaw, the Haywards and Lewallen are recommended.[15,16,17] I have copied most of them, and never had

any problems. My favorite is from Lewallen's Optimized QRP Transceiver, since it works as well as any, with fewer parts. Another good choice is the VFO/buffer portion of the Haywards' Ugly Weekender; PC boards are available from FAR Circuits.[18]

The LO level should be close to the value specified by the mixer manufacturer, +7 dBm in most cases. Some double balanced mixers will work fine with LO injection down to 0 dBm, with slightly reduced intermod performance. For best performance in high-density signal environments, high-level double balanced mixers are worth considering.

In any case, the LO should be well shielded, with the signal brought into the mixer through coax. A source of many of the problems associated with direct-conversion receivers is LO radiation, interaction with the local electrical environment, and subsequent pickup by the antenna. Two well-known cures for these problems are 1) completely shielding the VFO in a soldered-shut box; and 2) using a balun, balanced feed line and a balanced antenna system. A direct-conversion receiver with an unenclosed VFO, a speaker on one end and a few feet of wire stuck in the other end may not just hum, it may howl!

RF Input

The double balanced mixer RF port is nearly 50 ohms, and a filter should be used between the antenna and the mixer. In early tests an "Adequate Transmatch" (the Ultimate Transmatch circuit from the *ARRL Handbook*, hastily assembled with junk-box parts) was used between the open-wire feed line on the 40-meter dipole and the mixer port, with excellent results. The only drawback was that 15-meter signals could be heard leaking through when the band was open.

Later versions have all used a simple two-resonator band-pass filter built on a separate piece of unetched board (see Fig 10). It would have been simple to include a pattern for the filter on the main

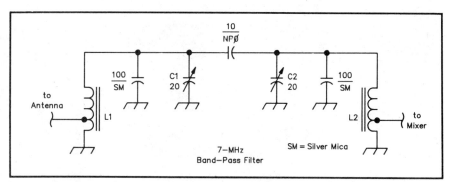

Fig 10—Here's one design for a 40-meter band-pass filter to provide RF-input selectivity for the Classic 40.

C1, C2—3-20 pF film trimmer (Digi-Key SG3007 or equiv).

L1, L2—32 turns of #26 enameled wire on a T-50-6 toroidal, powdered-iron core. Tap 5 turns up from the ground end.

PC board, but this receiver works fine from 10 kHz to 750 MHz (depending on the choice of double balanced mixer), so the RF filter is left off the board for maximum flexibility. Appendix 2 of *Solid State Design* (see note 17) contains excellent information on designing and building band-pass filters for many different frequencies.

Packaging

A receiver this good deserves a nice box. As shown in the photographs, Classic 40 is enclosed in a solid oak wraparound case with polished brass front panel, black lettering and a National Velvet Vernier dial that I picked up at a flea market. The only controls other than the tuning dial are the volume control and on-off switch. The front panel is 4 × 5½ inches, and the box is 5½ inches deep. The VFO is completely enclosed in a soldered-shut PC board case, but the receiver board is unshielded inside the wooden box. It looks as good as it sounds, on the picnic table with a dipole thrown up in some nearby trees, or in the corner of the living room.

Sisu

The basic R1 PC board works so well with different LOs on different bands that I built a second version for an entirely different purpose—to transceive with any of the popular QRP transmitter circuits. A number of CW transceiver circuits have been published in recent years,[19,20,21,22] but most have used the NE602 as a product etector, with its attendant dynamic range and distortion problems. Sisu was built to provide a high-performance receiver that can be easily tacked on to a VFO-controlled CW transmitter. Only three interconnec-

tions are needed: an RF-input line from the TR switch, an LO line with +7 dBm from the VFO, and a mute line from the key. Some RF selectivity is needed. This can be provided by the low-pass filter in the transmitter output stage, or the antenna tuner, if one is used, or by an outboard filter as in the Classic 40. Lewallen's Optimized QRP Transceiver and Roger Hayward's The Ugly Weekender II[23] illustrate the necessary interconnections.

Sisu has been tested on several bands from 160 meters through 432 MHz, with excellent results. Above 40 meters, a preamp is useful for digging out weak signals, but even at 432, with just a VXO and a single stripline filter in the RF line, the local SSB and CW signals come booming in. This receiver would mate nicely with a little 222.1 DSB CW transmitter for grid hopping during the June VHF contest.

Sisu is not an acronym for Signal Interface Sensing Unit. Sisu is a Finnish word for a character trait. A person with sisu is able to quietly get the job done, without complaining or begging for attention, in circumstances where most people would quit. This little receiver has sisu.

Speaker

Amateur receivers used to require external speakers. These days, little 3-inch speakers of remarkably low fidelity have become standard in amateur equipment. It seems to make little sense to put a good quality speaker on the output of a radio with IF distortion, hyperactive AGC and a 10% THD audio amp, but even the poorest radios will benefit from a high-quality external speaker. Conversely, a distortion-free radio will sound awful con-

nected to an unenclosed 3-inch speaker lying on the bench.

My favorite speaker for Amateur Radio applications is the compact Minimus 7, available for $49.95 from Radio Shack. It is too heavy for portable work, unless you are combining QRP operation with bodybuilding. I "built" a good portable speaker by buying a 3-inch stereo speaker with the heaviest magnet I could carry and mounting it in a cardboard box. A 3 × 4 × 2-inch cardboard box with all the seams taped shut sounds pretty good for speech and CW.

Measurements

It is one thing to listen to a receiver on the 40-meter band and determine subjectively that it is an improvement over previous designs—it is another thing to take it into the lab and measure its performance. Three receivers were measured for gain, sensitivity/noise figure, 3rd-order intercept point and minimum detectable AM signal. All measurements were done in the CW portion of the 40-meter band. The results are shown in Table 2.

Table 2 has some good news and some bad news. The good news is that the 3rd-order intercept point and blocking performance are outstanding, equal to the best available amateur equipment. This is to be expected, since the 3rd-order intercept point measurements are made with 20-kHz and 40-kHz signal-generator spacing, and the band-pass diplexer effectively terminates these IF signals in a resistive load. The only nonlinear component seen by the 20-kHz and 40-kHz offset carriers is the double balanced mixer, and it performs exactly as specified in the data sheet.

Sisu is a compact version of the R1 board configured to transceive with any of the popular QRP transmitter circuits. Only three interconnections are needed: an RF-input line from the TR switch, an LO line from the VFO and a mute line from the key. RF selectivity can be provided by the low-pass filter in the transmitter output stage, an antenna tuner, or an outboard filter as in the Classic 40.

Although the R1 board wasn't designed to be particularly compact, Sisu with a companion VFO takes up little tabletop space. *(photo by the author)*

Table 2

Measured Receiver Performance

Radio	Receiver Bandwidth	Minimum Discernible Signal	Intercept Point	IMD Dynamic Range	Noise Figure	AM Sensitivity
Classic 40	3.5 kHz	−118 dBm	+12 dBm	87 dB	20 dB	3 mV
Sisu	2.7 kHz	−119 dBm	+15 dBm	90 dB	20 dB	3 mV
R1 with high-level mixer	0.6 kHz	−128 dBm	+19 dBm	98 dB	18 dB	2.5 mV

The bad news is that the noise figure is higher than expected. I initially suspected that the measurements were in error, but minimum-detectable-signal measurements confirm the measured noise figures. This disappointing performance was a puzzle. The loss of the 40-meter RF filter was measured at less than 0.5 dB. The mixer loss was measured at 6 dB, and the data sheet said "noise figure within 1 dB of conversion loss." The band-pass diplexer loss is about 2 dB, and the 50-ohm preamplifier noise figure is 5 dB. The noise figure of this receiver front end should have been about 14 dB. The measured noise figures are 4 to 6 dB worse.

A number of tests revealed that excess noise was present at the mixer IF port. The following quote from page 1.4 of the 1990 Merrimac *RF & Microwave Processing* book [24] supplied the answer: "The noise introduced by the mixer consists of the conversion loss (SSB), thermal noise in the series resistance of the diodes and other components, and the 1/f noise figure produced by the Schottky Barrier diodes which is only appreciable below 10 kHz."

More information was found in the Hewlett Packard *Microwave and RF Designers Catalog*, pages 4-68 and 4-69.[25] A plot on page 4-69 shows the noise performance of various mixer diodes with IFs from 1 MHz down to 100 Hz. Even the best diodes have 14 dB more noise at 100 Hz than at 20 kHz.

I confirmed the 1/f noise contribution by measuring the spot minimum detectable signal of Sisu at a series of audio output frequencies from 300 to 3000 Hz using an HP3582A audio spectrum analyzer.

I don't know how to reduce the 1/f noise. It may be possible to improve the noise figure a few dB by using a home-brew double balanced mixer with low-flicker-noise diodes. On 160, 80 and 40 meters, a 20-dB noise figure is good enough, as long as the receiver is properly matched to a full-sized dipole. Above 40 meters, a preamp may be necessary. The preamp will reduce the intercept point and the dynamic range. Fortunately, the intercept point is so high that reducing it by 10 or 20 dB with a preamp still leaves a very good receiver.

Classic 40 and Sisu, with standard-level double balanced mixers, have two-tone dynamic range near 90 dB, low audio distortion, zero spurious responses (aside from the audio image), and no synthesizer noise. For operation in hostile RF environments, a 98 dB dynamic range can be obtained by replacing the standard-level double balanced mixer with a high-level TAK-3H mixer.

Conclusion

How does the Classic 40 sound? Like a compact disk recording of CW signals straight off the air. I have compared it side-by-side in the corner of my living room with radios by Collins, Kenwood, Yaesu and

ICOM, using a pair of identical Minimus 7 speakers. The other radios all sound about the same, but the clarity and presence of the Classic 40 is instantly recognizable. A good CW pileup sounds like music, and subtle differences between SSB transmitters are instantly recognizable. There are no whistles, birdies or other spurious sounds from this receiver. It is silent with the antenna disconnected, over the entire tuning range. I am pleased. The audio gain was chosen for comfortable listening using a speaker in a quiet room with a 40-meter dipole. If the volume control is set for a just-audible 40-meter noise floor, then the amplifier clipping level is 60 dB higher! (The clipping level is only about 45 dB above the noise floor in FM stereo broadcasting.)

What are the shortcomings of the Classic 40? First, it is a simple direct-conversion receiver with no provision for removing the audio image. This is fine for casual operating, since the receiver sounds so good with multiple signals, but for serious work, having twice as many interfering signals in the audio passband is a major drawback.

Second, the tuning rate is rather quick and the frequency readout poor. It is tempting to try and count the VFO directly with a simple frequency counter, but beware! The audio amplifier has 100 dB gain. Any attempt to run a frequency counter on the same battery, let alone in the same box, as a 100-dB-gain audio amplifier is probably doomed to failure because of all the digital noise you'll hear. A battery-powered counter in a separate shielded box with a high-isolation preamp is one possibility that might serve for portable work.

Third, the low-distortion audio amp sucks the batteries dry in a few hours. Overall receiver current drain is more than 100 mA at 12 V, which compares favorably with most commercial gear, but is a factor of 10 larger than a Neophyte or Sudden receiver using ICs designed for portable telephones.

Finally, the R1 board is large. The inductors and capacitors take a fair amount of board real estate, even when packed closely together. The 2.5- × 3.5-inch circuit board doesn't even contain a VFO or RF-input filter. An entire Neophyte receiver circuit can be built in a 1.375 × 2 × 0.675-inch matchbox, and the Sudden kit from Blue Rose Electronics uses all surface-mount components on a postage-stamp-sized circuit board! The Classic 40 runs circles around them in performance, but they win the prizes for being cute.

Next Steps

The band-pass diplexer network between the mixer and audio amplifier offers a textbook solution to the selectivity and mixer termination problem, and results in an exceptionally well-behaved receiver with predictable performance. Is it optimized?

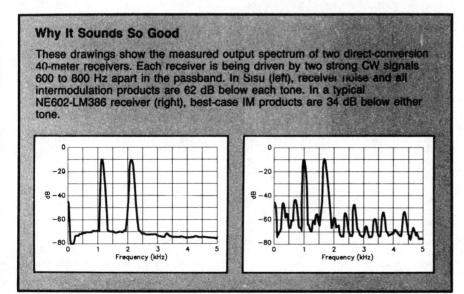

Why It Sounds So Good

These drawings show the measured output spectrum of two direct-conversion 40-meter receivers. Each receiver is being driven by two strong CW signals 600 to 800 Hz apart in the passband. In Sisu (left), receiver noise and all intermodulation products are 62 dB below each tone. In a typical NE602-LM386 receiver (right), best-case IM products are 34 dB below either tone.

Not necessarily! Although this receiver's AM rejection is about 20 dB better than an NE602-LM386 receiver tested under identical conditions, there is still room for improvement. Hayward and Lewallen have experimentally determined that AM suppression improves when the mixer IF port is ac coupled. I measured an improvement in AM suppression on the 40-meter band by removing the 22-ohm low-frequency termination resistor from the diplexer circuit in Fig 3. Removing this resistor also improved the LO-to-RF-port isolation in the double balanced mixer. Do these results hold at other frequencies, with other mixers? Is the dynamic range still predictable? I don't know, and the current textbooks don't say! We need some more work in this area, and then a set of updated textbooks!

Future Receivers

The R1 board can be used as a building block for other receiver designs. I've used it in several other projects, following the design and construction philosophy presented in "A Progressive Communications Receiver" by Lawson and Hayward.[26] The designs are:

1) *R2*, a *single-signal* direct-conversion receiver or IF for use on any frequency from VLF to microwaves.

2) *20-Meter Microscope,* a superselectivity, low-distortion, crunch-proof superhet for 20-meter CW.

3) *PCR 144,* a laboratory-grade two-channel 144-MHz receiver used as an IF for advanced propagation experiments, exploration of binaural signal processing techniques, and as a tunable front end for DSP experiments.

Acknowledgments

The Classic 40 receiver design was conceived, the engineering tasks identified, and much of the circuitry imagined during the 14-hour drive home after a pleasant chat with the Rev. George Dobbs, G3RJV of the G-QRP Society at the Dayton HamVention in 1991. I would like to thank him for his leadership in keeping the home-brewing side of Amateur Radio alive, and for providing all those back issues of *SPRAT* to read at the rest stops on the way home. This work follows the long tradition in Amateur Radio of improving on previous receiver designs. I hope I have kept the standards as high as the authors cited in the references. Wes Hayward, W7ZOI, and Roy Lewallen, W7EL, have been most helpful during the review period of this manuscript. Thanks are also due to Jim Davey, WA8NLC, for all the hours on the phone, fax, E-mail, 75 meters and 40 meters discussing this project.

Notes

[1]Etched, plated and drilled PC boards (double-sided with plated-through holes) and parts kits for the R1 board are available from Applied Radio Science, PO Box 225, Houghton, MI 49931. Prices: PC board only, $10; board and parts kit, $75 for a receiver with 1-kHz or 3-kHz elliptical filter, $70 for a receiver with a 4-kHz Butterworth filter. Please specify filter type when ordering. An etching template/part-overlay package for a single-sided version of the R1 PC board is available from the ARRL for an SASE. Address your request for the CAMPBELL R1 BOARD TEMPLATE to Technical Department Secretary, ARRL, 225 Main St, Newington, CT 06111. All parts except the SBL-1 mixer are available from Digi-Key, PO Box 677, Thief River Falls, MN 56701-0677, tel 800-344-4539. One source for the SBL-1 mixer is Oak Hills Research, 20879 Madison St, Big Rapids, MI 49307, tel 616-796-0920.

[2]*PSPICE1* Circuit Analysis Software is available from the Microsim Corp, 20 Fairbanks, Irvine, CA 92718, tel 714-770-3022.

[3]J. Dillon, "The Neophyte Receiver," *QST*, Feb 1988, pp 14-18.

[4]G. Dobbs, "The 'Sudden' Receiver," *SPRAT* no. 58, Spring 1989, pp 16-19.

[5]G. Dobbs, "The Sudden Receiver," *73 Amateur Radio Today,* Oct 1991, pp 8-12.

[6]"The Sudden Receiver Goes SMD," *SPRAT* no. 61, Winter 1989-90, pp 19-20. (Kit available from Blue Rose Electronics, 538 Liverpool Road, Great Sankey, Warrington. WA5 3LU England.)

[7]R. Lewallen, "An Optimized QRP Transceiver," *QST*, Aug 1980, pp 14-19; also see Feedback, *QST,* Nov 1980, p 53. The Optimized QRP Transceiver also appears on pages 30-37 to 30-40 of *The 1992 ARRL Handbook,* and in the second printing of *QRP Classics* (available from the ARRL Bookshelf as #3169).

[8]G. Breed, "A New Breed of Receiver," *QST*, Jan 1988, pp 16-23.

[9]N. Hamilton, "Improving Direct Conversion Receiver Design," *Radio Communication,* Apr 1991, pp 39-44.

[10]Roy Lewallen and Wes Hayward, private correspondence.

[11]S. Niewiadomski, "Passive Audio Filter Design," *Ham Radio,* Sep 1985, pp 17-30.

[12]See Chapter 2 of the *National Semiconductor Audio/Radio Handbook 1980,* M. Giles ed., National Semiconductor Corporation, 2900 Semiconductor Drive, Santa Clara, CA 95051.

[13]P. Horowitz and W. Hill, *The Art of Electronics,* 2nd ed, (New York: Cambridge University Press, 1989), pp 91-96.

[14]Although this view is valid from an engineering standpoint, it may be more instructional to say that AGC (originally AVC, for *automatic volume control*) has historically been necessary for AM reception because people don't like being blasted out of their chairs by loud radios. Invented in 1926 by Harold A. Wheeler of the Hazeltine Corporation, AVC was the radio industry's solution to the problem of "two-hand" AM-broadcast reception. Before AVC, the wide strength difference between local and distant stations required broadcast listeners to tune with one hand and ride audio gain with the other. Listener convenience, not detector dynamic range, put AVC in "virtually every radio on the market" by 1932. See Robert E. Grinder and George H. Fathauer, *The Radio Collector's Directory and Price Guide* (1986: Scottsdale, AZ, 1986), pp 47-48.—*WJ1Z*

[15]D. DeMaw, "Build a Universal VFO," *QST,* Jun 1991, pp 27-29.

[16]D. DeMaw, "Transmitter Design—Emphasis on Anatomy Part 1," in *QRP Classics,* pp 75-78 (available from the ARRL Bookshelf as #3169).

[17]W. Hayward and D. DeMaw, *Solid State Design for the Radio Amateur,* available from the ARRL Bookshelf as #0402.

[18]R. Hayward and W. Hayward, "The 'Ugly Weekender,'" *QST,* Aug 1981, pp 18-21. The Ugly Weekender also appears on pages 30-33 to 30-36 of *The 1992 ARRL Handbook.* Etched, plated and drilled PC boards for the VFO/buffer are available from FAR Circuits, 18N640 Field Ct, Dundee, IL 60118-9269. Price is $4; add $1.50 for shipping and handling to each order. Use the board's AUX OUT output for the correct drive level for the SBL-1 mixer.

[19]Z. Lau, "The QRP Three Bander," *QST,* Oct 1989, pp 25-30.

[20]G. Breed, "A Portable QRP CW Transceiver for 20 and 30 Meters," *The 1992 ARRL Handbook,* pp 30-26 to 30-32.

[21]R. Littlefield, "The QRP-15 CW transceiver," *CQ,* Sep 1990, pp 43-49.

[22]I. Keyser and G. Dobbs, "The CSP 14 MHz CW/SSB Transceiver," *SPRAT* no. 67, Summer 1991, pp 21-29

[23]R. Hayward, "The 'Ugly Weekender' II: Adding a Junk-Box Receiver," *QST,* Jun 1992, pp 27-30.

[24]1990 *Merrimac RF & Microwave Processing M-90* book, p 1.4.

[25]Hewlett Packard *Microwave and RF Designers Catalog 1990-1991,* pp 4-68 and 4-69.

[26]W. Hayward and J. Lawson, "A Progressive Communications Receiver," *QST,* Nov 1981, pp 11-21. Also in Chapter 30 of recent editions of *The ARRL Handbook.*

A classic portable station: Ricky, the author's son, with a Classic 40, antenna tuner, 20-mW CW transmitter, key, battery and speaker. *(photo by the author)*

5. Accessories/Components

From QST, August 1992, p 66:

Lab Notes

Conducted By Steve Ford, WB8IMY, Assistant Technical Editor
and the ARRL Laboratory Staff

Substituting Parts

You need to replace a 470-ohm resistor in your 2-meter power amplifier. Any 470-ohm resistor you have in your junkbox should do the trick—or will it? Did you check to see if the substitute resistor was a carbon-composition or wire-wound type? Contrary to what you may think, it makes a big difference in RF applications! ARRL Laboratory Engineer Zack Lau, KH6CP/1, offers many important tips to consider before you start swapping parts in your equipment.—WB8IMY

Q: Many construction articles say that I can substitute higher-wattage resistors for lower-wattage ones. Are there cases where this doesn't work?

A: The most obvious problem results from the larger size of the higher-wattage resistors: They may not fit in the same space as smaller resistors. Inductance is also related to size. At VHF and above, larger resistors may have too much inductance for circuits to work properly.

Q: How does the inductance of metal-film resistors compare with that of carbon-composition resistors?

A: The metal-film resistors made today seem to be quite low in inductance, and are comparable to carbon types. I've used them well into the VHF range with little difficulty. However, these should not be confused with *wirewound* resistors, which are probably too inductive even in the MF/HF spectrum.

Q: How about capacitors? Why is a given value available in so many types?

A: Manufacturers usually use the cheapest capacitor that will work well in a given circuit. Depending on the application, you end up with a menagerie of capacitors made from various materials, including ceramic, mica, polystyrene and so on.

Q: I can't seem to find the polystyrene capacitors specified in an oscillator project. Is there another type of capacitor I can use?

A: If it's an RF project, NP0-type (that's zero, not "oh") ceramic disc capacitors work just as well or better. For audio or very-low-frequency projects, polyester capacitors are a good substitute. If you manage to find polystyrene capacitors, take care when you solder them in place. Polystyrene capacitors are easily damaged by defluxing solvents and heat.

Q: The mica capacitors in my transmitter filter are getting awfully warm, yet I used the 500-volt capacitors specified in the article. What's going on?

A: When you're using capacitors in power circuits, the *current* rating of the capacitor is just as important as the voltage capacity. Unfortunately, current ratings are not usually specified. I look for larger capacitors with thicker leads when I have an application that requires the capacitor to handle high currents. An alternative is to use several smaller capacitors in parallel.

Q: I want to use disc capacitors to filter my ac line cord. How can I convert the dc voltage rating of the capacitors into an ac voltage rating?

A: Rather than use the conversion approach—which is a bit risky—the better course of action is to use ac-rated capacitors intended for across-the-line use. Another option is to use filtered line-cord connectors. They're often very cheap on the surplus market.

Q: I know that the tuning range and plate spacing of air-dielectric variable capacitors is important. Is there anything else I should worry about?

A: Size can be an important consideration—especially if the capacitor has to fit inside the box you're using! Loss is sometimes a factor as well. For instance, small tuned loops for transmitting require low-loss tuning capacitors to work efficiently. Expensive vacuum-dielectric variables are often used in these applications. However, if the author got away with an air variable, chances are you can, too. Some types of equipment, such as VFOs, also require capacitors with a high degree of mechanical stability.

Q: How come an author merely specified "ferrite bead" without specifying its size or material type?

A: In many cases, the ferrite bead was added as insurance against RF intrusion and the author merely grabbed whatever was available. It's difficult, but not impossible, to differentiate the various ferrite materials by color and texture. For example, type 43 material has a pronounced metallic sheen compared to type 72. Type 75 material usually appears to be dull and dark.

Q: I've purchased some mystery toroids at a recent hamfest. I'd like to substitute them in one of my amplifiers. How do I calculate the proper number of windings to use?

A: First, you have to determine the inductance, and possibly the Q, of the inductors you're replacing.

Once you've determined the inductance of the inductor you want to replace, make your best guess at the number of windings required on your mystery toroid. Wind the wire through the toroid and measure the resulting inductance.

If you find that it's impossible to maintain the proper turns ratio to get the inductance you need, your toroid is unsuitable. Also, if the loss is excessive, the Q of your toroid probably isn't high enough.

Q: I checked my parts-substitution directory and found that a 1N5767 PIN diode is similar to a 1N914 small-signal diode. I thought they were completely different. What gives?

A: A PIN diode is a specialty device that shares *some* characteristics with small-signal diodes. However, the publisher of your directory failed to take the special characteristics of PIN diodes into account. To add to the confusion, 1N914s *can* be used as RF switching diodes, but they have much higher losses (often approaching 50%) compared to a few percent or less for a properly designed PIN diode switch.

Q: Why do some circuits require a specific transistor while others operate with just about anything?

A: Good designers add extra parts to compensate for device variations. This allows a wide variety of devices—transistors, for example—to function in the circuit. In some cases, designers find that optimum performance can only be obtained by using a specific device. In other cases, cost calls the tune. A circuit designed to accommodate a variety of substitute parts requires extra effort...and extra expense!

Q: The project I'm building specifies a certain wire gauge to use when making the inductors. Can I get away with using a different wire size?

A: Maybe—if the size of your substitute wire is reasonably close. Much thinner wire will result in more inductance and lower Q—even if you're winding a toroid. This can make the difference between a working circuit and a dead circuit! Too much Q, on the other hand, can result in unwanted oscillation. Broadband circuits are usually less critical with regard to circuit Q.

Q: I want to replace the tubes in my radio with solid-state devices. Isn't there a company that sells replacements?

A: Sorry. The last manufacturer of solid-state tube replacements closed up shop a long time ago. Even building your own isn't easy. The necessary high-voltage field effect transistors are difficult to find these days.

Q: Why can't I use the fifth overtone of a cheap microprocessor crystal for my microwave transverter?

A: Nothing says you can't. However, the microprocessor crystals I've examined have strong spurious responses. If you attempt to use the fifth overtone of these crystals, be prepared to see your oscillator unexpectedly jumping frequencies. Unlike your microprocessor crystal, a crystal made for a particular overtone is cut to keep spurious responses to a minimum.

Q: I have a bad crystal in an FT-243 case. Can I replace it with a crystal in an HC-6 case?

A: Possibly, but be careful. The HC-6 crystal is a more modern vintage. Older crystals generally can handle more power than most modern crystals. This means you have to be cautious when using a modern crystal as a replacement in an older piece of equipment. Crystals will fracture if you apply too much power to them!

Q: What about using plastic-insulated wire when copying antenna designs that use bare or enameled wire?

A: Insulated wire will make a difference in the antenna's resonant frequency, though for HF antennas the antenna's placement has just as much effect. Besides, if the finished antenna isn't resonant on the desired frequency, a little shortening or lengthening will do the trick. For VHF and microwave antennas, the effect is more pronounced, and correcting the problem is more difficult.

Q: Does it make any difference whether I use phenolic or glass-epoxy circuit board?

A: Yes! Phenolic boards are junk compared to glass-epoxy boards. Assuming that you'll have to make a modification or repair to the circuit at some point, glass-epoxy is a wise investment. A phenolic board is brittle and will break easily.

Q: Is it really necessary to have my PC boards tin plated?

A: Not at all. They'll look better and won't oxidize as quickly as unplated copper, but you can always scrape the copper clean if you need to do a modification in a couple of years.

Q: What can I use for coil forms?

A: Polystyrene and Teflon make great coil forms, even though polystyrene cracks and melts easily. Fiberglass, Delrin and wood have also been used, apparently with good results. Some hams have tried PVC, but I've heard several reports of problems with this material. (One ham reported melting an antenna coil wound on PVC!)

Q: I can't seem to find audio-taper potentiometers. Can I use linear-taper potentiometers instead?

A: It depends on the circuit and how fussy you are. The wrong taper can make the difference between a smooth control and a touchy control. Audio tapers provide the smoothest adjustment for audio circuits, assuming the designer used them in the right place.

Q: Can I use anodized aluminum for my antennas?

A: Anodizing is an electrochemical process that has one huge disadvantage—it forms an excellent *insulator* on the surfaces of metal objects. I once encountered a TV antenna that seemed to be mysteriously nonfunctional—until I sanded off the coating to establish electrical contact!

Q: When is it appropriate to use IC sockets in a circuit?

A: Let the author's design be your guide. Sockets are usually safe for RF applications, although the author may have a perfectly valid reason to avoid them (too much inductance, high reliability requirements and so on).

Q: Can I use UHF connectors instead of those N, BNC, or SMA connectors so often specified in UHF and microwave projects?

A: No. Despite their name, UHF connectors have poor SWR characteristics at UHF and higher frequencies. They should not be used above 420 MHz. However, if the rig in question uses UHF connectors, its circuitry is probably designed to accommodate the mismatch they cause.

Q: Can I substitute a 6146B RF power amplifier tube for an ordinary 6146?

A: In most cases you can, although the B-suffix version's slightly higher grid-to-plate capacitance may cause problems if the range of the neutralization circuit is marginal. In addition, while the plate dissipation of the new tubes may be greater, don't try to squeeze more power out of the circuit. Your power supply may not survive the additional stress! For tube-type amplifiers, it's often the power supply that limits the amplifier, not plate dissipation.

Q: I found some high-quality Teflon cable at a hamfest. Can I use it in place of regular coax to reduce loss?

A: This is actually two questions. Yes, you can usually replace regular coax with its Teflon dielectric equivalent *in applications where the velocity factor doesn't matter*. But Teflon cable generally isn't less lossy than standard cable of the same impedance and diameter.

Q: How can I determine the impedance of the cable I bought?

A: Unless it has an RG-type number, forget about looking it up. It's easier just to measure the dimensions and calculate it. You can confirm your calculation by attaching a long piece of the cable to a dummy antenna and measuring the SWR.

Q: I copied an antique transmitter almost exactly, except that I used aluminum instead of steel for the chassis and shields. How come it's full of unwanted oscillations?

A: Assuming the original design didn't have oscillations its builder didn't know about, the aluminum is probably the problem. The use of steel, a lossy material, effectively lowers the gain of RF circuits, making it difficult for oscillations to occur. This is why old steel chassis were often copper plated—and one reason why old rigs on bare-steel chassis were relatively easy to tame.

We welcome your suggestions for topics to be discussed in *Lab Notes*, but we are unable to answer individual questions. Please send your comments or suggestions to: Lab Notes, ARRL, 225 Main St, Newington, CT 06111. ▭

From QST, March 1996, p 32:

By James "Jay" Craswell, WBØVNE

Weekend DigiBrain

Now you can free up your computer by teaming May 1995 *QST*'s popular DDS VFO with a programmed microcomputer for stand-alone operation.

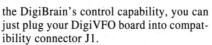

Reports of the demise of home-brewing appear to be premature. Hundreds of you have called and written me about the original DigiVFO article. The applications for a simple gadget like this apparently are innumerable. One fellow told me he was using his as a VFO for his WW II BC-610 transmitter. Another wanted to use the DigiVFO for some sort of sea-ice measurement system—fantastic! I guess I shouldn't be surprised that a basic gadget like this is not limited to ham radio projects. One letter informed me that because of the quality of articles (not just mine, of course), the author was going to replace his subscription to the *Proceedings of the IEEE* with ARRL membership, so he would receive *QST*! The general reaction to the DigiVFO article in the now-classic May 1995 issue of *QST* has been quite gratifying. Yet, with all of this praise there was a recurring complaint. Many of you want a stand-alone version for homebrew radio projects and so on. So from the inner sanctum of my little home electronics lab, I present the Weekend DigiBrain, an expanded DigiVFO that sports a real tuning dial and a liquid-crystal display (LCD) panel to display the VFO's relative frequency. Like the Weekend DigiVFO, it's available as a kit,[2] and my hope is that it can become a building block for all sorts of new home-brew gear in addition to serving as a stand-alone outboard VFO for commercial rigs. So warm up those soldering irons, and let's get to work!

Figure 1, the DigiBrain's circuit, contains the components of the Weekend DigiVFO (see Figure 1 of the May 1995 article) and then some. The original DigiVFO components include U4, a Harris HSP45102 direct digital synthesizer (DDS); U5, a Harris CA3338 digital-to-analog converter (DAC); and a 40-MHz clock module (U6). The "Brain" consists of a programmed Motorola 68HC705J1A microprocessor (U1), two 74LS574 latches (U2 and U3), and an MDL-16265 LCD panel (Z1). If you already have a DigiVFO and just want to add

the DigiBrain's control capability, you can just plug your DigiVFO board into compatibility connector J1.

I described how the DigiVFO works in the May 1995 *QST* article, so please go back and read that if you want to know how the DigiVFO generates RF. As in the DigiVFO, no filtering follows the DigiBrain's DAC. This is significant because the unfiltered output of a DDS's DAC contains many unwanted signals in addition to the signal you want. This is acceptable with the DigiVFO and DigiBrain operating as "external VFO" substitutes for commercial gear because the associated transmitter or transceiver provides additional filtering. For the Digi-Brain, I add another recommendation: Don't transmit while tuning the DigiBrain. Not only is "swishing" very bad manners, but many transient spurs appear in the DigiBrain's output as its DDS changes frequency and its DAC settles.

See May 1995 *QST*'s DigiVFO article for more information about the system's output purity.

How It Works

Microprocessor U1 runs the program necessary to tell the Harris DDS chip what frequency to produce. (You can reset U1 without powering down the DigiBrain by momentarily grounding the circuit's **RESET** line.) Two 74LS574 latches turn the 8 bits of U1's Port A (using two additional bits for control) into 16 bits to control the DDS chip and LCD display panel, Z1. Tuning knob unit Z2 does two things: Twisting its knob signals the microprocessor, which translates Z1's output into commands that tell the DDS chip to increase or decrease its

output frequency. Pushing the VFO knob in cycles the DigiBrain through its six tuning steps (1 Hz, 10 Hz, 100 Hz, 1 kHz, 10 kHz, 100 kHz). Z1 displays the DigiBrain's relative output frequency in megahertz (**xx.652.093**, for instance) and indicates the current step size.

One of the things going for the Motorola CPU was its cost. (You know me!) A 68HC705J1A Designer's Kit[3]—you don't need one unless you want to custom-design your own DigiBrain software—cost less than a hundred bucks. The Motorola kit includes an integrated editor/assembler/debugger as well as a sample of the erasable version of the CPU, and a CPU programmer that plugs into your PC's serial port and a sample of the erasable version of the part. It even includes an emulator pod! This is mighty handy for testing code before you program any chips. With it, I tried out routines and determined the CPU's inputs on my bungled prototype board! (Yep, I forgot my pullup resistors!) This seems fantastic to me because only a few years ago an in-circuit emulator cost over $30,000!

What About the Software?

Some of the letters and phone calls about the DigiVFO software ask, "Why don't you elaborate on it in your articles?" The main reason is that software listings are notorious for boring the pants off prospective readers. In addition, they fill the magazine unnecessarily when the full source is available with the kit and through the HIRAM BBS or Internet FTP.[3] If you're interested in learning how the program works, I urge you to study the source code. It contains many comments—often in almost painful detail!—that

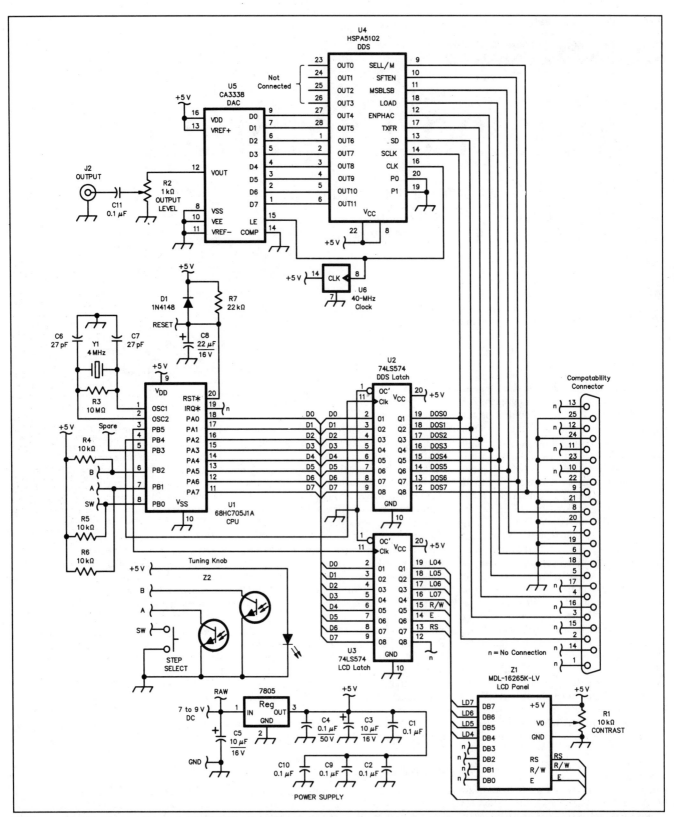

Figure 1—The DigiBrain relieves the DigiVFO's dependence on external computer control by using a 68HC705J1A microcontroller to translate pulses from optical shaft encoder Z2 into commands for the system's direct digital synthesizer (U4). LCD panel Z1 displays the system's relative frequency and tuning step. If you already have a DigiVFO (May 1995 *QST*), you can plug it into the compatibility connector (J1) and omit C11, R2, J2, U4, U5, and U6.) The circuit's resistors are ¹/₄-W carbon film; its polarized capacitors are aluminum or tantalum electrolytics; and the remainder of the capacitors are general-purpose ceramics.

R1—10-kΩ trimmer potentiometer
R2—1-kΩ, 10-turn potentiometer
U1—Motorola 68HC705J1A programmable
    microprocessor. This part must be
    programmed with the DigiBrain control
    software for the DigiBrain to work.
U2, U3—74LS574 octal D flip-flop.

U4—HSP45102PC-40 12-bit numerically
    controlled oscillator IC (Harris
    Semiconductor)
U5—CA3338AE 8-bit video DAC IC with
    voltage output (Harris Semiconductor)
U6—40-MHz, TTL-output clock module,
    14-pin DIP

U7—7805 5-V, 1-A voltage-regulator IC
    (equip this part with a heat sink)
Y1—4-MHz microprocessor clock crystal
Z1—Grayhill 61C11-01-08-02 optically
    coupled rotary encoder
Z2—Varitronics Limited MDL-16265K-LV
    LCD module

describe the actions of the program's subroutines. If all else fails, you can always drop me a letter—or better yet, send me an e-mail—and I'll try to remember how (or why) I did my code in a certain way.

Building It

If you build the full DigiBrain, there's no need to install the compatibility connector; none is supplied if you order the kit that way. The only tricky things to worry about are the orientation of the parts and proper soldering. Like the DigiVFO, the DigiBrain's digital circuitry can generate considerable radio noise, so I recommend mounting the board in a metal enclosure.

The 68HC705J1A's CMOS architecture and the LCD panel's low current keep the DigiBrain's current drain low.

Operation

Power up the DigiBrain, and the LCD shows the frequency (**xx.000.000**) and frequency step currently in use—no silly **HELLO** message or other such rubbish. As in the DigiVFO's control programs, the DigiBrain's LCD panel does not display megahertz digits. (There is a place reserved for them because a different version of the 68HC705J1A software can operate the VFO as a stand-alone signal generator.) When you turn the dial, you'll find that the tuning knob has a rubbery, detented bump-bump feeling. (I particularly like this because it reminds me of the tuning knob on a good German car radio. I want better control than I perceive with the free-wheeling tuning used on many rigs.)

The control software in some commercial transceivers makes them tune faster if you spin their tuning dials faster—when you savagely twist the knob, you get larger steps

than when you turn it slowly. I wanted accurate, predictable control, and got it with the DigiBrain's switch-selectable steps. To change the step size, just push the knob in and watch the display to see what step you've selected. Some people will rebel at this, and no doubt I will be talked into doing a more "standard" version of the controller code someday! For now, it's my chance to convince you that my way is "better." Try it; you *might* like it!

The standard DigiBrain kit produces output from 5.05 to 6.05 MHz. If you need a different range, such as the 5.5 to 6-MHz span common to many older Kenwood transceivers, make sure you indicate it in your order. I'm also willing to do a reverse-tuning VFO—one that moves lower in frequency as its dial readout moves higher—for Yaesu users. All you have to do is ask.

That New Golden Age Gets Brighter!

There's no reason I should have all the fun. The Motorola design tools that allowed me to test my hardware and software without programming a single chip cost a fraction of what I was used to a scant five years ago! Sure, many of my ham friends get a glazed or outright disgusted look when computer talk starts up at a hamfest or local swap meet. I'd prefer more "radio content" in ham-radio swap meets myself! But I hope that my fellow home designers will also see the merit in including microprocessors in new radio designs. Micros are now priced very reasonably, and can (if used creatively) replace scads of popcorn electronics. The tools we now have access to make designing with microprocessors much easier than the good old days. Anyone who thinks home-brewing ham gear is dead must not

have a wall calendar marked *1996*!

Acknowledgements

I thank Dave Newkirk and Paul Pagel at HQ for the help with the DigiArticles. Thanks again to Roger-Bob, WAØVLL, for the free LCD (which I "blowed up real good"), and the expert comments on switches and CPU selection; *Circad* author Fred Lehman (still not a ham <sigh>) for programming advice; Robert-Bob, WØAUS, for moral support; and Jim-Bob, WBØCHL, for the extra CPU chips, tea and sympathy.

Jay Craswell, WBØVNE, can be contacted at 321 W 4th St, Jordan, MN 55352-1313, or via e-mail at 73016.27@compuserve.com.

Notes
[1] James "Jay" Craswell, WBØVNE, "Weekend DigiVFO," *QST*, May 1995, pp 30-32.
[2] DigiBrain kits are available from Dover Research Corporation. #321 West 4th St, Jordan, MN 55352-1313, tel 612-492-3913. A DigiBrain kit for use with the original DigiVFO (includes compatibility connector J1; excludes C11, J2, R2, U4, U5, U6 and an enclosure) is $65 in US funds. A complete stand-alone DigiBrain/VFO with all parts (except J1, an enclosure and an ac power supply) is $89.95. A preprogrammed DigiBrain 68HC705J1A microprocessor is $10. Please include appropriate funds for shipping; Minnesota residents, add 6% sales tax. Remit by check, money order or traveler's check; VISA, Mastercard and AmEx are not accepted. when writing for information, please enclose a self addressed envelope in your correspondence.
[3] The M68HC705J1ACS Development Kit is available from Motorola's CSIC Microcontroller Division, 6501, William Cannon Dr W, MD OE17, Austin, TX 78735, tel 512-891-6568, World Wide Web http://design-net.com/csic/Dev_Sys/DevTool_Overview.html.
[4] The DigiBrain program files are available from the ARRL BBS (860-594-0306), and ARRL FTP (Web address: ftp://oak.oakland.edu/pub/hamradio/arrl/qst-binaries) and its mirror-site analogs, in the archive file **dbrain.zip**.

QST

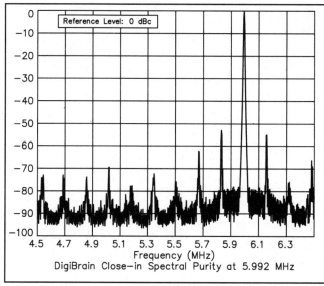

Figure 2—The DigiBrain's representative spectral purity in the 4.5 to 6.5-MHz region. The operating frequency is 5.992 MHz.

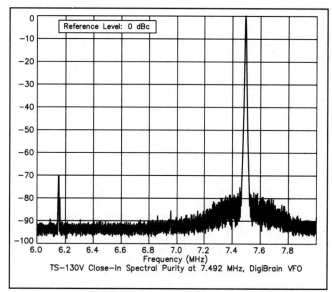

Figure 3—The 7.492-MHz output of a Kenwood TS-130V transceiver operating (into a dummy antenna, of course!) with the DigiBrain set to 5.992 MHz and acting as the TS-130V's external VFO. The 130V's output with its internal L-C VFO set to 5.992 MHz is essentially spectrally identical because of the electronic filtering performed by the 130V's phase-locked loop (PLL) circuitry.

From QST, June 1995, p 40:

Build a Super-Simple SWR Indicator

You don't need an actual *meter* to indicate reflected power if all you want to do is dip it. Here's a simple HF SWR indicator that provides positive indication of the matched-antenna condition down to very low power levels.

By Tony Brock-Fisher, K1KP
15 Webster St
Andover, MA 01810
e-mail: fisher@hp-and.an.hp.com

As a club project, the Hewlett-Packard ARC decided to build copies of the 40-40 QRP rig by Dave Benson, NN1G.[1] Many club members were interested in using this rig backpack or vacation style, with simple wire antennas and tuners, so the need for a companion SWR bridge arose. The resulting design is a simple, but effective, SWR indicator that can be used with a tuner to tune wire antennas, and is useful down to very low power levels (about 200 mW). The circuit can easily be squeezed into all but the smallest of QRP rigs, or it can be packaged into its own enclosure with a 9-V battery for a completely self-contained SWR indicator.

To save cost, we investigated the idea of using LEDs as indicators, instead of the traditional panel meter. In this application, it isn't really necessary to know exactly what the SWR is. We're more interested in just minimizing reflected power than in knowing that the antenna has an SWR of, say, 1.569:1. So we added a simple op-amp circuit to a traditional SWR-bridge design to create a much less expensive SWR indicator than the usual panel-meter approach. Additionally, the high-impedance LED driver circuit we developed allows the bridge to work down to very low power levels.

How It Works

See Figure 1. The bridge circuit is similar to the one described in *QST* and several editions of *The ARRL Handbook*,[2] but simplified (by the omission of a trimmer capacitor on the **XMTTR** side of T1) in that we don't need the bridge to be precisely balanced in this application. D1 and D2 act as half-wave diode detectors for the forward and reverse voltages. In traditional SWR-meter circuits, the output of these detectors feeds a panel meter via a

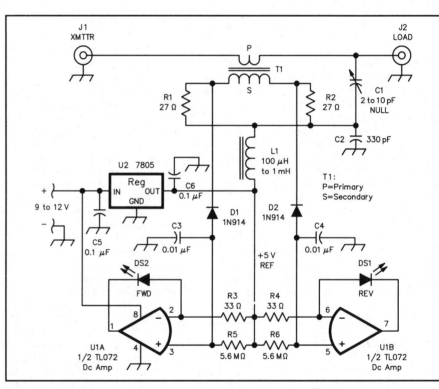

Figure 1—A standard directional coupler design teamed with a TL072 dual operational amplifier work together in this simple SWR indicator.

C1—Ceramic, plastic or air-dielectric trimmer
C2-C6—Ceramic
D1, D2—1N914 (or equivalent) silicon switching diode
J1,J2—Coaxial jacks
L1—RFC choke, 100 μH to 1 mH.
DS1, DS2—Light-emitting diodes (LEDs); red for **REV** and green for **FWD** suggested
R1, R2—5% or 10%-tolerance carbon film or composition

R3, R4—5% or 10%-tolerance carbon film or composition. The value of these resistors sets the bridge's power sensitivity; see text
T1—Toroidal transformer wound on a T-50-2 powdered-iron core. Secondary: 30 turns of #30 enameled wire; primary: 1 turn (just pass the wire through the core)
U1—TL072 dual JFET-input operational amplifier IC
U2—7805 or 78L05 5-V regulator IC

FORWARD/REFLECTED switch and a scaling resistor, which typically provides the detector diodes with a load on the order of 25 kΩ. This relatively low load impedance limits the diodes' performance at low

power levels because it causes their forward voltage drop to be higher than the sampled RF voltages to be detected.

To use LEDs (DS1 and DS2) as indicators, some sort of dc amplifier was needed.

We decided to use operational amplifiers because their high input impedance lets us load the diodes so lightly that their detection range can extend down to about 50 mV. U1A and U1B, halves of a TL072 dual JFET-input op amp (Figure 1), do the dc amplification.

The dc voltage developed by each detector is presented to its op amp across a 5.6-MΩ resistor. The 5.6-MΩ input resistor reduces the offset voltage, caused by input offset currents, to a negligible value. Each op amp operates at a voltage gain of 1 (unity), but provides enough current gain to drive an LED and to cause a matching voltage to appear across R3. (The current gain of the op amp is 5.6 MΩ ÷ 33 Ω, or about 170,000.) The LED's forward voltage drop is absorbed automatically by the op amp.

To provide each half of U1 with split (positive and negative) power supplies in environments in which only single-polarity, negative-ground supplies are typical, it was necessary to provide an artificial ground. U2 provides a stiffly regulated dc voltage between ground and the positive supply. (Note that the bridge circuit's dc reference is also set to +5 V because the RF-grounded end of L1, which is connected to dc ground in traditional directional-watt-meter circuits, is also connected to the +5 V supply provided by U2.)

Because we intended to use the bridge with a particular QRP transceiver design that operated at a known output power, Figure 1 includes no provision for adjusting the bridge's sensitivity. The overall sensitivity of the circuit can be adjusted to match the power level expected by changing the values of R3 and R4 to drive the LEDs with an appropriate current level. If you use different LEDs or want to use the bridge at a different power level, you may want to adjust these resistor values according to the formula

$$R3 \text{ and } R4 \text{ (ohms)} = \frac{\sqrt{P_0 \times 50}}{30 \times I_{f(LED)}}$$

where P_0 is the transmitter power in watts (1.5 W for the NN1G transceiver), 50 is the system impedance in ohms, 30 is T1's turns ratio, and $I_{f(LED)}$ is the current level (in amperes) that produces the LED brightness you need (we designed for an $I_{f(LED)}$ of 10 mA, or 0.01 A). With the resistor values chosen to light the **FWD** LED (DS2) brightly, the **REV** LED (DS1) will be easily visible at SWRs around 2:1, allowing no-guess SWR dipping with tuner adjustment.

Construction

Construction is straightforward—especially because an etched, drilled PC board is available.[3] The title photo and Figure 2 show this version of the SWR indicator. We built our first prototypes dead-bug style. If you decide to build it this way, construct the circuit's bridge portion on the copper ground plane afforded by a piece of

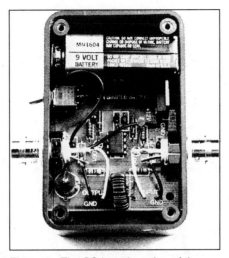

Figure 2—The PC-board version of the SWR indicator fits neatly into a Radio Shack 270-230 box with room to spare for a 9-V battery.

unetched PC-board material for good RF integrity. U1 and U2 can be arranged to suit the enclosure used. The unit has been tested with 9 and 12-V power supplies. It draws about 10 mA from a 9-V battery, which should provide about 10 hours of use—but shut it off between uses to save the battery. The unit can be combined inside your favorite QRP rig or built into an enclosure of its own, with 9-V battery and power switch.

Adjustment

C1, **NULL**, must be adjusted so the SWR indicator can correctly indicate minimum reflected power. To do this, connect a QRP transmitter or transceiver to the **XMTTR** jack and connect a 2-W, 51-Ω resistor between the **LOAD** jack's center pin and chassis. Power up the indicator circuit and put the rig into transmit on its highest-frequency HF band. Adjust the **NULL** trimmer to the center of the range over which the **REV** LED is dimmest. (Because we're not adjusting the bridge for the absolute best balance

possible, if you view the indicator in a darkened room, you may see the **REV** LED still lighting dimly at an SWR of 1. Also, if you can't make the **REV** LED go out by adjusting C1, you may have T1's secondary leads reversed. Interchange them and try again.) Remove the load resistor, connect the rig to the **XMTTR** jack, and you're ready to go.

One for the Road

This circuit's meterless reflected-power indication is all that's necessary for many ham radio applications, and its circuitry can be made small and compact for excellent portability. Using LEDs as indicators instead of a meter or meters keeps its size down and makes it inexpensive, too. I hope you'll find it a useful addition and companion to your travel/QRP rig.

Acknowledgment

I thank Paul Kranz, W1CFI, for his advice and encouragement in this project.

Notes

[1]First described in the April 1994 issue 72, the QRP 40-40 appeared in November 1994 QST in "A Single-Board Superhet QRP Transceiver for 40 or 30 Meters" and in the 1995 ARRL Handbook as "A Compact Single-Band Transceiver for 80 through 20 M."

[2]Doug DeMaw, W1FB, "QRP Person's VSWR Indicator," Hints and Kinks, QST, Aug 1982, p 45. This circuit also appeared in the ARRL Handbook as follows: on pp 34-11 to 34-12 of the 1985 through 1987 editions, and pp 34-9 to 34-10 of the 1988 through 1991 editions.

[3]PC boards are available from FAR Circuits, 18N640 Field Ct, Dundee, IL 60118-9269. Price, $4, plus $1.50 shipping (one to four boards).

First licensed in 1968 as WA1IKP, Tony Brock-Fisher got his Extra in 1976. Tony received a BS in physics from Southeastern Massachusetts University in 1972 and an MS in ocean engineering in 1976 from the University of Rhode Island. He is currently working as an R&D engineer for the Hewlett-Packard Company, where he designs medical ultrasound systems. He enjoys contesting, DX, QRP and home brewing, and is treasurer of the Hewlett-Packard Andover Radio Club. **QST**

From QEX, June 1995, p 16:

Refinements in Crystal Ladder Filter Design

Improved design techniques can result in much better wide-bandwidth filters.

By Wes Hayward, W7ZOI

Hams have been building their own crystal filters since the earliest days of single sideband. Early motivations were economic; commercially built filters were either too expensive or unavailable. Quartz crystals offered a method for achieving the selectivity needed in SSB transmitters and receivers. The trend continues, especially among QRP enthusiasts.

Recent work by Carver and by Makhinson has taken the process further.[1,2] Both examined the construction and design of very high-performance crystal filters. Their goal was to build filters offering performance that was not commercially available. This work produced some spectacular filter performance. Both

7700 SW Danielle Ave
Beaverton, OR 97008

based their work on one of several versions of *X.EXE*, a computer program for crystal filter design that I wrote several years ago.[3]

Recent communications (including those with Makhinson) mention limitations in the design method used in *X.EXE*. Wide filters were difficult, if not impossible. Examination of the underlying filter theory revealed a simple *circuit modification* to extend the design methods. This circuit extension produces filters with wider bandwidths at a greater variety of center frequencies, including filters using overtone modes. The new freedom allows us to build filters with improved time-domain performance, the primary goal in the filter designs of Carver.

Before examining circuit modifications, the original mathematical methods will be presented—allowing the limitations to be evaluated—be-

ginning with a review of L-C filters using crystal-like circuits. The problems encountered when we substitute crystals into this framework are then presented, leading to the methods used in *X.EXE*. Finally, the circuit modifications are presented that extend the capabilities.

This article is practical to the extent that it produces filters that are inexpensive and relatively easy to build. The filters really work well. The methods, however, are mathematical. Hence, the article is more analytical than is usual in amateur literature.

L-C Filter Background

The bandwidth of a band-pass filter defines a filter Q. This parameter, $Q_f = F_{center}/Bandwidth$, must be less than the unloaded Q of the resonators. A filter is then completely determined if the following conditions are met:

1) The singly loaded end section Q is

established in accordance with the polynomial of choice (Chebyshev, Bessel, etc).

2) The couplings between resonators are set to fit the polynomial.

A practical, although uncommon, example would use L-C *series* tuned circuits with large L and small C. This topology is presented in Fig 1.[4]

Unloaded resonator Q is easily measured. Once known, a *normalized* Q can be calculated for a filter as the ratio, $Q_o = Q_u/Q_f$. Tables in Zverev list the values of Q_o that are needed for a given polynomial filter to be realizable.[5] If the resonators are not good enough, it will be impossible to realize some filter types.

Consider an example, a 4th-order Butterworth filter, which has normalized parameters $q_1 = q_4 = 0.765$, $k_{12} = 0.841$, $k_{23} = 0.541$, and $k_{34} = 0.841$. Assume that the inductors are 10 μH while the series capacitor is 101.3 pF. Assume also that both L and C are fixed; we can't adjust them. (This restriction is the same one we encounter with crystals.) The L-C combination is series resonant at 5 MHz. Assume further that $Q_u = 250$, a typical value for toroid inductors. Examination of Zverev's tables shows that $Q_o > 3.7$ will allow the construction of a 4-resonator Butterworth filter. The unloaded resonator bandwidth is 20 kHz, so 4th-order Butterworth band-pass filters with a bandwidth of 74 kHz or more are realizable. We will design this filter for $B = 200$ kHz, so $Q_f = 25$ at 5 MHz.

The end section Q is denormalized according to the equations summarized on page 92 of Note 3:

$$Q_{END} = \left(\frac{1}{q \cdot Q_f} - \frac{1}{Q_u} \right)^{-1} \qquad \text{Eq 1}$$

where q (lower case) is the normalized end Q. The value for q was 0.765 for both ends of the Butterworth filter, so denormalized $Q_{END} = 20.71$. The inductor reactance at the filter center frequency is $\omega L = 314.2$ Ω, so the end sections will have a singly loaded Q of 20.71 if the end termination is 15.2 Ω. The coupling coefficients are denormalized with regard to Q_f:

$$K_{12} = \frac{k_{12}}{Q_f} \qquad \text{Eq 2}$$

where k_{12} (lower case) is the normalized coupling coefficient between the 1st and 2nd resonator. The coupling capacitor is then:

$$C_{12} = \frac{C_o}{K_{12}} \qquad \text{Eq 3}$$

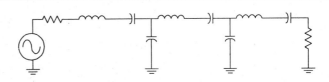

Fig 1—L-C filter topology using series tuned circuits.

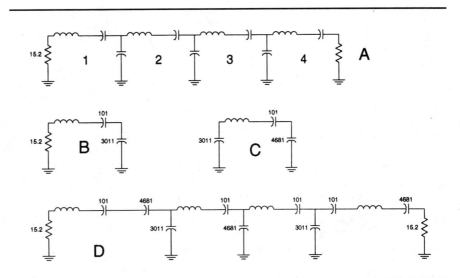

Fig 2—Evolution of a 4-resonator band-pass L-C filter including tuning. See text.

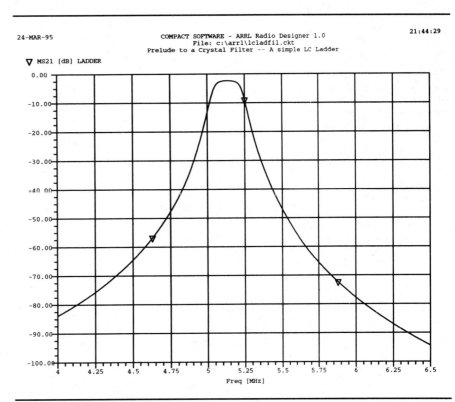

Fig 3—L-C filter response. The filter is that of Fig 2D.

where C_o is the nodal capacitance for the resonator, 101.3 pF for the example. With $k_{12} = 0.841$, the coupling capacitor is $C_{12} = 3011$ pF, a large but realizable value. C_{34} has the same value. A similar process generates the middle coupling capacitor, $C_{23} = 4681$ pF.

The almost-complete filter is shown in Fig 2A. We must still tune the filter. The simple resonators all started on the same 5-MHz frequency, but this synchronous tuning was upset when we inserted coupling capacitors. Mesh 1, shown in Fig 2B, is resonant at 5.084 MHz while mesh 2 (Fig 2C) tunes to 5.137 MHz. Owing to symmetry, mesh 3 is identical to mesh 2 while mesh 4 is the same as mesh 1. A filter becomes properly tuned when we insert extra series C in meshes 1 and 4, forcing all four meshes to be resonant at the same frequency, 5.137 MHz. The final circuit is shown in Fig 2D. The calculated response of this filter is presented in Fig 3.

The Quartz Crystal

The equivalent circuit for a crystal is given in Fig 4. The motional parameters, L_m and C_m, form a series tuned circuit while ESR, the *equivalent series resistance*, models crystal losses. This is, so far, no different from the series tuned circuits considered in the previous L-C example. However, the quartz crystal is complicated by an additional element, C_o, the parallel crystal capacitance. This component is the result of the basic physical crystal structure, a slab of quartz with metalization on both sides. This is a simple parallel-plate capacitor that is unrelated to the piezoelectric properties of the material. C_o of Fig 4 includes any stray capacitance that might be in the crystal package. The value for C_o is usually related to the motional capacitance by an approximation, $C_o = 220 C_m$.[6]

The component values are much different than what we might realize with off-the-shelf L and C. For example, a 10-MHz crystal that I've used

for numerous filter experiments has $L_m = 0.02$ H, $C_m = 12.67$ fF, and $C_o = 3$ pF. (1 fF = 0.001 pF = 1 femtofarad.)

As an initial approximation, the filter designer might ignore C_o. The crystal is then nothing more than a series resonator, and the design of filters is *exactly* like the L-C example. Unfortunately, this works only for the narrowest of filters. As the filter becomes wider, the discrepancy between design and measured results is extreme. (It is not necessary to build the filters to see these effects. The difficulties are quite evident in computer simulation with C_o included in the crystal model.) The coupling capacitors calculated when C_o is ignored are too large and may not be in the right ratio. The result is a bandwidth that is too narrow and a distorted shape. A smaller value of motional C should be used when calculating coupling elements. But what are appropriate motional elements? An answer was found in a *reactance slope approximation*, the method that formed the basis for *X.EXE*.

Consider a simple lossless series tuned circuit, Fig 5. The complex impedance is given as:

$$Z = j \cdot X = j\left(\omega \cdot L - \frac{1}{\omega \cdot C}\right) \qquad \text{Eq 4}$$

where $\omega = 2\pi f$. At resonance:

$$\omega_o \cdot C = \frac{1}{\omega_o \cdot L} \qquad \text{Eq 5}$$

which allows us to eliminate C:

$$j \cdot X(\omega) = j\left(\omega \cdot L - \frac{\omega_o^2 \cdot L}{\omega}\right) \qquad \text{Eq 6}$$

Differentiating this expression with respect to angular frequency, ω:

$$\frac{\partial X}{\partial \omega} = L + \frac{\omega_o^2 \cdot L}{\omega^2} \qquad \text{Eq 7}$$

This expression can be solved for inductance as a function of reactance slope with frequency, providing a new definition for effective inductance:

$$L = \frac{\dfrac{\partial X}{\partial \omega}}{1 + \dfrac{\omega_o^2}{\omega^2}} \qquad \text{Eq 8}$$

Consider now the equivalent circuit for the crystal shown in Fig 4. Ignoring ESR, the series tuned circuit portion has the impedance:

$$Z_{SER} = j\left(\omega \cdot L - \frac{\omega_o^2 \cdot L}{\omega}\right) \qquad \text{Eq 9}$$

This is converted to an admittance, $Y = 1/Z$, and the admittance of the parallel capacitance, C_o, is added, yielding:

$$Y = j\left[\frac{\omega \cdot C_o \cdot L \cdot (\omega^2 - \omega_o^2) - \omega}{L \cdot (\omega^2 - \omega_o^2)}\right] \qquad \text{Eq 10}$$

Converting back to impedance form, the reactance becomes

$$X = \frac{L_m \cdot (\omega_o^2 - \omega^2)}{\omega \cdot C_o \cdot L_m \cdot (\omega^2 - \omega_o^2) - \omega} \qquad \text{Eq 11}$$

This reactance is differentiated with respect to angular frequency, ω, with the result inserted into Eq 8 to produce the desired result, an expression for effective resonator inductance of a crystal in a filter:

$$L_{EFF} = L_m \cdot \left[\frac{2 \cdot A}{(A-1)^2 \cdot \left(1 + \dfrac{\omega_o^2}{\omega^2}\right)} \frac{1}{A-1}\right] \qquad \text{Eq 12}$$

where

$$A = L_m \cdot C_o \cdot (\omega^2 - \omega_o^2) \qquad \text{Eq 13}$$

We define $X(\delta f)$ as the ratio of the effective inductance to the motional inductance, with δf being an offset frequency in Hertz above the crystal resonance. Then, Fig 6 shows $X(\delta f)$ plotted as a function of offset for a typical 5-MHz crystal with $L_m = 0.098$ H. Two parallel capacitance values are used, resulting in the two curves. The lower curve is for $C_o = 2$ pF while the upper one is for $C_o = 5$ pF. The effective inductance ratio is plotted for offsets up to 2500 Hz. The effect is dramatic, especially when C_o is large.

This effect, an increase in effective inductance resulting from added parallel capacitance, is a familiar one. It happens when we parallel an inductor in a low-pass filter to generate fre-

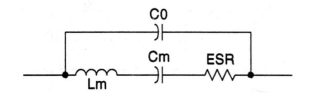

Fig 4—Quartz crystal model.

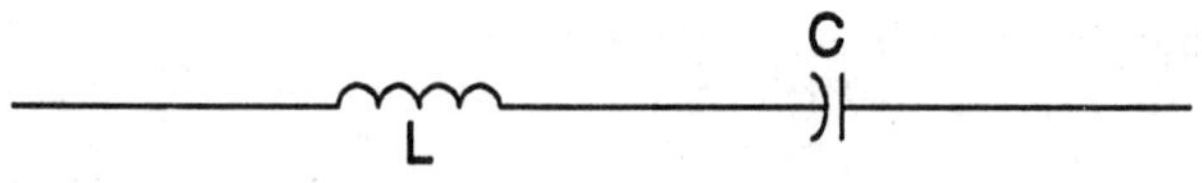

Fig 5—Ideal series tuned circuit.

quencies of high attenuation in the stopband (elliptic filters). It also happens when we build a trap for use in an antenna. In both cases, the addition of parallel C causes the inductor to behave like one with a larger value.

Crystal Filter Design

Now that we have isolated an effect—increased effective inductance due to holder capacitance—that will complicate filter performance, we can try to compensate for it. From Fig 6, if the filter is narrow, with a bandwidth of only a few hundred Hertz, the inductance ratio is very close to 1 over the entire band. We can then build effective filters by allowing the inductance to equal the motional value. Wider-bandwidth filters are built by evaluating the effective L over the passband. The L_{eff} value calculated at the top of the passband seems to work well for SSB filters. That value, and the resulting motional capacitances, are used for filter design. This is done in $X.EXE$.

The results shown in Fig 6 describe a particular 5-MHz crystal, although the effect is a general one. Going to a higher crystal frequency partially alleviates the problem, while lower frequencies complicate the outcome. This is the effect that led Makhinson (Note 2) to observe that effective lower-sideband ladder filters with an SSB bandwidth are best built for center frequencies between 6 and 12 MHz.

The approach used in $X.EXE$ seems to produce useful and predictable filters when $L_{eff} < 2L_m$. The rest of the design is no different than the L-C method outlined above. The reader should review the results obtained by Carver and Makhinson to see what is possible with these methods.

Motional inductance and capacitance can be measured with a variety of methods. The scheme shown in the sidebar is the one I presently use with most crystals.

Additional Refinements

The methods presented are not new. Rather, they represent but one mathematical formulation for the design. This method grew from correspondence with Dr. Dave Gordon-Smith, G3UUR. Dave had used similar analytical techniques to derive a unique set of normalized filter tables for crystal filter design with arbitrary crystals with any value for C0.[7] While not published, Dave has freely distributed his work (and tables) to many amateur experimenters over the years. His analysis predated and contributed to

the "L_m effective" approach that I've presented above (Eq 12). Dave also originated the crystal measurement scheme presented in the sidebar.

Wider Bandwidth Crystal Filters

The design methods outlined so far do not work well (if at all) when wide-bandwidth filters are to be built. Even when the methods appear to be working with regard to filter shape and bandwidth, the resulting circuits may

have excessive group delay near one end of the passband. This is another consequence of C_o, the nemesis of our problem. There is a simple solution to the problem: add circuitry that will cancel the effects of C_o.

The modified design procedure will be illustrated with an example. The circuit desired is one with a bandwidth of 3 kHz, suitable for AM reception. The center frequency is 3.58 MHz, the frequency of readily available color-

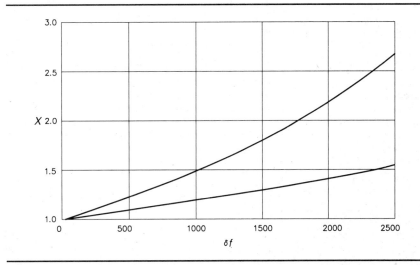

Fig 6—X, defined as L_{eff}/L_m, is plotted for frequency offset, δf, above the crystal series-resonance frequency in Hertz. These 5-MHz crystals had parallel C of 2 pF (lower curve) and 5 pF.

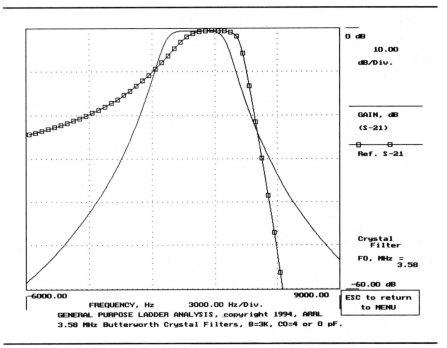

Fig 7

burst crystals. Circuit design begins with an attempt at using the standard methods. The available crystals have a motional L of 0.117 H and C_0 of 4 pF. This data, along with the k and q data for a Butterworth polynomial were entered into *X.EXE*. The resulting filter was then analyzed; the results are presented in the *reference plot* (small squares) of Fig 7. The filter is a poor one at best, showing severe asymmetry. Further, the bandwidth is slightly less than the desired 3 kHz. This attempt at synthesis is clearly unsuccessful; this is an application requiring the modified circuit.

The scheme that is used to cancel C_0, the parallel crystal C, is to add inductance in parallel with the crystal, creating a parallel resonance with C_0. The inductance is made a bit smaller than needed and a small trimmer capacitance is added, allowing for easy adjustment. The resulting filter is shown in Fig 8. The filter was designed with *X.EXE*, but with a value of 0 pF entered for C_0.

The added inductors are wound on ferrite toroids. This was required for this low frequency filter; the needed 150-µH inductance was not practical with iron-powder toroids. The solid curve in Fig 7 shows the calculated result for this filter. The shape is clean and very symmetrical, something of a rarity with lower-sideband-ladder crystal circuits.

This filter was built and tested with the results shown in Fig 9. The only subtlety encountered was with adjustment of the trimmer capacitors. I eventually shorted all four crystals with pieces of wire. Then the crystals were individually unshorted, the related capacitor was adjusted for a deep null about 20 kHz away from the passband, and the crystal was again short circuited. Only then were the shorts removed. No further adjustment was needed. This method should work well with filters with many more crystals.

It is not surprising that adjustment should be difficult. Fig 10 shows the calculated response for this filter over a wider frequency range of 3.4 to 3.8 MHz. The nulls (calculated!) next to the desired passband are over 150 dB below the desired response! The "wings" that reappear at wider separations from the desired responses can be a problem. The crystal filter will have to be "protected" with a suitable L-C band-pass circuit; one or two resonators will probably do the job.

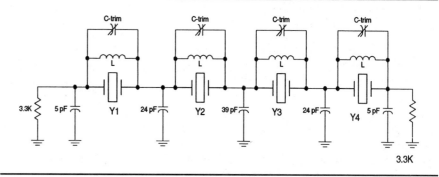

Fig. 8—A low-frequency AM filter with BW = 3.5 kHz.
Y1,2,3,4—3.58-MHz surplus color-burst crystals. L_m = 0.117 H, C_0 = 4 pF
L—151 µH, 48 turns #30 on FT-50-61 Ferrite toroid (Amidon).
C-trim—3-12 pF ceramic trimmer.

The G3UUR Method for Measuring Quartz Crystal Motional Parameters

This simple circuit may be used to measure the motional parameters of fundamental-mode quartz crystals. A crystal to be evaluated is placed in the circuit at Y1 and oscillation is confirmed. The frequency is measured. Then the switch is thrown and the frequency is measured again. Typical values are C_p = 470 pF and C_s = 33 pF. C_m will have the same units as C_s:
If

$$C_s \ll C_p$$

then

$$C_m \approx 2 \cdot C_s \cdot \frac{\Delta F}{F}$$

and

$$L_m = \frac{1}{\omega^2 \cdot C_m}$$

where $\omega = 2\pi F$ with F in Hertz. ΔF is the frequency difference observed when the switch is activated. Example: use capacitors mentioned above, 10-MHz crystal; $F = 1 \times 10^7$, ΔF = 1609 Hz, to yield L_m = 0.0239 H and C_m = 10.6 fF. (1000 fF = 1 pF.)

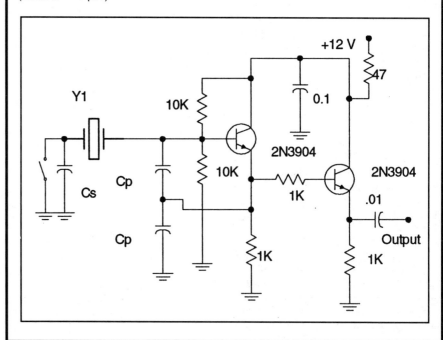

Filters with Overtone Crystals

The example filter used readily available low-frequency crystals. The instrumentation used for measurement is that available to most experimentally active amateurs. Similar filters have been built at VHF with overtone crystals. Such filters are not difficult if small inductors are added to each crystal, along with small trimmers. The inductors can now use iron-powder cores. The difficulty with overtone crystals results from the physical nature of the crystals: while motional inductance remains essentially constant, independent of overtone number, the motional capacitance decreases in proportion to the square of the overtone number. Hence, a third-overtone crystal will have one ninth of the motional C that is seen at the fundamental frequency. The coupling capacitors will be reduced by a similar ratio, complicating filter realization. Swept instrumentation will probably be required for the construction of really good overtone filters.

Conclusions

The filters that we have examined are very practical. Of greater significance are the general methods that allow the experimenter to move toward high-order filters with improved selectivity and more constant group delay.

Acknowledgments

Any long-term project like this one is the result of several sessions of midnight pondering and numerous discussions with others with similar interests. In this vein, I want to acknowledge discussions with Larry Lockwood, W7JBY, and Dr. Dave Gordon-Smith, G3UUR. It was Larry who first suggested that I examine reactance slope methods and Dr. Gordon-Smith who confirmed the approach through communications of his earlier works. More recent communications with Bill Carver, K6OLG/7, Jacob Makhinson, N6NWP, and Ulrich Rohde, KA2WEU, have provided the emphasis for the later work.

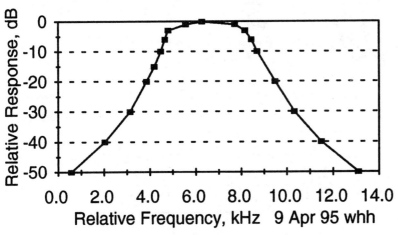

Fig 9—Measured response of an AM-bandwidth crystal filter at 3.58 MHz.

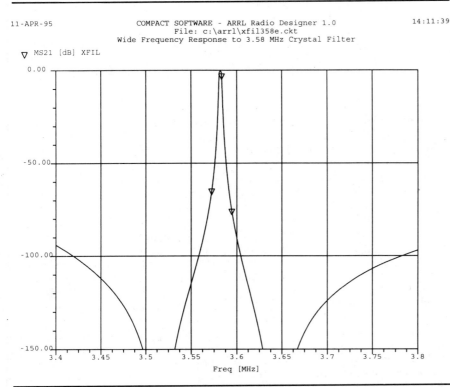

Fig 10

Notes

[1]Carver, Bill, "High Performance Crystal Filter Design," *Communications Quarterly*, Winter 1993.
[2]Makhinson, Jacob, "Designing and Building High-Performance Crystal Ladder Filters," *QEX*, January 1995.
[3]Hayward, Wes, *Introduction to Radio Frequency Design*, ARRL 1994. See the crystal filter design programs on the disk distributed with the book including *X.EXE* and *MESHTUNE.EXE*.
[4]See Note 3, page 92.
[5]Zverev, *Handbook of Filter Synthesis*, John Wiley and Sons, Inc, 1967.
[6]Bottom, V. E., *Introduction to Quartz Crystal Unit Design*, Van Nostrand Reinhold Co, 1982.
[7]Gordon-Smith, Dave, G3UUR, private correspondence, June 26, 1982.

From QEX, January 1995, p 3:

Designing and Building High-Performance Crystal Ladder Filters

Designing crystal filters for SSB is made easier using readily available software.

By Jacob Makhinson, N6NWP

Despite the several excellent articles about crystal filters that have been published in amateur magazines over the years, building high-quality crystal filters is still seen by many amateurs as either black magic or as a complicated procedure beyond the reach of the average builder.

A crystal filter, being the heart of a superheterodyne receiver, has a profound effect on its selectivity. A low-quality crystal filter in even a high-priced commercial transceiver can degrade its selectivity and dynamic range. On the other hand, a good crystal filter can significantly enhance receiver performance, whether in a simple "weekend" project or in a competition-grade station.

1100 N Sunset Canyon Dr
Burbank, CA 91504

Commercially available crystal filters are usually expensive and often discourage construction-minded amateurs from pursuing projects that include crystal filters. In addition, studies conducted in recent years conclude that in a high-performance receiver, a crystal filter may become the "bottleneck" restricting the receiver's dynamic range. So, the goal of this article is to provide design and building methods that can be used to construct crystal filters that rival or exceed the quality of commercially available filters. I will describe a simple, practical step-by-step procedure to design, construct and align crystal filters using equipment available to most construction-minded amateurs. The resulting filters achieve top-quality performance at a fraction of the cost of commercially available crystal filters.

Most of the crystal filters described

in amateur projects and those being sold commercially are lattice, half-lattice or cascaded half-lattice filters like those shown in Fig 1. A two- or four-crystal filter of this type can provide a symmetrical response with reasonably steep skirts. But the bandwidth of such filters is a function of the frequency separation of the crystals. If a steeper response is desired, designing a half-lattice filter with more than four crystals becomes more complex, requiring matched pairs of crystals and several adjustments. While it is reasonably easy to obtain matched crystal pairs for CW filters, it becomes considerably more problematic to obtain pairs of crystals separated by a couple of thousand hertz for use in SSB filters. In addition, the coils used for lattice filter alignment often use small cores, which can result in the degradation of dynamic range because of core saturation at high signal levels.

Another form of filter—which is the subject of this article—is the ladder filter shown in Fig 2. It typically has an asymmetrical response and is sometimes called the "lower-sideband ladder" configuration. But as we'll see, with a sufficient number of poles this asymmetry is significantly reduced. Ladder filters offer several advantages to the amateur experimenter:

- there is no need to pick crystals for proper frequency separation and no need for matched crystal pairs;
- the inherently simpler filter topology results in simple construction methods;
- no adjustable components are required after alignment is completed;
- the absence of coils allows a compact assembly and reduces the possibility of dynamic range degradation;
- the simple topology is conducive to a high number of poles, which allows very steep skirts; and

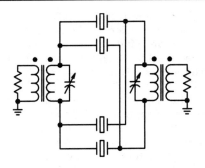

A) Lattice Crystal Filter

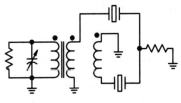

B) Half—Lattice Crystal Filter

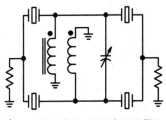

C) Cascaded Half—Lattice Crystal Filter

Fig 1—Lattice crystal filter circuits.

- a computer program is available that eliminates the need for empirical approaches or cut-and-try methods and allows the designer to shape the filter response with great accuracy.

This work was inspired by an article by Bill Carver, K6OLG/7.[1] Carver's work is quite remarkable; first, it proves that it is possible to build high-quality CW and SSB crystal filters with a predetermined frequency response "without black magic," and second (but of no less importance), it proves that the performance of filters built in a home lab using home-built equipment successfully rivals that of filters built using sophisticated professional equipment.

This article builds on Carver's work, refines the crystal filter design criteria and methodology, walks the reader through a complete design example, provides the results of measurements on several crystal ladder filters and analyzes the results.

The scope of this study has been limited to SSB filters, although most of the methods and conclusions are also applicable to CW filters.

The computer-design stage is based on a collection of computer programs designed by Wes Hayward, W7ZOI. The ARRL has just republished Wes Hayward's textbook *Introduction to Radio Frequency Design*, now including the software as part of the package.[2] The computer programs (which I will refer to as *IRFD*) run on an IBM PC or compatible computer. The computer requirements are minimal, since *IRFD* fits on a single floppy disk and the computer's speed is of no concern. A VGA card is required for graphic display, however.

The Design Procedure

Design and construction of these ladder crystal filters are performed using these steps:

- selection of the filter center frequency;
- measurement of crystal parameters;

[1]Notes appear on page 17.

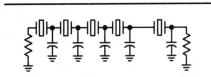

Fig 2—Circuit of a ladder crystal filter.

- selection of the shape of the response;
- computer design of the filter; and
- construction and alignment.

Frequency Selection

If the required filter frequency is not already defined, you can select an IF to suit your needs. In doing so, consider that certain frequencies may result in in-band intermodulation products. Tables and charts have been developed to help designers avoid these frequencies.[3] Practical considerations also impose some limitations on IF selection.

The crystals used in color-burst generators at 3.579 and 4.433 MHz are the most inexpensive crystals around and are widely available as surplus components. Unfortunately, the required termination resistances of filters built with such crystals may exceed 10 kΩ, which necessitates an impedance transformation with a very high ratio (for a 50-Ω system). As a result, very high voltage levels may be developed at the filter input, which may cause an overload condition. In addition, the required values of the coupling capacitors may be under 5 pF, making construction difficult due to stray capacitances. For these reasons, crystal filters with center frequencies under 6 MHz are not recommended.

The useful upper frequency limit is determined by the influence of stray capacitances at frequencies above 10 MHz and by the limitations imposed on the VFO circuit for multiband HF operation. Consequently, the recommended frequency range for an HF SSB crystal filter is between 6 and 12 MHz. The remaining criteria for the crystal frequency selection are the crystal Q and the price. Microprocessor crystals in HC18/U or HC49/U cases are reasonably inexpensive, but, being manufactured in large quantities, they are optimized for parameters other than Q.

Q is typically not specified by the manufacturer, and it varies significantly from batch to batch and from device to device within a batch. Therefore, the only way to find the Q of a specific type of crystal is to obtain several samples and to measure the parameters. This should be done before buying a large batch of crystals.

I originally intended to build crystal filters at 9 MHz, which is a popular IF within the amateur community, but it turned out that all the 9-MHz crystals I obtained (from different vendors) had Qs below 80,000. On the other hand, I found 8-MHz crystals with much higher Qs, so all of the crystal filters described in this article are built using 8-MHz (series resonance) crystals.

Crystal Parameters

The equivalent circuit of a quartz crystal is shown in Fig 3. The computer software we will use to design the ladder filter requires entry of the crystal parameters. These parameters are easily measured with the use of a lab-quality impedance analyzer, but they also can be measured quite accurately using home-built equipment. The test equipment required to measure crystal parameters has been described previously and is beyond the scope of this article.[1,4,5] The parameters needed for the design process are: ΔF, the frequency offset or deviation from the specified center frequency; r, the series resistance of the crystal; f_L and f_H, the 3-dB points required for the Q calculation; and L_m, the motional inductance, which is derived from the Q and r. C_o, the parallel or "holder" capacitance, can be measured, but an assumption that C_o is 5 pF (which I verified for several crystals in HC49/U cases) appears to be adequate in most cases.

There are several practical consid-

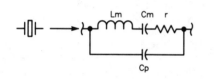

Fig 3—Equivalent circuit of a quartz crystal.

erations in selecting and handling the crystals you will use. For one thing, the design process is easier if the crystals to be used in a particular filter are selected from a large pool of crystals. Although it's not essential, the crystals can be matched for Q, L_m and ΔF. Buying a large batch of crystals may provide a volume discount and furnish you with several sets of filter crystals. To illustrate the point, I bought 100 8-MHz crystals for a total of $60. Out of that batch I used 14 crystals with an average Q of 145,000 for a 14-pole filter, 10 crystals with an average Q of 122,000 for a 10-pole filter and 12 crystals with an average Q of 110,000 for a 12-pole filter. I rejected the remaining 64 crystals. Three high-quality crystal filters for $60—not bad!

The crystals should be tagged before measurement, and the measurement results should be logged for future use. Invest sufficient time in this initial stage of the design since the accuracy of the data will affect the shape of the frequency response.

Take care to avoid heat transfer from your hands to the crystal cases, and allow 40 to 60 seconds between handling the crystals and performing the measurements to let the resonant frequency stabilize.

Once the measurements are completed, a preliminary group or groups of crystals with sufficiently high Q can be identified (grouped by Q within a certain range). Calculate the average motional inductance (L_{m-av}) and average Q (Q_{av}) for each group of crystals.

Filter Selection

An important part of the design process is selection of the desired filter parameters. The parameters you need

to select are:
- the filter response type—Chebyshev, Butterworth, Gaussian, etc,
- the number of poles,
- the filter bandwidth, and
- the value of terminating resistances.

The Chebyshev response with 0.1 dB of ripple is the most commonly used response type for SSB HF filters. It may be advantageous in the final filter design to deviate slightly from the 0.1-dB ripple value to obtain more convenient values for the end coupling capacitors. Decreasing the ripple level value will result in a slightly smoother frequency response but will degrade the shape factor; an increase in the ripple value causes the opposite effect.

Several factors have a significant influence on the number of poles chosen for the crystal ladder filter:
- the desired shape factor,
- the insertion loss,
- the degree of asymmetry of the frequency response,
- construction considerations, and
- the size and weight (for portable use).

The shape factor is defined as the ratio of the filter bandwidth at a level of –80 or –60 dB to its bandwidth at the –6-dB level. In this article I'll use the –80/–6 dB shape factor, $SF_{6:80} = \Delta f_{-80}/\Delta f_{-6}$.

The required shape factor depends on the complexity of the receiver, its architecture and its specifications. Filters with more poles have better shape factors. (For example, the XF-9B10, a 10-pole, 9-MHz SSB filter manufactured by KVG Inc, has $SF_{6:80} = 1:1.8$.) Fig 4 may help you select the needed number of poles,

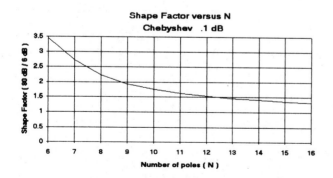

Fig 4—Graph of ladder filter shape factor (6:80) versus the number of poles for a Chebyshev response with 0.1 dB of ripple.

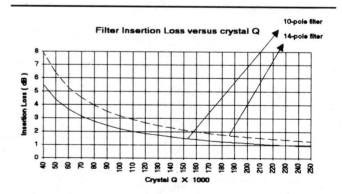

Fig 5—Graphs of filter insertion loss versus crystal Q.

based on the desired shape factor. Receivers having filters with good shape factors exhibit improved selectivity and a distinct "crisp" quality when tuning from one station to another.

Insertion loss, while strongly influenced by the Q of the crystals, also depends on the number of poles. The curves in Fig 5 show these effects. All other factors aside, the availability of good-quality crystals may be the deciding or limiting factor in selecting the number of poles. As shown in Fig 5, a 14-pole filter made of crystals having Qs of 160,000 has the same insertion loss as a 10-pole filter made of crystals having Qs of 110,000. The curves in Fig 5 were generated using *IRFD* and represent theoretical calculations performed by the program. Due to several limitations I'll discuss later, the practical results differ somewhat from the predicted values. But it is possible with a good degree of accuracy to make an estimate of the practical value of the insertion loss by adding 0.8 dB to the value obtained from Fig 5.

The asymmetry of the frequency response is inherent in crystal ladder filters, but by increasing the number of poles it is possible to overcome this shortcoming. While the asymmetry is obvious in a 10-pole filter, it becomes almost unnoticeable in a 14-pole filter.

Construction considerations will undoubtedly differ from one builder to another, but one observation is worth mentioning: I noticed during the construction of several ladder filters that to achieve good ultimate attenuation (more than 120 dB), the requirements for shielding between filter sections are considerably more stringent for a 10-pole filter than for a 12 or 14-pole filter.

Considering all the factors listed above, I recommend keeping the number of poles between 10 and 14. There is an advantage in having an even number of poles—it results in a symmetrical design, minimizing the number of different capacitor values needed.

Several factors influence the choice of bandwidth of the crystal filter:
- the desired selectivity—narrower filters may be preferred for contest work while wider filters may be more appropriate for casual rag-chewing,
- receiver sensitivity and dynamic range, and
- personal preference.

All of the filters discussed in this article have a bandwidth of 2500 Hz—mostly due to the last factor.

The value of the terminating resistance should be as low as possible to minimize the transformation ratio of the impedance-matching transform-

ers, and the value should exceed the *IRFD* recommended value by an amount that ensures that the end coupling capacitors are at least 15 pF. You should choose the lowest impedance value consistent with these two criteria from Table 1. (The transformer ratios assume you want to match the filter to 50-Ω source and load impedances.)

Computer Design

Before starting the computer design, make sure you have calculated the average Q (Q_{av}) and motional inductance (L_{m-av}) of the crystals and have selected the desired bandwidth, number of poles and the ripple value.

Note that if the actual desired bandwidth is used directly in the crystal filter design, the filter designed by the *IRFD* program will have a bandwidth narrower than predicted. (This occurs because of simplifying assumptions used in the equations and the use of *k*

Table 1—Termination Resistances and Transformer Design

Impedance ratio	Termination resistance (Ω)	Primary turns	Secondary turns
1:1.5	75	4	5
1:2	100	5	7
1:3	150	4	7
1:4	200	4	8
1:5	250	4	9
1:6.25	312	4	10
1:7.5	375	4	11
1:9	450	4	12
1:10.6	530	4	13
1:12.25	612	4	14
1:14	700	4	15
1:16	800	4	16

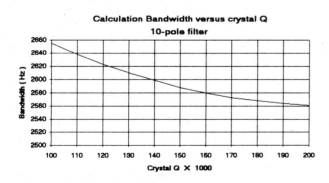

Fig 6—Graph of calculation bandwidth versus crystal Q for a 2500-Hz, 10-pole filter.

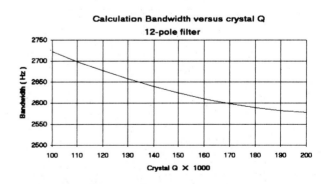

Fig 7—Graph of calculation bandwidth versus crystal Q for a 2500-Hz, 12-pole filter.

and q values based on lossless crystals.[4]) I've developed correction factors to compensate for this discrepancy. The bandwidth used for the computer calculations will be referred to as the calculation bandwidth (BWc), which can be obtained from the charts in Figs 6 through 8 for a desired bandwidth (BWd) of 2500 Hz.

To illustrate the design process, let's walk through the steps of an actual filter design. We'll begin by listing the design parameters:

Number of poles (N): 12
Desired bandwidth (BWd): 2500 Hz
Filter response type: Chebyshev, 0.1-dB ripple
Crystal (Q_{av}): 110,000
Motional inductance (L_{m-av}): 0.0155 H
Parallel capacitance (C_o): 5 pF
Nominal crystal frequency: 8 MHz

Four programs from the *IRFD* software package will be used to accomplish the design: *GPLA*, the general purpose ladder analysis program; *L*, the low-pass filter design program; *X*, the ladder crystal filter design program; and *MESHTUNE*, a utility for tuning meshes in a crystal filter. In each program, the menu selections are selected by typing the appropriate letter key. Entry of numeric values is done by typing the value, then pressing the **Enter** key. (See the IRFD2MAN.TXT file supplied with *IRFD* for details of program operation.)

To start the design process, use the *L* program to generate k and q values for the filter. Run *L*, then select **K** from the menu. Type **12** for the number of poles, then **0.1** for the ripple, in dB. (The program calculates the needed values and stores them in a disk file for the *X* program to use.) Press the **Enter** key until the *L* program exits.

Next, run the *X* program to perform the ladder filter design. Select **K** from the menu to load the k and q values from the disk file. Type **12** for the number of meshes, **8** for the nominal crystal frequency, **0.0155** for the motional inductance in henries, **1** for the overtone, **5** for the parallel capacitance in pF (assumed), and **110** for the crystal Q in thousands. *X* now wants you to enter the k and q values. Since they are on disk, you can just press the **Enter** key repeatedly to load the data generated by the *L* program, until *X* stops asking for the values and instead asks for the bandwidth in hertz. The bandwidth you enter, **2700**, is the bandwidth obtained from the chart in Fig 7, for a 12-pole filter with a desired bandwidth of 2500 Hz. Press **Enter** to get to the source termination resistance prompt. Although the end resistance value given by the *X* program in this step is 206 Ω, an attempt to use the 250 Ω given in Table 1 fails—the actual minimum possible termination is 274 Ω. But the use of that termination value would make for very small (2.2 pF) end coupling capacitors, so the next highest termination value is selected from Table 1. Enter **312**. *X* will next ask for the termination value for the load end of the filter. Just press **Enter**, as 312 is now the default. At this point the values of the coupling capacitors are displayed on the screen. You can print a hard copy by using your computer's print-screen key. The values of all the capacitors are practical and can be easily realized with either a single capacitor or two capacitors in parallel. The values of the coupling capacitors will not be altered during the alignment stage and should be considered final. Pressing **Enter** displays the second set of data vital to the design: the mesh offset frequen-

cies. You should print this screen as well, as this data will be used later in the design procedure. Another **Enter** displays the menu. It's useful at this point to closely examine the coupling capacitor values. If they appear satisfactory, you are done with this stage of the design and can save the designed filter to disk by pressing the **D** key. If you want to change the design, you can alter the termination resistances with the **R** key or change the calculation bandwidth with the **W** key.

Altering the termination resistances affects only the values of the end coupling capacitors; it is easy to vary these values and see the effect, so feel free to experiment. Altering the bandwidth affects all of the coupling capacitors. You shouldn't change the bandwidth by more than about 30 Hz from the initial value since it will invalidate the later stages of the design procedure.

Changing the ripple value is another option, but the design will have to be repeated from scratch since the k and q values have to be changed by the *L* program. Possible values for the filter ripple may be between 0.07 and 0.15 dB.

Be sure to store the final design in a file using the **D** key. For this example, we'll call the file **12POL1**. (The *X* program will automatically add .CIR to the end of the file name.) The stored file can be viewed or edited with a text editor. Make a hard copy of the file for future reference.

We can investigate the response of the filter we've designed using the *GPLA* program. If you have a VGA display, *GPLA* can plot the frequency response of your screen. Run *GPLA* and read in the saved circuit using the **R** key. Once the file has been read in, press the **P** key to select plotting, then press the **H** key to get the filter gain plot. The filter response should be displayed. After viewing the plot, press the **Esc** key to return to the menu. To find the theoretical insertion loss of the filter, we need to adjust the sweep parameters to get a close-in look at the pass-band response. Press **S** to set up the sweep, type **400** for the beginning frequency, **3500** for the end frequency, **30** for the frequency step, **310** for the grid spacing, **10** for the screen bottom, and **1** for the dB/division. Then press **P** followed by **H**. The theoretical insertion loss of the filter is the distance from the top of the plot to the highest point on the response curve, at 1 dB per division. The loss appears to be

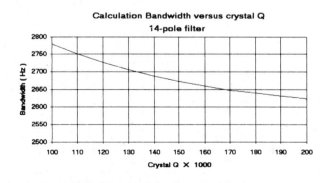

Fig 8—Graph of calculation bandwidth versus crystal Q for a 2500-Hz, 14-pole filter.

slightly over 2 dB. A practical value for the loss may be estimated by adding 0.8 dB to the theoretical loss, for a result of about 3 dB. To exit this screen press **Esc**.

If crystal resonators with frequency offsets equal to the mesh offset frequencies listed by the X program were available, the computer design would be finished at this point. Since that's unlikely, additional steps are required in order to tune the crystals to the required offset frequencies. making the use of crystals with random (but known) offset frequencies possible.

To accomplish this, tuning capacitors are inserted in series with the crystals. These capacitors allow considerable design flexibility and tune every crystal to the same "loop frequency."[1,4] This modification results in the schematic diagram shown in Fig 9.

Our next step is to "build" this new filter circuit for analysis using a utility program and the *IRFD* software. We will do this by creating a modified copy of the 12POL1.CIR circuit file.

Our new circuit file adds series tuning capacitances to the circuit and changes the original crystal offset frequencies calculated by the X program to the actual measured offset frequencies (ΔF) of the crystals we will use in the filter. All of the values we need to deal with are shown in Table 2.

If you investigate the coupling capacitor values and the mesh offset frequencies shown in Table 2 (or on your hard copy from the X program), you'll find that the values are symmetrical around the middle. Although it's not essential, it is helpful to arrange the crystals in pairs in an attempt to preserve the symmetry. Columns A and B in Table 2 help to illustrate the arrangement. The two crystals with the highest positive frequency offset are placed at the edges (X2 and X35). The two crystals with the highest negative offset are placed next (X5 and X32). The remaining crystals are arranged monotonically and symmetrically around the middle.

The *CLFMOD* program (see Listing 1) is a simple utility program written in BASIC by Jon Bloom, KE3Z, of ARRL HQ.[6] It reads the original filter circuit file output by the X program and writes the modified circuit file we will work with (call it 12POL2.CIR). This file adds the tuning capacitors to the original filter circuit, setting the value of each tuning capacitor to 200 pF. It will ask you to enter the measured frequency offsets of the crystals, as shown in column B of Table 2, and it will calculate and display the combined offset shown in column D of Table 2. These values will also be written to the OFFSETS.CLF file. (It's helpful to make a table like Table 2 so you don't get lost.) Note that if you arranged the crystals as recommended, the spread of the offset frequencies in the middle of column D is minimized, which leads to a narrow spread of the eventual tuning capacitor values, as shown in column F. (The coupling capacitor values obtained earlier are presented in column J.)

Now the values of the tuning capacitors should be calculated and entered into the circuit. We will use the

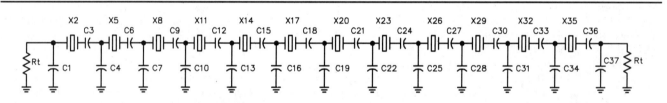

Fig 9—Schematic diagram of the example 12-pole crystal filter.

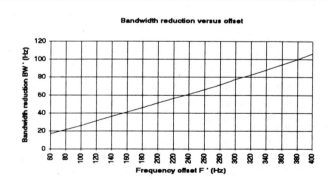

Fig 10—Bandwidth-reduction graph. The needed frequency offset can be obtained once the desired bandwidth reduction is found.

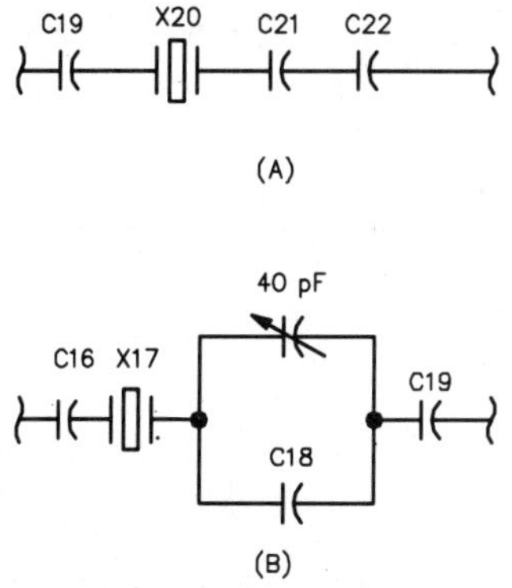

Fig 11—Filter alignment circuits. The resonant frequency of the reference loop is measured using the circuit at A. For the other loops, the required tuning capacitance is found by adjusting the variable capacitor at B to get the same resonant frequency.

MESHTUNE program to find the required tuning capacitor values. Run *MESHTUNE* and press **B** to start a new mesh. Type **8** for the nominal crystal frequency and press **Enter** for the crystal offset frequency. (Do *not* enter an offset frequency!) Type **0.0155** for the motional inductance and **0** for the crystal parallel capacitance. Press **Enter** to get to the interior/exterior prompt, then press **I**. Enter **10000000000** (1 followed by 10 zeroes) for the left-hand coupling capacitor and the same value for the right-hand coupling capacitor. Enter **300** for the initial value for the tuning capacitor. For the target offset frequency, enter the target offset frequency calculated by *CLFMOD* for this mesh (column D of Table 2). The actual mesh offset frequency and the target offset frequency will be displayed. Note whether the mesh is tuned too low or too high. (It's too low in this case.) Press **Enter** to get back to the menu. If the mesh was tuned too low, press the down arrow key to reduce the tuning capacitor; if the mesh is tuned high, press the up arrow key instead. The new tuning capacitor value will be displayed, as will the target and new actual mesh frequencies. Continue pressing the same key until the mesh frequency crosses over the target frequency.

To fine-tune the capacitor value, press the **S** key to set the tuning capacitor step. Enter **0.1** for the step size. Now, using the arrow keys, tune back across the target frequency until it again changes from too high to too low, or vice versa. At the point where

it changes, the displayed tuning capacitor value will be within 0.1 pF of the perfect value—close enough! Enter the final capacitor value into column F of the table.

To obtain the next tuning capacitor value, start over by pressing **B**. Note now that most of the values you entered previously default to the correct numbers, so you can just press **Enter** for those parameters. Remember to enter the correct target offset frequency for the crystal you are tuning. Repeat the tuning process. For some crystals, the required value of tuning capacitance may be quite large. In such cases, you may want to increase the tuning step size using the **S** command. It's easy to watch the actual mesh frequency as you tune and get a feel for whether you need to raise or lower the step size for effective tuning.

The above tuning procedure may seem cumbersome, but once you get the hang of it, things go pretty quickly.

We now need to create the final filter circuit file so we can check its response using *GPLA*. Use a text editor such as DOS *EDIT* or *Windows Notepad* to open the 12POL2.CIR file. Each tuning capacitor entry consists of three lines:

```
cap   <ref>
ser
200
```

where <ref> is the reference designator of the component (e.g., C3). For each tuning capacitor, C3, C6,...C36, change the line reading 200 to the value for that capacitor from column F of Table 2. For C3, the result is:

```
cap   c3
ser
279.8
```

Do not change any of the other lines in the file. When all of the tuning capacitor values have been changed, save the file as 12POL3.CIR.

Next, run *GPLA* and press **R** to read in the 12POL3.CIR file. Then press **S** to set up the sweeps for a beginning frequency of **0**, an end frequency of **4000** a frequency step of **40**, a frequency grid spacing of **200**, a screen bottom of **10** and **1** dB per division. Then press **P** followed by **H** to see the filter response curve. Make an estimate of the insertion loss in the middle of the pass-band. Press **Esc** to return to the menu.

Determine the −3 dB points by changing the sweep settings to make the bottom of the screen 3 dB below the insertion loss. The insertion loss in this example is about 2.3 dB, so set the bottom to 2.3 + 3 = 5.3. When you redisplay the gain plot, the −3 dB level will be at the bottom of the screen, and a rough estimate of the bandwidth can be done by determining the two points at which the filter response curve meets the bottom of the chart. A more accurate estimate can be performed by modifying the sweep such that the gain curve originates at the beginning of the sweep interval and finishes at the end of the sweep interval. This sweep modification may require several tries to get it just right. In this example, you should end up with a sweep range of about 520 to 3225. The −3-dB bandwidth can be easily calcu-

Table 2—Design Parameters for the Example 12-Pole Filter

A	B	C	D	E	F	G	H	I	J
Crystal #	Crystal offset (Hz)	Mesh offset (Hz)	Combined offset (Hz)	C#	Tuning capacitor (pF)	New offset (Hz)	New tuning capacitor (pF)	C#	Coupling capacitor (pF)
2	+17	381.99	364.99	3	279.8	534.99	190.9	1	23.84
5	- 67	0	67.0	6	1524	237	431.0	4	77.20
8	- 60	320.66	380.66	9	268.3	550.66	185.5	7	103.26
11	- 55	383.96	438.96	12	232.7	608.96	167.7	10	109.54
14	- 15	405.96	420.96	15	242.6	590.96	172.8	13	111.79
17	- 4	413.86	417.86	18	244.4	587.86	173.7	16	112.70
20	0	413.86	413.86	21	246.8	583.86	174.9	19	112.95
23	- 9	405.96	414.96	24	246.1	584.96	174.6	22	112.70
26	- 34	383.96	417.96	27	244.4	587.96	173.7	25	111.79
29	- 55	320.66	375.66	30	271.9	545.66	187.2	28	109.54
32	- 61	0	61.0	33	1674	231	442.1	31	103.26
35	+26	381.99	355.99	36	286.9	525.99	194.2	34	77.20
								37	23.84

lated: $BW_3 = 3225 - 520 = 2705$ Hz.

This bandwidth is too high for the final design, but that was done intentionally. The final step in the computer design involves adding an additional frequency offset to reduce the bandwidth to a predetermined value. The purpose of this procedure is twofold: first, it reduces the value of the tuning capacitors, making it more practical to use two parallel capacitors; second, it further narrows the range of capacitor values (see column H of Table 2), possibly minimizing the number of required capacitor values.

The target bandwidth for the computer design is 6.5% higher than the desired bandwidth: $BW_t = 1.065 \times BW_d = 1.065 \times 2500 = 2662$ Hz.

The bandwidth reduction: $BW' = BW_3 - BW_t = 2705 - 2662 = 43$ Hz. The additional frequency offset required to accomplish this bandwidth reduction can be obtained from Fig 10. From the chart, a 43-Hz reduction requires an additional frequency offset, $F' = 170$ Hz. Offset F' is added to the value of the combined offset in column D of Table 2, and the new value is entered in column G. (The *CLFOFS* program, included with the *CLFMOD* program, can be used to perform these calculations.) By using the *MESHTUNE* program and the tuning procedure described earlier new values for the tuning capacitors are obtained and entered in column H of Table 2. File 12POL3.CIR should be modified one more time to include the updated capacitor values and saved as 12POL4.CIR.

Finally, the filter bandwidth should be checked again. If the −3 dB bandwidth (BW_3) is within 15 Hz of the target bandwidth ($BW_t = 2662$ Hz), the computer design is completed. Other-wise modify the value of offset F' using the chart in Fig 10 as a guideline and calculate new tuning capacitor values to obtain the required target bandwidth.

Construction and Alignment

The construction method described in this section is an alternative to a printed-circuit board. The filter components are mounted on a piece of Vector board (Vector part no. 8007). The crystals, matching transformers and the attenuator are mounted on the copper side, which is used as a ground plane. All ground connections are made directly to the ground plane. The capacitors and the intersection shields are mounted on the pad side of the board. The interface with other stages is done through BNC connectors which can be soldered directly to the board, or via coaxial cables which can be soldered to Vector pins (Vector part no. T44). Photo 1 shows the filter assembly.

The construction involves several steps. In the first step, only the crystals are mounted on the board. The crystals identified previously should be arranged on the board in the sequence determined in column A of Table 2. The separation between the leads of adjacent crystals is 0.2". The leads should be soldered to the pads while making sure that the crystals are mounted firmly against the ground plane. I do not recommend you ground each crystal case via a wire ground strap; the risk of altering the crystal parameters during soldering is too great to take. The crystal leads should be clipped to ⅛ inch. It is helpful at this point to label the crystals on the pad side of the board for easy identification.

The second step is the formation of the coupling capacitances (see column J of Table 2). These are formed by paralleling capacitors, taking into account the approximately 3 pF of stray capacitance present:

C1, C37: 10 pF + 10 pF (+ 3.84 pF of stray capacitance)
C4, C34: 47 pF + 27 pF (+ 3.20 pF of stray capacitance)
C7, C31: 100 pF (+ 3.26 pF of stray capacitance)
C10, C28: 68 pF + 39 pF (+ 2.54 pF of stray capacitance)
C13, C25: 82 pF + 27 pF (+ 2.79 pF of stray capacitance)
C16, C22: 100 pF + 10 pF (+ 2.70 pF of stray capacitance)
C19: 100 pF + 10 pF (+ 2.85 pF of stray capacitance)

The selection process is greatly facilitated if the capacitors are picked from a 5% or 10% stock using a capacitance meter with at least 0.1-pF resolution. The parallel combinations of the selected capacitors should be formed by soldering them together and trimming the leads to ³⁄₁₆ inch. The capacitors should then be tagged with their component number for easy identification.

To complete the design, the final values of the tuning capacitors must be determined. The values calculated in column H of Table 2 are preliminary but indicative of the capacitance range required for tuning. The tuning procedure is based on the fact, from filter theory, that each loop in the ladder filter should be resonant at the same frequency.[1,4] In other words, each crystal-and-tuning-capacitor combination, when put in series with the coupling capacitors on each side of it, should resonate at the same loop frequency.

Photo 1

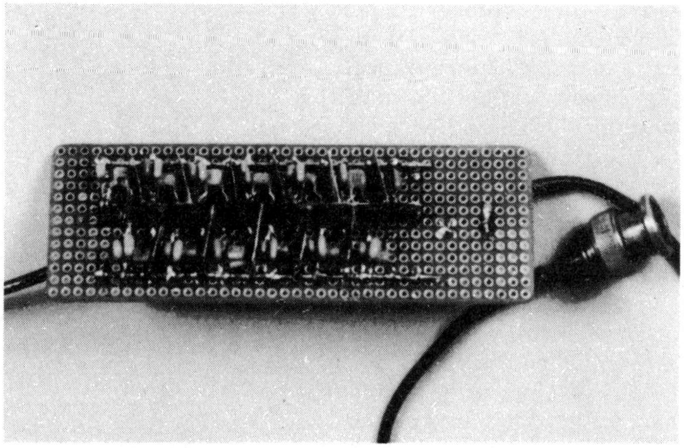

Photo 2

To find a starting point, refer to column H of Table 2. A convenient value from the middle of the column is selected: C21 = 174.93 pF = 150 pF + 22 pF (+ 2.93 pF of stray capacitance). Connect this parallel combination of two capacitors in series with crystal X20 (see Fig 9) and the two coupling capacitors on either side of the crystal, C19 and C22, as shown in Fig 11A. The series-resonant frequency of this circuit can be found with the aid of a crystal tester. This becomes the loop frequency, and all remaining loops have to be tuned to this frequency. Note that the predicted values of the tuning capacitors in the center section of the filter vary within a narrow range.

To determine the value of the next tuning capacitor, connect a parallel combination of a 150-pF capacitor and a 40-pF variable capacitor in series with crystal X17 (see Fig 10) and the two coupling capacitors on either side of the crystal, C16 and C19 (see Fig 11B). Use the crystal tester to measure the resonant frequency of this series combination, tuning the variable capacitor until the circuit is resonant at the loop frequency. The proper value for C18 is then found by measuring the value of the parallel combination of the 150-pF capacitor and the variable capacitor. Form this capacitance using paralleled fixed-value capacitors and tag it as C18. This procedure is repeated for all of the tuning capacitors except those at either end of the filter. During this procedure, each coupling capacitor is used twice: once while selecting a tuning capacitor on its left and again while selecting a tuning capacitor on its right.

The procedure for determining the values of the tuning capacitors at the ends of the filter differs only slightly: A 316-Ω resistor (the termination resistance) is placed across the end coupling capacitor, C1, when determining the value of C3 and across capacitor C37 when determining the value of C36. The terminating resistors lower the Q of the circuit, so the tuning of C3 and C36 is not very critical. Remember that when you perform filter measurements the scope probe capacitance (approximately 10 pF) and the generator output capacitance (approximately 5 pF) will be added to the respective terminals. Therefore, after the tuning process has been accomplished the values of capacitors C1 and C37 have to be modified to compensate for the source and load capacitances.

Once the values of all of the tuning capacitors have been determined, filter construction can continue. Construct the ground bars and mount them on the pad side of the board before installing the capacitors. Each ground bar is made from #16 copper wire (stripped of insulation), cut to a length of $[(0.2 \times N) + 0.5]$ inches, where N is the number of crystals. Place each ground bar symmetrically, 0.35-inch away from the pins of the crystals (see Fig 12) and solder it to the ground plane every 0.2 inch (every other hole) using jumpers made out of small-diameter hook-up wire. Next, solder the tuning capacitors in place following the placement diagram shown in Fig 12. Take care not to overheat the crystals during soldering. The load coupling capacitor, C37, and tuning capacitor, C36, are soldered to a Vector pin.

Install the coupling capacitors following the diagram of Fig 12. While the tuning capacitors are mounted horizontally, the coupling capacitors are placed vertically to conserve space. Make the capacitor leads as short as practical, keeping in mind that longer leads can cause excessive crosstalk between sections, and very short leads can lead to capacitor cracking during the soldering process. Provide sufficient clearance between adjacent sections to accommodate the shield ribs. These are made from ⅜-inch-wide strips of metal. Brass, copper or tinned 0.02-inch steel will do, providing it can be easily soldered to the ground plane. The shield is arranged in a "fish-bone" fashion. The center section is cut to a length of $[(0.2 \times N) + {}^3\!/_{16}]$ inches and is

placed vertically exactly in the middle between the pins of the crystals (see Photo 2). Keep it in place by soldering it to ⌐ shaped posts. These are made from #18 copper wire (stripped of insulation), with the short end soldered to the ground plane. Insert the intersection ribs between adjacent sections of the filter and solder them to the center rib on one side (at the top only) and to the ground bars on the other side. More comprehensive shielding can be accomplished by fully encapsulating the filter components in a metal enclosure, but I've obtained adequate performance without this precaution.

Matching transformers are used to present a 50-Ω input and output impedance to the outside world. The winding information is taken from Table 1. The transformers are wound with #32 enameled wire on two-hole ferrite balun cores (see Fig 13). In Table 1, "primary turns" refers to the number of turns from the tap to ground, and "secondary turns" refers to the number of turns of the entire winding. Mount both transformers on the ground-plane side of the board in close proximity to the crystals. Solder the tap leads to Vector pins on the ground-plane side of the board. The Vector pin on the input side is also connected to the output of a 3-dB attenuator (see Fig 14). Place the attenuator components on the ground-plane side of the board as well, making the connections on the pad side. Then con-

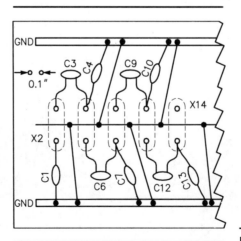

Fig 12—Layout diagram of the crystal filter.

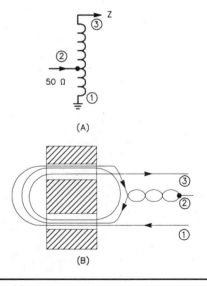

Fig 13—The matching transformers are tapped autotransformers (A), wound as shown at B.

nect the attenuator input to another Vector pin, which serves as the filter input terminal. The board area taken by the entire 12-pole filter circuit is 3¾ × 1⅛ inches.

Measurements

Now that the filter is finished, we need to measure its response, which should match the design objectives: shape of the response, −3 dB points, bandwidth, amount of ripple, insertion loss and the symmetry of the response. Making the measurements is a trivial task when a spectrum analyzer is at hand, or at least a good synthesized generator and a scope. Since few amateurs have the luxury of using lab-quality equipment, I suggest a simple method that should be within reach of the average experimenter. It requires the construction of a variable-frequency crystal oscillator (VXO). The VXO should tune from 8.000 MHz to at least 8.005 MHz. (One of the rejected filter crystals can be used in the VXO—use the one with the most negative offset.) The VXO should have a level adjustment control and adequate buffering at the output to prevent frequency pulling when being loaded by

the crystal filter. Many variations of VXO design have been covered in the amateur literature.[4,7,8,9,10] A frequency counter with 1-Hz resolution and an oscilloscope are also needed to perform the measurement.

The block diagram of the measurement setup is presented in Fig 15. The measurement procedure is to vary the frequency of the VXO in small increments (20 to 80 Hz) while monitoring and recording the signal level at the output of the filter at each frequency. Hold the VXO output level constant at every measurement point.

I used lab-quality test equipment (a Hewlett-Packard HP3585A spectrum analyzer) to measure three ladder filters—10-pole, 12-pole and 14-pole—designed and constructed using the procedures outlined in this article. The measured response curves of these filters are shown in Fig 17, with the ripple level for the 14-pole filter shown in Fig 18. The measured bandwidth of all three filters is within 2% of the desired bandwidth, and the shape factor is within 3% of the calculated value. The ripple level is slightly higher than the projected value but significantly better than several commercial units I tested.

To compare the performance of my home-built ladder filters to that of commercially available crystal filters, I made a series of measurements using laboratory-grade measurement equipment. The block diagram of the measurement setup is given in Fig 16. The amplifier used in the measurement has an output third-order inter-

cept point (OIP) of +48 dBm and a −1 dB output compression point of +27 dBm. One of my objectives was to study each crystal filter's dynamic range and its effect on the output intercept point of the driving amplifier.

Four crystal filters have been evaluated: a 2.2-kHz, 8-pole SSB filter from Fox-Tango Corp (part no. 2309) and the three home-built ladder filters mentioned previously. The Fox-Tango filter requires a 500-Ω impedance termination, so it was coupled to the amplifier via a 1:9 transformer. The test results were very similar for all three ladder filters, so they will be referred to collectively as the "ladder crystal filter."

The input impedance of the filters was examined using an HP impedance analyzer and re-examined after inserting an attenuator between the amplifier and the crystal filter. For the ladder filter, a 3-dB attenuator was used; a 6-dB attenuator was used with the Fox-Tango filter. Figs 19 through 22 show the results of these measurements.

To measure the IMD of the filters, I used two equal-level tones placed outside of the filter pass-band. The tone spacing was varied between 2 and 20 kHz without an appreciable effect on the third-order products measured at the output of the amplifier. These measurements were made at two different signal levels (+15 dBm and +10 dBm) in order to gauge the linearity of the system. The measurements were made while driving the filter directly by the amplifier and again

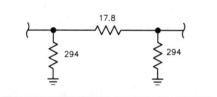

Fig 14—Schematic diagram of the 3-dB input attenuator used with the ladder filter.

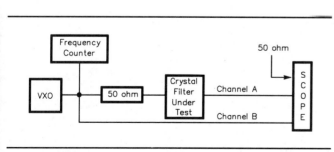

Fig 15—Block diagram of the filter evaluation test set-up.

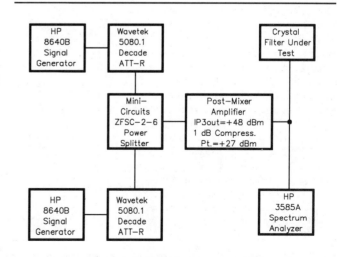

Fig 16—Block diagram of the filter IMD measurement test set-up.

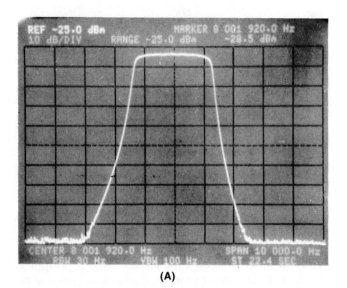

(A)

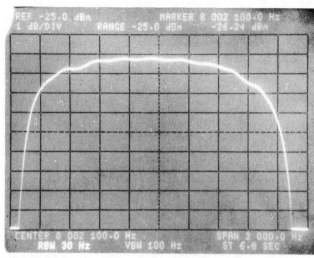

Fig 18—A close-in look at the response of the 14-pole ladder filter shows the pass-band ripple. Vertical divisions are 1 dB; horizontal divisions are 300 Hz.

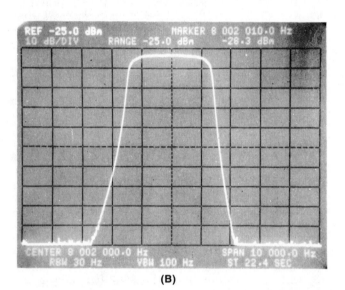

(B)

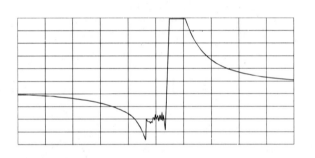

Fig 19—The measured impedance of a 14-pole crystal ladder filter. The vertical divisions are 20 Ω, with zero at the bottom. The horizontal divisions are 4 kHz each.

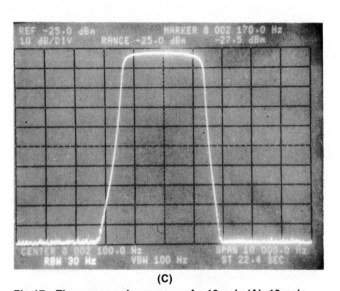

(C)

Fig 17—The measured response of a 10-pole (A), 12-pole (B) and 14-pole (C) ladder filter built using the techniques described by the author. Vertical divisions are 10 dB; horizontal divisions are 1 kHz.

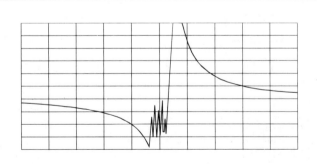

Fig 20—The measured impedance of a Fox-Tango crystal lattice filter. The vertical divisions are 20 Ω, with zero at the bottom. The horizontal divisions are 4 kHz each.

while driving the filter through a resistive pad. The measurement results are given in Table 3. The output intercept point of the amplifier was degraded by 5 dB by the ladder filter and by 12 dB by the Fox-Tango filter. I tried using resistive pads with different attenuation values in an attempt to "smooth out" the impedance presented to the amplifier. A 6-dB pad is required in the case of the Fox-Tango filter to improve the OIP by 5 to 6 dB, and a 3-dB pad is sufficient in the case of the ladder filter to improve the OIP by 3 to 5 dB.

In the next experiment, one of the tones was placed in the center of the pass-band and the second tone was –20 kHz away. In this measurement, the OIP of the amplifier was degraded by 4 dB in the case of the ladder filter and by 11 dB in the case of the Fox-Tango filter. A 3-dB resistive pad in front of the ladder filter reduced the degradation by 1 to 3 dB, and a 6-dB pad in front of the Fox-Tango filter reduced the degradation by 6 to 7 dB.

Finally, one of the tones was placed at the leading edge of the filter passband (notice the impedance dips in Figs 19 and 20). Due to the severe impedance mismatch presented to the two tones at both frequencies the OIP of the amplifier is degraded by 11 dB in the case of the ladder filter and by 22 dB in the case of the Fox-Tango filter. Resistive pads have a profound effect on the performance in this case: a 3-dB pad in front of the ladder filter reduces the degradation by 5 to 6 dB, and a 6-dB pad in front of the Fox-Tango filter reduces the degradation by up to 17 dB!

The following conclusions can be drawn from these measurement results:

- Because of the highly reactive nature of its input impedance, a crystal filter has a significant loading effect on the preceding stage. This may become the limiting factor when calculating the overall dynamic range of a receiver.
- The experiments suggest that it is more meaningful to evaluate the effect of the filter on the preceding stage than to attempt to measure the OIP of the crystal filter itself.
- Some non-linear behavior was observed (the degradation of the OIP of the preceding stage depends on the signal level). The filter behavior is more predict-

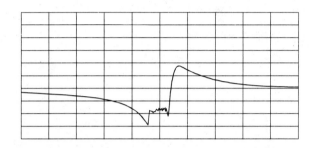

Fig 21—The measured impedance of a 14-pole crystal ladder filter with a 3-dB attenuator at the input. The vertical divisions are 20 Ω, with zero at the bottom. The horizontal divisions are 4 kHz each.

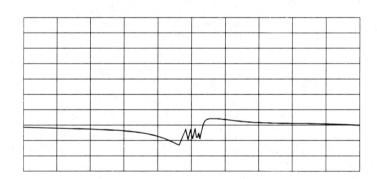

Fig 22—The measured impedance of a Fox-Tango crystal lattice filter with a 6-dB attenuator at the input. The vertical divisions are 20 Ω, with zero at the bottom. The horizontal divisions are 4 kHz each.

Table 3—Measurement results
Third-order output intercept point of the amplifier (+dBm)

Tone location relative to the passband	Ladder filter		Fox-Tango filter		Tone level (+dBm)
	No pad	3-dB pad	No pad	6-dB pad	
Both tones outside	45	47	38	43	15
of passband	43	45	36	42	10
One tone inside	44	46	37	44	15
of passband	45	46	37	43	10
One tone at the	38	42	30	43	15
edge of passband	37	42	26	43	10

Listing 1

Page 1: BASIC

```
' Modify IRFD circuit files contining crystal-ladder filters
' to add tuning capacitors for offset crystal frequencies.
'
' From "Designing and Building High-Performance Crystal Ladder
' Filters," QEX, January, 1995
'
' J. Bloom, KE3Z
' 12/08/94
'
' Note: Little checking of the input file is performed. Only files
' written by the IRFD program "X" should be used as input files.

CLS
PRINT "CLFMOD -- Modifies IRFD ladder crystal filter circuit files for tuning"
PRINT
INPUT "Enter name of original circuit file: ", f1$
OPEN f1$ FOR INPUT AS #1
INPUT "Enter name of output circuit file: ", f2$
OPEN f2$ FOR OUTPUT AS #2
OPEN "OFFSETS.CLF" FOR OUTPUT AS #3
' Get the number of circuit elements
INPUT #1, x
N = (x - 2) / 2        ' Number of poles
' Write the new number of circuit elements, including tuning caps
PRINT #2, N * 3 + 2
' Copy the unchanging parameters
FOR i = 1 TO 14
    INPUT #1, x
    PRINT #2, x
NEXT i
' Loop through each of the meshes, annotating the elements with
' component designators as in Fig 9, adding the tuning capacitors,
' and replacing the crystal offset frequencies with those of the
' real crystals.
FOR i = 0 TO N - 1
    ' Coupling capacitor
    INPUT #1, x$
    PRINT #2, x$, LEFT$(x$, 1) + MID$(STR$(i * 3 + 1), 2)
    INPUT #1, x$
    PRINT #2, x$
    INPUT #1, x
    PRINT #2, x
    ' Crystal
    INPUT #1, x$
    y$ = LEFT$(x$, 1) + MID$(STR$(i * 3 + 2), 2)
    PRINT #2, x$, y$
    INPUT #1, x$
    PRINT #2, x$
    INPUT #1, x
    PRINT "Crystal"; i + 1; "("; y$;
    INPUT ") delta F: ", y
    PRINT #2, y
    PRINT "Target offset frequency for mesh"; i + 1; "= "; x - y
    PRINT #3, x - y
```

Listing 1 (continued)

Page 2: BASIC

```
    ' Tuning capacitor
    PRINT #2, "cap", "c" + MID$(STR$(i * 3 + 3), 2)
    PRINT #2, "ser"
    PRINT #2, 200
NEXT i
' Load end coupling capacitor
INPUT #1, x$
PRINT #2, x$, LEFT$(x$, 1) + MID$(STR$(N * 3 + 1), 2)
INPUT #1, x$
PRINT #2, x$
INPUT #1, x
PRINT #2, x
' Should only be one line left, but "just in case," copy to
' end of file
WHILE NOT EOF(1)
    LINE INPUT #1, x$
    PRINT #2, x$
WEND
' Clean up and exit
CLOSE
SYSTEM


' CLFOFS -- Generates final offsets for ladder crystal filter design
'
' From "Designing and Building High-Performance Crystal Ladder
' Filters," QEX, January, 1995
'
' J. Bloom, KE3Z
' 12/08/94

CLS
PRINT "CLFOFS -- Calculates final design offsets for ladder crystal filters"
PRINT
INPUT "Frequency offset for bandwidth reduction: ", f
OPEN "OFFSETS.CLF" FOR INPUT AS #1
WHILE NOT EOF(1)
    INPUT #1, x
    PRINT x + f
WEND
CLOSE
SYSTEM
```

able at the flat portions of the frequency response and less predictable when extreme impedance changes are encountered. Resistive pads tend to improve the linearity.
- If no resistive pad is used, the degradation of the amplifier's OIP is reduced by at least 7 dB if the Fox-Tango filter is replaced by a ladder filter.
- A 6-dB resistive pad is required to significantly reduce the degradation of the amplifier's OIP in the case of the Fox-Tango filter. A 3-dB pad is sufficient to produce the same effect in the case of the ladder filter.
- The level of the third-order products at the output of the Fox-Tango filter deviates from the calculated value by more than 6 dB, even with a 6-dB resistive pad. In the case of the ladder filter, this deviation is reduced to a value under 1 dB if a 3-dB resistive pad is employed.

- Examination of the plot of input impedance of the two types of filters (Figs 19 and 20) reveals that the ladder filter has a much smoother response in the passband. This must be one of the reasons for the ladder filter's superior performance.

Summary

I've shown that home construction of high-performance crystal filters is quite practical, and that laboratory-grade equipment, although helpful, is not required. Home-built ladder filters can exhibit performance superior to that of commercially available filters at reasonable cost. The design and construction procedure outlined above enables the amateur to tailor the frequency response of the filter to fit the needs of the project.

Acknowledgments

I wish to express my appreciation to Wes Hayward, W7ZOI, Bill Carver, K6OLG/7, Colin Horrabin, G3SBI and Peter Chadwick, G3RZP for the helpful discussions that enabled me to better understand this subject and the encouragement to pursue this project.

Finding Parts

Crystals: The most consistent results were obtained using crystals from Fox Electronics (Tel: 813-693-0099), part number: FOX080. These are series-resonance microprocessor crystals in an HC49/U case. Ask for a list of distributors in your area.

Capacitors: Use monolithic ceramic capacitors from Panasonic or equivalent quality capacitors. Panasonic capacitors are available from Digi-Key Corporation (Tel: 800-344-4539), P4800 series. COG ceramic parts are recommended for good temperature stability. Low loss is an important requirement. 5% or 10% tolerance is acceptable.

Transformer cores: Use two-hole balun cores, part number: BN-43-2402 from Amidon Associates (Tel: 310-763-5770).

Board: The project board, with a ground plane on one side, is part number 8007 from Vector (Tel: 800-423-5659; 800-426-4652 inside California). The Vector pins are part number T44. (Digi-Key is one of the nationwide distributors for Vector.)

Notes

[1] Carver, B., K6OLG/7, "High-Performance Crystal Filter Design," *Communications Quarterly*, Winter 1993, pp 11-18.

[2] Hayward, W., W7ZOI, *Introduction to Radio Frequency Design*, ARRL, Newington, Connecticut, 1994, chapters 2 and 3.

[3] Drentea, C., WB3JZO, *Radio Communications Receivers*, Tab Books Inc, Blue Ridge Summit, 1982, pp 69-75.

[4] Hayward, W., W7ZOI, "A Unified Approach to the Design of Crystal Ladder Filters," *QST*, May 1982, pp 21-27.

[5] DeMaw, D., W1FB, "A Tester for Crystal F, Q and R", *QST*, January 1990, p 21.

[6] The source code and executable versions of *CLFMOD* and *CLFOFS* are in the QEXCLF.ZIP file, available for download from the ARRL BBS (203-666-0578) or via the Internet by anonymous FTP to ftp.cs.buffalo.edu, in the /pub/ham-radio directory.

[7] Hayward, W., W7ZOI and DeMaw, D., W1FB, *Solid State Design for the Radio Amateur*, ARRL, Newington, Connecticut, 1977, p 171.

[8] *The ARRL 1986 Handbook*, ARRL, Newington, Connecticut, 1985, p 10-3.

[9] Noble, F., W3MT, "A Variable Frequency Crystal Oscillator," *QST*, March 1981, pp 34-37.

[10] DeMaw, D., W1FB, "Some Practical Aspects of VXO Design", *QST*, May 1972, p 11.

From QST, December 1991, p 29:

The Double-Tuned Circuit: An Experimenter's Tutorial

Although the double-tuned circuit is popular with Amateur Radio experimenters, its response can sometimes be misleading. Here's how to evaluate and adjust double-tuned circuits for maximum performance.

By Wes Hayward, W7ZOI
7700 SW Danielle Ave
Beaverton, OR 97005

The double-tuned circuit, among the most common filters found in radio equipment, consists of two tuned circuits, or resonators, that are coupled together, allowing energy in one to be shared with the other. Designing a double-tuned circuit for use at HF and below is not difficult,[1] yet builders commonly encounter practical difficulties in building and adjusting the double-tuned circuit, especially at VHF and above. The result may be a circuit that does not meet the filtering goal.

Although HF double-tuned circuits differ greatly in physical appearance from those built for microwave frequencies, all double-tuned circuits share many similarities. This tutorial emphasizes their universal properties. In it, I'll examine the double-tuned LC circuit from an experimental viewpoint, emphasizing measurement, evaluation, and adjustment.

Basic Characteristics of the Double-Tuned Circuit

I'll examine the fundamentals of the double-tuned circuit by describing the 40-m filter shown in Figs 1 and 2. Fig 3 graphs an analysis of the circuit. The solid-line plot shows gain versus frequency for a single-tuned circuit filter. The dashed plot shows the performance of a double-tuned circuit filter. Both filters are designed to be doubly

terminated, with 50 Ω at input and output. Both have a 7.1-MHz center frequency and a 200-kHz bandwidth. The response magnitudes are similar for the single- and double-tuned circuits; their differences become significant only at frequencies removed from passband center—in the filter stopband. We use double-tuned-circuit filters in place of single-tuned designs because double-tuned filters provide higher stopband attenuation.

The two tuned circuits shown in Fig 1 use toroidal transformers (T1 and T2) tuned with mica-dielectric compression trimmer capacitors (C1 and C2, **TUNING**). A 2-to-24 pF air-dielectric capacitor (C3, **COUPLING**) couples the resonators. Two-turn links provide input/output coupling to and from 50 Ω. (I originally used three-turn links; I'll describe later why I reduced them by one turn.)

First, I set the **COUPLING** capacitor to maximum and adjusted the two **TUNING** capacitors for maximum response with the signal generator set to 7.1 MHz. Then I tuned the generator from 6 to 8 MHz to examine the filter's overall response. Fig 4 shows the result: an *overcoupled* filter

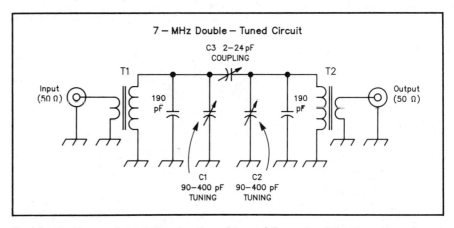

Fig 1—A double-tuned-circuit filter for 40 m. C1 and C2 are mica-dielectric compression trimmers; C3 is an air-dielectric variable. (There is usually no justification for using a variable coupling capacitor in practical double-tuned circuits for frequencies of 30 MHz and lower; instead, use a fixed capacitor of the value required by the filter design. This filter's variable coupling capacitor varies the filter response to illustrate concepts discussed in this article.) The tuned windings of T1 and T2 consist of 17 turns of #22 enameled wire on T-50-6 toroidal, powdered-iron cores; the transformers' untuned links at first consisted of three turns of insulated wire but were later reduced to two turns. See text and Fig 2.

Fig 2—An HF (7.1-MHz) double-tuned-circuit filter constructed for lab analysis.

tuned circuit's second peak if you merely adjust its resonators for maximum response at a single frequency!

Fig 6 shows the other extreme, the *under-coupled* double-tuned circuit. I obtained this single, sharp peak by adjusting C3, **COUPLING**, to its minimum value (2 pF). This filter is too narrow; its insertion loss is excessive.

The desired double-tuned-circuit-filter response is usually *critical* coupling, shown by the reference plot in Figs 3 through 6. A critically coupled filter has only one peak, without excessive insertion loss. (I'll discuss the difference between excessive and proper insertion loss shortly.)

You can experimentally achieve critical coupling as follows: Set up the circuit for undercoupling and align the filter in this condition. Loss will be large. Increase coupling in small steps, readjusting the filter tuning capacitors and sweeping the filter response after each coupling increase. Continue this procedure until you observe

response in which two peaks bound a region of increased attenuation.

This "double-humped" response is not the result of stagger tuning—that is, it's not caused by tuning the resonators to slightly different frequencies. Rather, both resonators are tuned to the same frequency. The peak amplitude of the double-humped response of Fig 4 is about the same as that of the desired filter, labeled **REFERENCE**.

Fig 5 is a more extreme example of over-coupling: I added capacitance across C3 to

bring the coupling capacitance up to 65 pF. This moves the peaks even farther apart and increases the depth of the valley between them. This situation can be especially perplexing to the home experimenter because either peak may appear to be the single peak expected of the filter. This illustrates the importance of swept-frequency instrumentation in evaluating double-tuned circuits—checking the filter response through a *range* of frequencies. You'll never notice an overcoupled double-

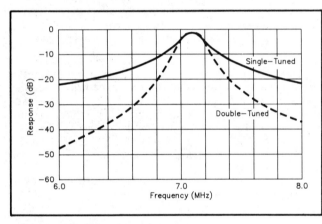

Fig 3—Analysis of the filter shown in Figs 1 and 2. The solid curve shows the response of a single-tuned circuit; the dashed curve, a double-tuned circuit. Both filters are adjusted for maximum response at 7.1 MHz. The gap between the filter-response maxima and the 0-dB line represents the filters' *insertion loss*. (A computer generated the data for this and the other graphs in this article; experiment confirmed the data.)

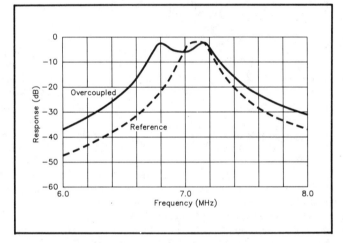

Fig 4—Too much resonator coupling (in this example, too much capacitance at C3) *overcouples* the filter resonators and produces a two-peaked response. This is *not* caused by tuning the resonators to different frequencies. The reference plot shows the desired single-peak response.

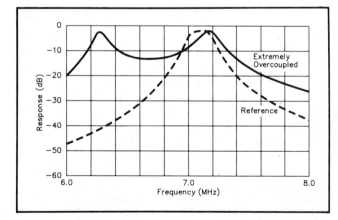

Fig 5—Extreme overcoupling can produce two widely separated peaks, either of which can appear to an experimenter operating with limited test equipment to be the single sharp response of a properly adjusted filter. The reference plot shows the desired single-peak response.

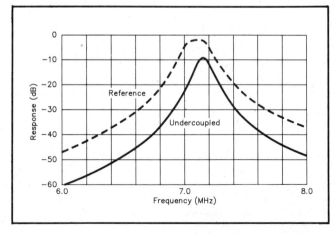

Fig 6—Insufficient resonator coupling produces a too-sharp peak and abnormally high insertion loss. As in Figs 4 and 5 (and the **Double-Tuned** plot in Fig 3), the reference plot shows the desired filter response—the response obtained by *critical* coupling.

Measuring Double-Tuned Circuit Performance

Simple, home-built instrumentation usually suffices for double-tuned-circuit adjustment at HF and VHF. The main parameter of interest is filter gain versus frequency; this can be measured with the test setup of Fig A.

The first element is a signal source. I usually use home-brew generators at HF and VHF, each with an available output of about 10 mW.*,+ Fixed attenuators in line with the input and output of the filter under test provide the filter with "clean" 50-Ω source and load terminations.

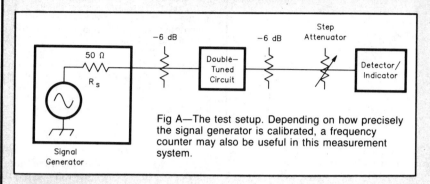

Fig A—The test setup. Depending on how precisely the signal generator is calibrated, a frequency counter may also be useful in this measurement system.

double peaking. Slightly decrease the coupling from the double-peak value and measure the filter bandwidth.

This procedure produced a smooth, single, almost flat response in the experimental 40-m filter. Initially, however, the bandwidth was too wide (324 kHz), with an insertion loss of 1.2 dB. I reduced the transformers' three-turn links to two turns and repeated the process. The result: a critically coupled filter that's 178 kHz wide, with just over 2 dB of insertion loss.

A VHF Double-Tuned Circuit

The double-tuned circuit and the adjustment methods just described can easily be applied at higher frequencies. I needed a filter for a 2-m SSB transceiver's receive and transmit signal paths—a filter no wider

The next element is a step attenuator. This block is very fundamental; it becomes the cornerstone for a system for home RF measurements. I use surplus and home-brew attenuators.††

The final element is a sensitive detector. This can be a 50-Ω-terminated oscilloscope, a spectrum analyzer or even a simple power meter. I made all measurements reported in this article with the circuit shown in Fig B—a "microwatt meter" consisting of a biased diode detector followed by an operational-amplifier meter driver. The detector is preceded by a two-stage amplifier using MMICs. The detector should be capable of responding to signals 30 to 60 dB weaker than the signal-generator output.

Begin your measurements with a calibration. Tune the generator to the frequency of interest and replace the filter with a direct coaxial connection between the fixed attenuators. Note the attenuator setting for a full-scale meter reading and record this in your notebook. Compare this figure with the peak-filter-response readings to determine insertion loss. Check the system's calibration often, for levels often drift with time.

This test setup can also measure filter bandwidth. Align the filter and adjust the generator frequency for maximum response. Set the attenuator to provide a full-scale meter reading. Increase attenuation by 3 dB. Carefully note the new, lower meter reading. Reset the attenuation to the previous level, bringing the meter back to full scale. Then tune the signal generator, first to one side of the filter peak and then to the other, stopping in each case when the response equals "the new, lower meter reading" just described. The frequency difference between these points is the filter's −3-dB bandwidth.—*W7ZOI*

Solid-State Design for the Radio Amateur, p 170. See main-text note 1.
†W. Hayward, "Beyond the Dipper," *QST*, May 1986, pp 14-20; Feedback, *QST*, Aug 1986, p 40.
††R. Shriner and P. Pagel, "A Step Attenuator You Can Build," *QST*, Sep 1982, pp 11-13.

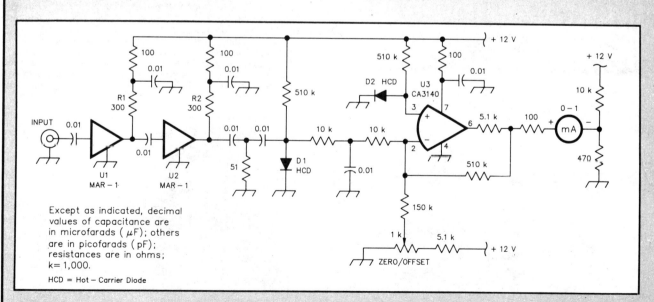

Except as indicated, decimal values of capacitance are in microfarads (μF); others are in picofarads (pF); resistances are in ohms; k = 1,000.

HCD = Hot — Carrier Diode

Fig B—A detector/indicator suitable for filter evaluation and alignment. All capacitors are disc-ceramic; all resistors are ¼-W, carbon-film. D1 and D2 are hot-carrier diodes (HP 5082-2672, 1N5711 or equivalent). U1 and U2, shown as Mini Circuits MAR-1 MMICs, can be directly replaced with Avantek MSA-0185 MMICs, or, if you use 270-Ω resistors at R1 and R2 instead of the 300-Ω resistors shown, with Motorola MWA-120 MMICs. Adjust the **ZERO/OFFSET** control for a meter indication of 0 with no RF present.

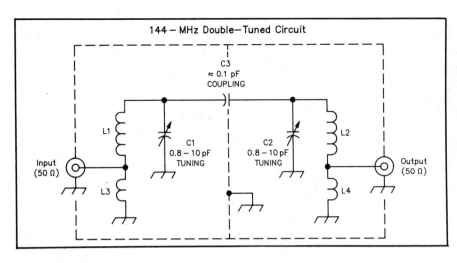

144 – MHz Double–Tuned Circuit

Fig 7—This VHF double-tuned circuit differs electrically from its HF relative (Fig 1) only in the means used to couple the filter ports to 50 Ω. The HF filter used small inductive links; this filter uses the autotransformer action of L1-L3 and L2-L4—in effect, tapped coils. C1 and C2 are 0.8- to 10-pF air-dielectric piston trimmers (Johanson); standard air-dielectric variables are also suitable. C3 is a wire probe, soldered at only one end (the C1-L1 junction in this case; it doesn't matter which) that passes through a hole in the filter shield partition for electrostatic coupling to the C2-L2 junction. L1 and L2 each consist of 7 turns of #14 tinned copper wire, ¼-inch inner diameter. L3 and L4 each consist of approximately 0.6 inch of #18 tinned copper wire. Fig 8 shows three filters constructed in this way.

than about 2 MHz to attenuate the image frequency (124 MHz in my application) by 50 dB. The filter I constructed becomes our second example.

Fig 7 shows the VHF-filter topology I used. Each resonator consists of two inductors. L1 and L2 contribute most of the resonator inductance; L3 and L4 are end-loading elements consisting of small lengths of #18 wire connected to circuit common. Coaxial connectors attach to the L1-L3 and

L2-L4 junctions. I find this topology easier to adjust than taps on a coil.

The filter is built on a scrap of circuit-board material. Vertical walls serve as shield sections for each resonator and provide for component mounting. You may not need to add a lid if the walls extend well above the board (perhaps 1.5 inches or more) and if you mount the components close to the board. A lid is mandatory, even during adjustment, if the walls are short.

A very low-value adjustable capacitor (C3 in Fig 7, illustrated by the three examples in Fig 8), couples the filter sections. C3 consists of a piece of plastic-insulated wire that's soldered to one of the tuning capacitors, routed through a hole in the shield partition and placed in proximity to the other tuning capacitor.

The partition is *necessary*; it eliminates stray coupling between filter elements—a fact confirmable through measurement.

(A)

Fig 8—Two VHF (A and B, for 2 m) and one UHF (C) double-tuned-circuit filters. The filter at A uses piston air-dielectric trimmers (Johanson); at B, standard air-dielectric trimmers (in this case, split-stator "butterfly" units with stators paralleled). Piston trimmers afford more precise adjustment and higher Q. C details one section of a 70-cm filter in which each resonator inductor (L1-L3 and L2-L4 in Fig 7) consists entirely of an L-shaped length of #14 tinned wire, the end-loading inductor (L2 or L4 in Fig 7) being the short section between the elbow and ground. In each filter, the coupling capacitor (C3 in Fig 7) consists of a wire probe that passes through the shield partition. Adjusting the wire's length (and the proximity of its unconnected end to the tuned circuit it probes) varies filter coupling.

Filter shielding, including an inter-resonator partition, is essential at VHF/UHF because even stray capacitance can overcouple a filter. Solenoidal resonators must be shielded for an additional reason: Unlike toroidal coils, they can couple to each other and associated circuitry via their external magnetic fields.

(B)

(C)

Double-Tuned Circuits: Not Necessarily "Top-Coupled"

Radio technologists sometimes characterize the Fig 1 and Fig 7 circuits as *top-coupled* because capacitance between the "tops" (ungrounded ends) of their resonators couples the filter sections. Top-coupled double-tuned circuits are common; one popular *QST* project* uses them in its RF-amplifier circuitry, for instance. The relative commonness of this special case of the double-tuned-circuit leads some experimenters to conclude that *double-tuned circuit* necessarily implies two top-coupled circuits. But this is not so.

Coupling two circuits together merely means that energy from one circuit somehow gets into the other; such coupling can be inductive, capacitive or both; top, bottom or both (Fig A). What matters more is that whatever coupling exists allows you to achieve the filter response you seek, and that whatever unwanted or stray coupling exists doesn't compromise that response—in the filter's passband *and* stopband—over the frequency range of interest. Predictable, repeatable filters minimize "coupling somehow" through builder and designer *know*-how.—*David Newkirk, WJ1Z*

*W. Hayward and J. Lawson, "A Progressive Communications Receiver," QST, Nov 1981, pp 11-21; Feedback, 1982 QST: p 47, Jan; p 54, April, p 41, Oct; also in the ARRL Handbook (1982 through present editions).

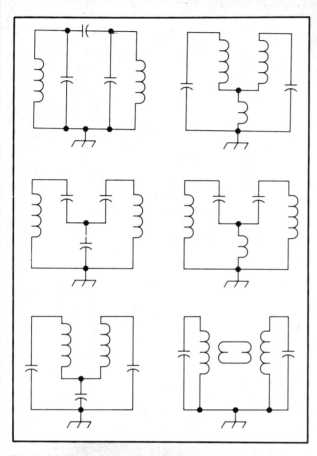

Fig A—Double-tuned circuits can be coupled inductively, capacitively or both; top, bottom or both. These examples show only a few of the possible combinations. Sometimes the mere proximity of circuit components suffices; see Fig B.

Fig B—ARRL Lab Engineer Zack Lau, KH6CP, who lives 1 mile from W1AW, originally built this undercoupled double-tuned filter to knock down W1AW at 3581.5 kHz during QRP contests centering at 3560 kHz. Now reconfigured for 75-m SSB, the filter specs out like this: −3-dB bandwidth, 8 kHz; −60-dB bandwidth, 310 kHz; insertion loss, 21 dB. Each coil consists of 17 turns of #16 wire on a T-200-6 toroidal, powdered-iron core (Q_u = 482 at 3.8 MHz). The tuning capacitor in each section consists of paralleled 56-pF silver-mica, 240-pF chip and 2- to 19.3-pF air-dielectric capacitors. Silver-mica end-loading capacitors (10 pF, between each resonator top and the BNC jacks) couple the filter to 50-Ω reality.

The resonators are exactly 1 inch apart, core to core (the spacing is adjustable). Can we *accurately* calculate the tiny capacitance between them? Should we characterize this filter as capacitively top-coupled? Maybe what matters more is that using this filter on a band where you usually kick in a 20-dB attenuator anyway also makes your receiver front end *8 kHz wide!*

(Likewise, the outer walls prevent coupling between the filter elements and external circuitry.) In one version of this filter with 0.7-inch-high shield walls, enough stray coupling existed to produce a severely over-coupled response with C3 (the probe wire) absent! The coupling disappeared when I placed a lid over the two compartments. Good lid-to-wall electrical contact is mandatory; I used **C** clamps during alignment. Eventually, I'll solder a lid in place.

VHF/UHF double-tuned circuit adjustment resembles the procedure I described for the 7-MHz example. Install a longer-than-necessary coupling wire and bend it close to the probed resonator's "hot" (ungrounded) end. Tune the filter and sweep its response. You should observe a double-humped response. If you can't find two peaks, increase the coupling until you do. Once you observe overcoupling, decrease coupling by reducing the wire length or changing its position. Then measure the filter's bandwidth and insertion loss. The bandwidth probably won't be right at first; you can set the filter's bandwidth by adjusting the end-loading inductors (L2 and L4) and adjusting the coupling after each loading change.

The 2-m filter performs as expected, exhibiting a bandwidth of about 2 MHz and an insertion loss of 3 dB. (A similar filter I built uses #18 wire instead of #14 wire for the main inductors. Although I can adjust it to obtain a 2-MHz bandwidth, its insertion loss exceeds 6 dB.)

How Narrow is Narrow?

Experiments like these clearly indicate a

relationship between filter selectivity and insertion loss. Loss is also related to the components' unloaded Q (Q_u). The parameter Q_0 (normalized Q) summarizes these dependencies. Q_0 is defined as the ratio Q_u/Q_f, where Q_u is unloaded resonator (inductor) Q and Q_f is the filter Q, which equals filter center frequency divided by filter bandwidth. Fig 9 graphs filter insertion loss versus normalized Q.[2]

The 40-m filter of Fig 1 has a design bandwidth of 200 kHz—hence, a Q_f of 7/0.2, or 35. Building this filter using resonators with an unloaded Q of 250 results in a normalized Q of 250/35, or 7.1. The Fig 9 curve shows an insertion loss of about 2 dB for Q_0 = 7; this agrees with my measurements.

Fig 9 also shows that insertion loss becomes very large for normalized Qs of less than 2. As a reasonable limit, double-tuned-circuit filter Q should be no more than about 40% of the unloaded resonator Q.

Summary and Additional Thoughts

The double-tuned circuit can be summarized as follows:

1. Double-tuned circuits can be characterized by degree of coupling. A circuit may

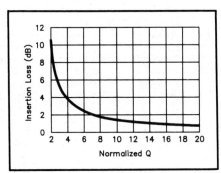

Fig 9—Double-tuned-circuit insertion loss versus normalized Q, Q_0 (unloaded Q [Q_u divided by filter Q [Q_f]). Higher insertion loss accompanies narrower bandwidths; a reasonable limit for the double-tuned circuit is $Q_0 > 2.5$.

be undercoupled, overcoupled or critically coupled.

2. A double-humped response indicates overcoupling, and rarely has anything to do with stagger tuning.

3. An experimenter may overlook the "other" peak in a severely overcoupled circuit because it may be far removed in fre-

quency from the observed peak. Builders should take special care to avoid mistaking one of two peaks as the single peak of a critically coupled circuit.

4. Align double-tuned circuits by adjusting their coupling from slight overcoupling toward critical coupling. You should observe slight overcoupling during the alignment process.

5. Higher insertion loss accompanies narrower bandwidths. A reasonable limit for the double-tuned circuit is $Q_0 > 2.5$.

All of the concepts governing the double-tuned circuit may be extended to filters of other orders. For example, a single-tuned circuit has an insertion loss related to bandwidth and unloaded Q. Similar relations exist for filters consisting of multiple coupled resonators. Crystal filters, arrays of dielectric resonators, and coupled microstrip sections all behave similarly. They can all be tuned with these methods.

Notes

[1]W. Hayward and D. DeMaw, *Solid-State Design for the Radio Amateur*, Appendix 2, "Band-pass filters," p 239 (Newington: ARRL, 1986). Also see W. Sabin, "Designing Narrow Band-Pass Filters with a BASIC Program," *QST*, May 1983, pp 23-29.
[2]Insertion loss (dB) = 20 log (Q_0 / (Q_0 − 1.414)) $\boxed{\text{QST}}$

From QST, December 1993, p 37:

Measuring and Compensating Oscillator Frequency Drift

How stable is the VFO in your rig? A frequency counter, a simple environmental chamber, and a home-built electronic thermometer can allow you to measure and even compensate the drift in your oscillators.

By Wes Hayward, W7ZOI
7700 SW Danielle Ave
Beaverton, OR 97005

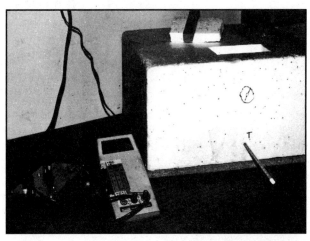

(photos by W7ZOI)

An oscillator's *stability* characterizes its relative freedom from undesired frequency change. Many factors can cause unwanted frequency shift. Variations in loading (termination) can cause *pulling*. Altering the oscillator power supply voltage can cause *pushing*. Circuit noise can modulate an oscillator, leading to *phase-noise* sidebands.

The most common form of oscillator instability, however, is that related to temperature. The inductors, capacitors, crystals, and/or transmission lines that determine oscillator frequency have values that depend upon temperature. Temperature changes arise either from internal heating, which causes *warm-up drift*, or from changes in the environment surrounding the circuitry. Both of these are called *thermal drift*.

Variable frequency oscillator (VFO) drift has always been a topic of vital concern to the radio amateur. Articles on the subject abound, with each author presenting his or her own recipe for achieving oscillator stability. Some of this lore is well-founded—that is, based on careful observation and sound thinking, and correspondence between the two. Other contributions depart from science. The collective result is confusing, if not chaotic. Believing the lore may cause us to build ill-conceived circuits while we ignore others that might offer wonderful stability.

VFO design is an ever-evolving pursuit. Internal heat generation was the major problem we fought with vacuum-tube oscillators. Although less severe, these thermal effects persist with solid-state oscillators. A more recent difficulty adds further complication: Some critical VFO components are no longer commercially available. Stable fixed-value capacitors and high-quality variable capaci-

tors are relatively difficult to find. (Some fixed-ceramic capacitors advertised as having an NP0 temperature characteristic do not really qualify. More later on this.) The smooth, double-bearing "variables" used in our vintage rigs have been largely replaced by smaller, but more rugged and robust tuning diodes. The diodes are easy to use and offer wonderful mechanical stability, but they also tend to have terrible temperature characteristics and be lower-Q than the mechanical variables they replace. They can also generate noise.

Thermal stability problems can be solved through careful measurements. The requisite tools for oscillator measurement include a frequency counter and a simple environmental chamber with a controlled, measured temperature. An initial measurement (at power up) determines the oscillator's "cold" output frequency. Further measurements at the same chamber temperature quantify what warm-up drift occurs. Heating the chamber then adds the factor of rising ambient temperature. Further temperature and frequency measurements then characterize the oscillator's thermal stability.

Many experimenters already own frequency counters, so this article will describe a simple thermal chamber I built for oscillator evaluation. I'll also present several methods for temperature measurement—a vital part of the process—and show how to use the counter, temperature chamber and thermometer for oscillator evaluation.

Once the measurement tools are in place, the details of temperature compensation can be explored. I'll discuss some of the things that cause drift in oscillators, and how components are specified for temperature stability. I'll then present some examples that illustrate the compensation process.

Temperature Measurement

The ambient temperature in a ham shack is usually around 20 degrees Celsius (°C). A reasonably useful ham environmental chamber would produce temperatures from –20 to +70 °C. The chamber I'll describe is less ideal; it operates only at room temperatures and above. It is still nonetheless useful to be able to measure temperatures on either side of 20 °C.

A mercury thermometer, available from a chemical supply house, serves as an easy-to-use and traditional solution. For some experiments, I've used a Curtin Matheson Scientific Inc type CM-8 (catalog #248-422), which covers –20 to +150 °C. A hole in the chamber passes the thermometer. Most of the thermometer remains outside the chamber; its mercury bulb enters the chamber at the same height above the bottom of the chamber as the circuit under test.

A photographic shop may also carry a thermometer you can use: Photo thermometers, typically priced around $20, operate over a temperature range that includes most of the one we need. Some home thermometers may even work, although many lack useful resolution. The restricted range of medical thermometers makes them unsuitable for our purposes.

If you already have a digital multimeter (DMM), you can cheaply and easily build the ultimate solution, an electronic digital thermometer. (If you're an avid experimenter who doesn't have a DMM, put one on your "wish list.") Two possible circuits (Fig 1) use National Semiconductor's LM3911 IC temperature sensor. The simpler circuit, Fig 1A, provides a readout in kelvins. The LM3911 has an output of 10 mV/°C, so this circuit provides 0.1-°C resolution when used with a DVM capable of 1-mV resolu-

Accessories/Components 5-35

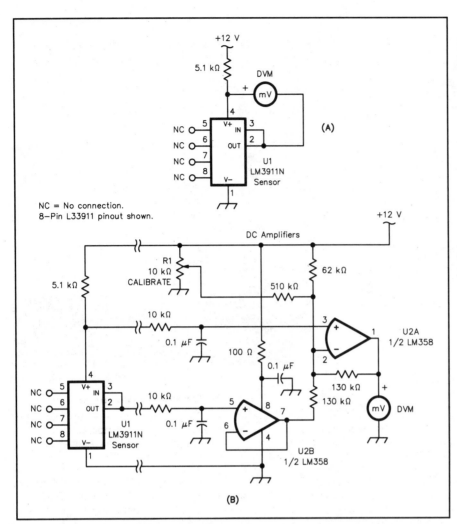

Fig 1—Two solid-state thermometers based on the LM3911 temperature sensor IC, one with readout in kelvins (A) and another (B) with readout in degrees Celsius. The circuit's fixed resistors are ¼-watt carbon-film; the capacitors, general-purpose ceramic. R1, **CALIBRATE**, is a trimmer potentiometer.

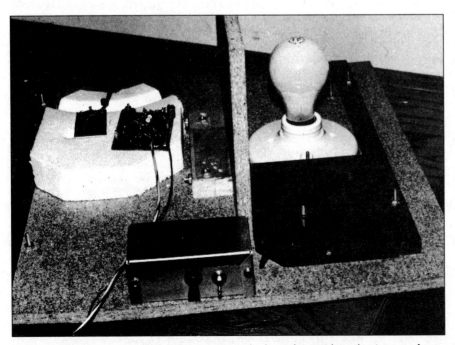

Inside the chamber, a vertical partition separates the incandescent-lamp heat source from the circuit under test. The switch box controls the lamp and exhaust fan.

tion at the 3-V level. Fig 1B shows a version with direct readout in degrees Celsius.

The TO-46 metal-can LM3911 I used in my thermometer needed a small heat sink to guarantee accuracy. Without it, self-heating in the sensor IC can generate errors of several degrees, even with the IC dissipating only 5 mW. An 8-pin plastic LM3911 (LM3911N) is available from Digi-Key for about $2. This plastic IC can be epoxied to a small, junk-box heat sink. Alternatively, the LM3911N may provide accurate results without a heat sink if its unused pins (5, 6, 7, and 8) are soldered to the surface where temperature is being measured. Some experiments may be required here.

I built the Fig 1B circuit in two sections. A small scrap of PC-board material carrying the LM3911 resides in the temperature chamber. A box away from the chamber contains the offset amplifier. There is nothing critical about the offset circuit and any construction form is suitable. R1, the **CALIBRATE** pot, should afford high resolution.

The electronic thermometer can be calibrated at room temperature using a chemical thermometer as a standard. Absolute temperature accuracy is not especially important for this application. What's more important is the ability to measure temperature *changes* with accuracy and repeatability.

The Chamber

The thermal chamber (see title photo) can be as simple or as elaborate as you would like it to be. The oven described here emphasizes simplicity, but it still provides a great deal of information.

A thermal chamber consists of a source of heat and an enclosure to spatially confine the heat. A 60-watt light bulb serves as the heat source. The only control is a toggle switch. The bulb resides in a ceramic socket mounted on a piece of fiberboard about 16 inches square (see photo this page). Another piece of fiberboard, placed vertically between the light bulb and the part of the chamber containing the circuit under test, prevents direct bulb radiation from reaching the circuit under test.

The chamber itself is a 9-inch deep Styrofoam box originally used as a shipping container for tropical fish. (At a supermarket, I located a suitable substitute box in the form of a Styrofoam picnic cooler. A usable substitute could be fabricated from plywood, or even cardboard.) The box is inverted and placed over the fiberboard base. Wood strips on the base locate the Styrofoam, simplifying the box's quick removal and replacement when inserting test circuits.

The box confines the light-bulb heat through the excellent insulation properties of Styrofoam. Lining the inside surface with aluminum foil would further improve the chamber's thermal performance by providing reflection as a second isolation mechanism. The metal would, however, act as a thermal load and slow the rate at which the

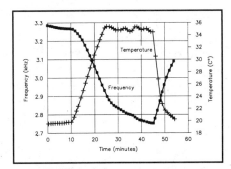

Fig 2—Results of a drift run made on the Ugly Weekender (JFET Hartley) VFO operating with its enclosure closed.

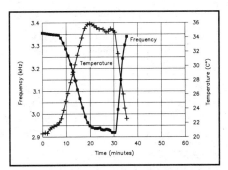

Fig 3—An Ugly Weekender drift run made with the transceiver's enclosure open. The quicker response of the VFO components to test-chamber temperature changes is clearly evident.

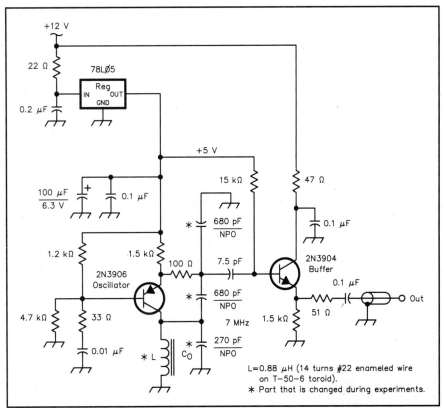

Fig 4—The 7-MHz bipolar-junction-transistor Colpitts VFO used for temperature-compensation experiments. Its resistors are ¼-watt carbon-composition; all of its nonpolarized capacitors not marked NP0 are general-purpose ceramics.

chamber temperature can be changed.

My chamber also contains a small fan configured to exchange room and chamber air. This allows quick cooling of the chamber air to ambient temperature. Air exits through a small outlet hole in the Styrofoam. A Styrofoam plug normally closes a hole in the top of the box; removing the plug allows room air to enter when cooling is desired. (The cooling fan is a convenience and is not essential. The chamber would be effective without it.)

Another useful chamber refinement would be a small internal fan to circulate the air within the chamber. Such a fan must be carefully mounted to avoid inducing mechanical vibrations that might compromise oscillator performance.

Thermometer measurements indicated that the chamber temperature is higher at the top when the heat source is on. It's therefore useful to put the circuit under study on a small pedestal made from a piece of Styrofoam packing material. The thermometer should be close to, and at the same height as, the circuit under study.

Testing and Using the Chamber

My initial experiments with the chamber dealt with thermometer calibration. I began oscillator testing only after confirming proper operation of the chamber and thermometer.

The first oscillator tested was a 7-MHz VFO from a portable QRP transceiver. This circuit, a design based on earlier lore that promoted Micrometals SF (-6 designation)

toroid inductors and NP0 capacitors,[1,2] was built in a small aluminum box. Although drift has certainly been observed with this circuit, it has been tolerated. The transceiver has seen considerable use over a decade-long period from locations as thermally diverse as sun-drenched ocean beaches and mountaintops to snow caves in winter.

I placed the entire VFO box in the chamber with the electronic thermometer in close proximity. Cabling carried signal and power connections for the thermometer and circuit under test. After placing the Styrofoam box over the chamber base, I applied power to the VFO and measured its frequency with the counter. The frequency dropped by about 150 Hz over the first 10 minutes of operation; this is the *warm-up drift*. A slight increase in chamber temperature accompanied oscillator warm-up. Fig 2 shows the experiment's frequency and temperature versus time for this period.

Ten minutes after powering up the VFO, I turned on the chamber heat. As Fig 2 indicates, the temperature immediately began to increase. The accompanying frequency change, however, was not immediate. Only after a couple of minutes of increasing temperature did the VFO frequency begin to drop. The time delay results from the thermal isolation provided by the VFO box.

I kept the heat on until the chamber temperature reached 35 °C—for 24 minutes. Then I cycled the heat on and off in short

bursts to maintain a chamber temperature around 35 °C. The VFO's frequency decreased more slowly during this interval, but never reached equilibrium. At 45 minutes into the test, I turned on the fan. The thermal insulation properties of the VFO box again complicated the measurements by slowing the onset of cooling inside the box. Such thermal isolation is very useful; it is a major reason for building a VFO in a separate box!

I removed the VFO from the environmental chamber immediately after obtaining the data for Fig 2. Then I removed the transceiver cover, returned the VFO to the chamber, and repeated the measurements. Fig 3 shows the results on the same time scale used in Fig 2. The VFO was still warm from the previous experiment, so the starting temperature was higher. The warm-up was similar to the earlier one, but when I applied oven heat at 7 minutes into the experiment, the VFO started to change frequency almost immediately. The frequency changed in direct response to changing temperature. Moreover, the frequency was relatively stable as soon as I turned the heat off at 20 minutes. Also, the chamber took less time to reach 35 °C than in the earlier run. Clearly, VFO enclosures should be removed or opened for temperature compensation measurements.

A small circuit board carrying an experimental oscillator should be much more responsive to thermal changes than one in an enclosure. I confirmed this with the design

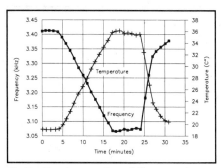

Fig 5—One temperature-drift run made with the oscillator of Fig 4. The circuit was not enclosed in a shield box.

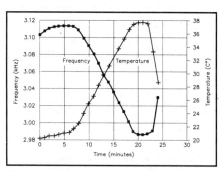

Fig 6—Thermal drift characteristic of the Fig 4 oscillator with some of its NP0 tuned-circuit capacitance replaced by polystyrene-film units. The polystyrenes' negative temperature coefficient offsets drift in the oscillator inductor. (In this case, the result was modest *overcompensation*; see text.) As in the Fig 5 test, the oscillator was not enclosed in a shield box.

presented in Fig 4. A PNP transistor serves as a Colpitts oscillator. The PNP circuit's collector operates at dc ground when powered from a negative-ground supply—convenient when biasing a tuning diode. I used NP0 ceramic capacitors for the circuit's three frequency determining elements. The inductor value chosen produced oscillation very close to 7 MHz, the same value as was used earlier. The inductor was wound on an SF toroid, a T-50-6.

Fig 5 shows frequency and temperature versus time for this circuit. I turned the oven on at 4 minutes and off at 17 minutes into the test. The oscillator seemed to follow the chamber temperature with virtually no time lag. Additional experiments to higher temperatures showed that the frequency continued to drop as temperature increased to values as high as 50 °C. The run shown in Fig 5 went from room temperature to 35 °C, producing a frequency change of about 3.5 kHz.

Fig 6 shows the results of a first attempt at temperature compensation. I replaced a 270-pF NP0 capacitor with a 100-pF NP0 capacitor paralleled by a 150-pF polystyrene capacitor. This resulted in a drift of 1.3 kHz for the same temperature swing that initially produced 3.5 kHz.

These measurements suggest a simplified way of using the oven: Rather than recording data at one-minute intervals, record the initial frequency and temperature in your notebook. Then apply heat to the oven for a long enough time to produce a temperature rise of 10 to 15 °C. Record the final conditions. This is enough information to calculate a temperature coefficient of frequency (TCF) for the circuit. I used this abbreviated procedure for almost all of the measurements reported in this article.

Temperature Compensation by Numbers

Frequency drift with temperature is usually specified in terms of a fractional change per degree of temperature change. The run in Fig 6 produced a change of about 80 Hz for each degree-Celsius of temperature swing with the oscillator operating at 7 MHz. This corresponds to a change of 0.0011 percent per degree. A more convenient specification replaces percentages with parts per million (ppm). The TCF for the VFO of Fig 6 is –11.4 ppm/°C. The negative sign indicates

that frequency decreases with increasing temperature.

Components are specified in a similar way. The *temperature coefficient of inductance* (TCL) for a coil wound on a carbonyl SF toroid (Micrometals –6 designator) is +35 ppm/°C. That is, the inductance will increase by 35 millionths of the total inductance for each degree-Celsius increase in temperature. Note, however, that this value predominantly describes how the *core* permeability changes. The inductor TC is often higher, usually because its wire is not wound tightly against the core. (Heavier wire results in higher Qs but is harder to wind tightly than thinner wire; a more stable coil may therefore result from the use of smaller wire than might be optimum for Q.)

The TCF is related to the coefficients of the individual components by the equation given in the sidebar, "Calculations in Temperature Compensation." There is a factor of one half in the sidebar's Eq A; The TCF is half of the temperature coefficient of the components. The sidebar example analyzes a parallel tuned circuit with one inductor and two capacitors with combined value of C_{total}. The overall temperature-compensating effect of a capacitor diminishes by the ratio of its value to the circuit's total capacitance.

Capacitor manufacturers specify their parts' thermal characteristics, but this data may be omitted in distributors' catalogs to save space. The most stable capacitors have a temperature coefficient of *NP0*. NP0 is a shorthand designation for *negative-positive-zero*. This characteristic depends mainly on the material from which the capacitor is made. Because manufacturing processes operate within tolerances that allow some degree of error and variation, temperature coefficients are sometimes specified in greater detail. These specifications include terms like C0G, C0H and C0J, all of which are variations on the NP0 specification. A C0G capacitor has a TC of 0 ppm/°C with an uncertainty of ±30 ppm/°C.

Temperature compensation involves counteracting an oscillator's inherent thermal instability by adding instability equal in value but opposite in sign. Drift attributable to an oscillator's tuned-circuit inductor usually plays the largest role in thermal instability, although this may not be true if some especially "bad" or poorly specified capacitors are present. Inductor TC is usually positive and can be compensated by a capacitor with a negative TC. A common temperature-compensating capacitor type (a ceramic "mix") has a TC of –750 ppm/°C; this is designated as a *N750* part. The compensating capacitor's coefficient is usually much larger than that of the inductor to be compensated because the compensating component replaces only a tiny fraction of the total resonator capacitance.

As an example, consider the oscillator evaluated in Figs 4 and 5. Based on data recorded at 5 and 17 minutes, the oscillator TCF (as determined using the sidebar's

Eq A) was –28.0 ppm/°C. The circuit used all NP0 capacitors. Assuming that these parts are drift-free, the inductor has a temperature coefficient of +56 ppm/°C.

The modified oscillator that produced the data of Fig 6 used parallel capacitors, 440 pF of NP0 plus 150 pF of polystyrene (TC, –150 ppm/°C). According to the sidebar's Eq A, the approximately compensated oscillator should have a TCF of –9 ppm/°C. The measurements on which Fig 6 is based reflect a TCF of –11.5 ppm/°C. Compensation would be exact with 220 pF of N150 and 370 pF of NP0 capacitance.

Observations on the Method and Its Limits

The methods presented are incomplete because the test chamber is capable only of positive temperature excursions. Extending the process to cooler extremes should not be difficult. For example, a small thermal chamber could be put inside a household freezer. After a suitable cooling period, the heat source could be turned on to bring the oscillator under test up to room temperature.[3]

The compensation process should not be asked to deliver miracles. The folly of such an effort is evident from the sidebar's Eq A, which shows how two or three thermal effects are balanced against each other. As one component becomes less stable, the others must be made similarly unstable, but in the opposite direction, such that the overall result is zero net drift.

As a better design procedure, use the most stable inductor available. Resonate it with the most stable capacitors available to you. Then use compensation only to make this good design even better. This approach illustrates a concept that finds its way through much of science: Two large effects are not expected to balance each other unless there is good physical justification for the balance. This idea, applied to VFO design, was emphasized by Roy Lewallen, W7EL, in his earlier work.

Ham junk boxes typically do not contain capacitors with negative temperature coeffi-

Calculations in Temperature Compensation

If a tuned circuit consists of an inductor with a temperature coefficient of TC_L that is paralleled by two capacitors, C_1 and C_2, with temperature coefficients TC_{c1} and TC_{c2}, respectively, the temperature coefficient of frequency is then TCF, where

$$TCF = -\frac{1}{2}\left(TC_L + TC_{c1}\frac{C_1}{C_{total}} + TC_{c2}\frac{C_2}{C_{total}} \right) \quad \text{Eq A}$$

If a compensating capacitor, C_c, is paralleled with a capacitor C_p and the combination is placed in series with a capacitor C_s, the combination has a net capacitance C with a net temperature coefficient TC_n, where

$$C_{net} = \frac{1}{\left[\dfrac{1}{C_s} + \dfrac{1}{\left(C_p + C_c \right)} \right]} \quad \text{Eq B}$$

$$TC_n = \frac{C_{net}\, C_c}{\left(C_c + C_p \right)^2}\, TC_c \quad \text{Eq C}$$

cients. One major exception to this is common: polystyrene film capacitors. Most of the polystyrene capacitors I've used have come from Mouser Electronics. They were specified to have a temperature coefficient of −150 ppm/°C. Such relatively stable, low-TC performance should be used in preference to smaller-valued, but higher-coefficient N750 parts.

Examining compensation more closely further complicates the process. Especially at higher frequencies, the parasitic reactances of a circuit's active devices become significant. The analysis presented in this article assumes that drift is linear with temperature. Linearity implies that a component temperature coefficient is constant, but this only approximates reality. Compensating an oscillator over a wide temperature range can be a very difficult chore.

Conclusions and Quasi-Lore

I found this project very enlightening, and it suggests the following conclusions and observations. Some of these are rather specific, often pertaining to technical lore long believed by amateur constructors, while others are more general.

The first, and certainly the strongest, conclusion that emerges is that temperature compensation is neither difficult nor expensive. The equipment needed is usually available in an experimenter's collection of goodies. While lore provides a starting point for design, it is no substitute for measurement.

I'll now present as lore some of the generalities that have come from the experiments, with the thought that they can and will be confirmed through additional reader measurements:

• Excellent components are available to radio amateurs of today. This allows good compensation results to be realized with *single-point* methods. That is, we can do one TC measurement between two relatively close temperatures and be assured that the results will apply over a wider range.

• There is no fundamental thermal stability difference between a Hartley or a Colpitts oscillator, or any other topology that I have tried. It's important that the oscillator operate with current limiting.[4] Voltage limiting can severely degrade resonator Q, leading to

compromised stability.

• Micrometals -6 toroid material, when used with high-quality NP0 capacitors, form the most stable starting configuration I have found. The run of Fig 5 is typical (TCF = −28 ppm/°C). After compensation, several oscillators have yielded TCFs between 1 and 2 ppm/°C. I have not yet investigated the newer -7 material that some builders have found useful.

• Warm-up drift is interesting as a measure of self-heating. However, it is a poor indicator of stability when compared with a temperature run in a simple thermal chamber.

• A search for readily available, inexpensive NP0 capacitors that perform as advertised produced two viable sources. One part tested was a 470-pF monolithic ceramic (Mouser Electronics 21RD647). The other part tested was a 220-pF ceramic (Digi-Key P4460, manufactured by Panasonic). Other parts from the same catalog groups are probably as stable. This experience is much more encouraging than a similar experiment done a few years ago.

• A tuning diode I examined (a Motorola MV209) exhibited, as expected, a high TC (+442 ppm/°C). Work continues on active compensation circuits, however. Voltage-regulator circuitry used with tuning diodes must be designed with care because Zener-diode temperature drift can confuse compensation results.

• Some builders (amateur and otherwise) have been building oscillators from available, but apparently mismatched components. Experiments confirmed the variable performance of these methods. One oscillator, built using a -6 toroid and polystyrene capacitors alone (no NP0 units), was overcompensated (TCF = +24 ppm/°C—better than expected, but not recommended). Another test oscillator, built with a -2 ("carbonyl E") core, exhibited a TCF of −63 ppm/°C when tuned with NP0 capacitors. Replacing the NP0 capacitors with polystyrenes yielded a TCF of +8.2 ppm/°C. This topology is also not recommended, because its temperature depends on two relatively large coefficients working against each other. As mentioned earlier, better designs aim for the best stability with each and every component.

• Coils should be conditioned for best sta-

bility. Bending and stretching the coil wire during winding creates mechanical stresses in the windings. Heating the coil, and then allowing it to cool to ambient, relieves those stresses. I readily observed this effect with the temperature chamber: A new coil, just wound and subjected to a thermal cycle, starts at a frequency that is different than the final one. Subsequent cycles, however, show repeatable, reversible behavior. Temperature-chamber tests confirmed a method of annealing an inductor in boiling water as suggested by W7EL.[5]

• This article considers only toroidal inductors. They are presently available, offer higher Q for a given volume than other forms, and are well-characterized. Some workers continue to advocate slug-tuned or air-core coils, but have not offered specifications or measurements.

Science can help you build better oscillators if you give it a chance. You can have "rock stable" oscillators if you're willing to build and apply some simple measurement gear.

Acknowledgments

I'd like to extend my thanks to numerous ham colleagues who have shown an interest in this project, especially W7EL; Terry White, KL7IAK; and K8BHZ. Thanks also to Steve Bingham, who contributed an LM3911 from his junk box.

Notes
[1]R. Lewallen, "An Optimized QRP Transceiver," *QST*, Aug 1980, pp 14-19; also see Feedback, *QST*, Nov 1080, p 63. The Optimized QRP Transceiver article also appears in re-edited form in the 1992-1994 *ARRL Handbooks*.
[2]R. Hayward and W. Hayward, "The 'Ugly Weekender,'" *QST*, Aug 1981, pp 18-21. (The Ugly Weekender also appears in re-edited form in the 1992-1994 *ARRL Handbooks*.) Also see oscillator comments in W. Hayward and D. DeMaw, *Solid-State Design for the Radio Amateur* (Newington: ARRL, 1977 and 1986).
[3]Brian Mattson, K8BHZ, has suggested using the Peltier-effect coolers that are now available as 12-volt-powered mini-refrigerators. Relatively inexpensive and available in a size intended to cool six-pack-sized objects, they might be an ideal basis for a small environmental chamber.
[4]W. Hayward, *Introduction to Radio Frequency Design* (Englewood Cliffs, NJ: Prentice-Hall, 1982), Ch 7.
[5]See Note 1.

From QST, April 1995, p 60:

Build the Camper's Portable Hamshack

When you're hamming in the great outdoors, do it in style!

By Bill Jones, KD7S
83 Redwood Ave
Sanger, CA 93657

NEW HAM COMPANION

The CPH holds my Heathkit HW-8 QRP (low power) transceiver, an MFJ-948 antenna tuner and a homebrew iambic keyer. In addition, it includes an expanded-range voltmeter, internal 7 A-h gel-cell battery, headphones, Mr. MouseKey,[1] plus storage for extra fuses, spare keyer battery, pens, paper, log book, flashlight, digital clock and so on. A fuse holder and SO-239 antenna connector are mounted on the bottom section of the rear panel. Also at the rear are binding posts for external power, solar panel or a conventional battery charger. Except for the antenna itself, it is a complete, self-contained station.

The CPH enclosure is built mainly of $^{1}/_{2}$-inch-thick particle board. The shelves, rear cover and sub-panel are cut from a piece of $^{1}/_{4}$-inch particle board. The front cover is hinged and serves as a small desk when open. The two-piece rear cover is hinged to allow access to the back of the equipment, as well as the stored items. The entire assembly is held together with carpenter's glue and 1-inch wire brads. Two coats of enamel paint protect the wood and make the finished project look as good as it is functional.

Construction

Figure 1 shows how the various pieces fit together. The exact size will depend on

W hat could be better than the early morning sun touching the treetops, bacon sizzling over an open campfire and 40 meters alive with signals? If you've already experienced the joy of camping with ham radio, you know the answer—not much! You also know that packing ham gear for a camping trip is not for the faint of heart. Besides the rig itself, there are many less obvious parts and pieces that must be included. Items such as connecting cables, spare fuses, extra batteries, headphones, keyer paddles, log book and writing paper are easily overlooked.

The Camper's Portable Hamshack—CPH for short—takes the worry and guesswork out of operating in the field. Simply stated, the CPH is a custom-made wood box designed to house the portable station equipment in a single, compact package. Beyond that, it includes many accessories and convenience features that can mean the difference between worry-free operation away from home and just another camping trip.

Figure 1—CPH layout and materials list
(all lumber dimensions are depth × height × width, in inches)

2 ea—$11^{3}/_{8}$×$11^{5}/_{8}$×$^{1}/_{2}$ particle board (sides)

2 ea—$11^{3}/_{8}$×$11^{5}/_{8}$×$^{1}/_{2}$ particle board (top and bottom)

2 ea—$11^{1}/_{8}$×$11^{5}/_{8}$×$^{1}/_{4}$ particle board (shelves)

1 ea—11×$11^{5}/_{8}$×$^{1}/_{2}$ particle board (front cover)

1 ea—$11^{5}/_{8}$×$9^{1}/_{2}$×$^{1}/_{4}$ particle board (rear cover, top)

1 ea—$11^{5}/_{8}$×$2^{1}/_{8}$×$^{1}/_{4}$ particle board (rear cover, bottom part)

1 ea—$6^{1}/_{2}$×$2^{3}/_{8}$×$^{1}/_{4}$ thick particle board (sub panel)

Miscellaneous: Carpenter's glue, nails, hinges, chain, paint.

your own equipment. My cabinet measures 11⅝ inches wide by 11⅝ inches high by 12⅛ inches deep. Make a sketch of each item you want to include inside the box, including its dimensions. Be sure to allow sufficient space around the equipment for proper air circulation. Then, make a rough drawing of the enclosure. Use this drawing as a guideline for construction.

Begin construction by cutting the top, bottom and two sides from a piece of ½-inch particle board. A table saw makes it easy to cut the grooves for the shelves. If all you have is a handsaw, use stud-mounted shelf clips pushed into holes drilled in the sides of the box to mount the shelves. Dry-fit the assembly and make sure it's square. Glue and clamp the pieces together and let the glue cure overnight. Cut another piece of ½-inch board for the front cover. Set it aside for now.

From a piece of ½-inch particle board, cut out the parts for the two-piece back cover. Install a pair of small brass hinges between them. Confirm that everything is square and that the hinges move freely. Glue and nail the bottom part of the cover to the frame. Put the assembly aside long enough for the glue to cure completely. By the way, a simple way to hold the upper part of the back cover closed is to use a magnetic cabinet catch. If that doesn't appeal to you, use whatever you have on hand. Be creative. Now would also be a good time to cut the shelves and sub-panel to size. They will be used shortly.

Next, install the front cover. Take special care with this part of the project. Remember that the front cover will double as a desktop when it's open. Attach the front to the base with a pair of brass hinges. A piano hinge, if you can find a small one at a reasonable price, would be a better choice. Otherwise, use what you have available. Substituting longer screws than the ones provided with the hinges will result in a more durable arrangement. Drill small pilot holes for the mounting screws and fill the holes with a dab of glue or epoxy resin just before assembly. Install a pair of screw-eyes on the inside of the front cover toward the top. Put a second pair on the inside of each side panel. To these, attach two lengths of small, decorative chain to serve as a lid support when the cover is in the down position. Keep the lid closed with another magnetic cabinet latch.

Final construction consists of installing the shelves, sub-panel and connectors. If you would like some sort of carrying handle, browse the aisles of your hardware store. You will no doubt come up with a dozen different ideas.

I mount my CPH on a heavy-duty "yard-sale special" camera tripod. The adjustable legs are great for setting up shop on uneven terrain. Screw-on coffee table legs would work almost as well and are available at most building supply or larger hardware stores.

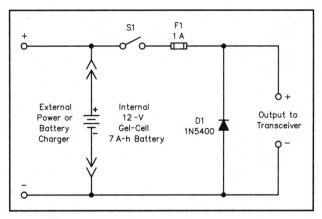

Figure 2—Schematic diagram and parts list for the reverse-polarity protection circuit (optional).
D1—1N5400 silicon diode (Radio Shack 276-1141)
F1—1-A fast-acting fuse
S1—SPST rocker switch (Radio Shack 275-690)

Bells and Whistles

As mentioned earlier, my portable hamshack includes a number of bells and whistles. Figure 2 shows how I provide reverse polarity protection for my transceiver. Under normal circumstances, diode D1 will not conduct because it is reverse biased. However, if the battery is connected backward, D1 conducts heavily and will quickly blow the 1-A fuse. D1 must be capable of handling two to three times the current rating of the fuse. A 1N5400 diode is rated at 3 A and should be adequate for low-power equipment. This approach avoids the 0.7-V drop of the conventional series-connected diode scheme.

An expanded-scale dc voltmeter helps to keep tabs on the status of my main battery. The circuitry is shown in Figure 3 and is borrowed from WB8VGE's QRP column in *73* magazine.[2] The meter, a 0-1 milliammeter, measures the difference between the 10-V reference set by the Zener diode and the battery voltage. Calibration is done with a variable power supply and digital voltmeter. Using the digital voltmeter, set the power supply for 15 V and adjust the 10-kΩ trimmer to read full scale on the expanded scale meter. Reduce the voltage to 12.5 V and your new meter should read half-scale. Redraw the meter face to read from 10 to 15 V.

Just to the right of the meter and master power switch are jacks for the headphones and keyer paddles. Bringing these connections to the front of the enclosure makes hookup quick and simple.

An inexpensive LCD digital clock from MFJ helps keep my logbook straight. The clock has an internal battery and can be set to display 12 or 24-hour time. I set mine for UTC. The clock is stored inside the CPH except when the station is in operation. Similar clocks are available from Radio Shack stores.

The space behind the keyer and meter sub-panel holds the headphones, paddles, spare fuses, writing materials, flashlight and all the other things I used to forget to bring along. The gel-cell battery is mounted behind the antenna tuner.

As a final test before leaving home I set

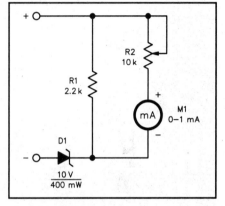

Figure 3—Schematic diagram and parts list of the expanded-scale dc voltmeter (optional).
D1—10 V, 400 mW Zener diode (Ocean State 1N758)
M1—0-1 mA milliammeter (Ocean State 20-6001-1)
R1—2.2 kΩ, ¼-W resistor (Radio Shack 271-1325)
R2—10 kΩ trimmer resistor (Radio Shack 271-343)
Ocean State Electronics, PO Box 1458, 6 Industrial Dr, Westerly, RI 02891; tel 401-596-3080.

the CPH up in my back yard. With one or two stations in the logbook, I'm confident that everything is ready to go. Inside the cabinet is a printed checklist that provides added insurance, however.

It takes about three minutes to set everything up in the field after the antenna is in the air. Compared to what it used to take, the CPH gives me more on-the-air time than ever before.

The peace of mind of knowing that nothing has been overlooked is very comforting. But then, that's why I built the Camper's Portable Hamshack in the first place. If it could just make a fresh pot of coffee every once in a while, it would be perfect.

Notes
[1]Bill Jones, KD7S "Mr. Mousekey," *QST*, July 1994, p 12.
[2]Michael Bryce, WB8VGE, "QRP," *73 Amateur Radio Today*, June 1991, p 70.

6. Resources

Periodicals of Interest to QRP Enthusiasts
Compiled by L. B. Cebik, W4RNL
From the *QRP-L* Internet Site

ARRL Publications for QRP Enthusiasts

6. Resources

Periodicals of Interest to QRP Enthusiasts

This list was compiled by L. B. Cebik, W4RNL. It appears on the World Wide Web QRP-L Resource Page, and is reproduced with the permission of L. B. Cebik, W4RNL. For those with access to the Internet, the Resource Page can be found at:

http://QRP.cc.nd.edu/QRP-L/

Periodicals of Interest to QRP Enthusiasts   Version 1.3
February 1, 1996
Compiled by L. B. Cebik, W4RNL   e-mail: cebik@utk.edu

Contents: This file contains basic information on periodicals of especial interest to QRP enthusiasts. It lists club-sponsored periodicals, independent journals, and club newsletters known to the compiler to the date of the present version.

NOT included are standard, general interest amateur radio journals, such as QST, CQ, Communications Quarterly, 73, RADCOM, and others from all over the world. Although these journals often contain articles of interest to QRP enthusiasts, they are too well known to require space here. Both 73 and World Radio have regular QRP features or columns.

Electronics books of interest to QRP enthusiasts and antenna books of interest to QRP enthusiasts will be found in separate listings.

Each entry in this list providess the following information: journal name, issues per year, source, cost per year, basis of subscription, average pages per issue, subscription or membership address, a brief description of the usual contents, and special notes.

In addition to the hams listed within each entry, special thanks go to WA8MCQ, DL8MFQ, N8ET, AA2UJ, W6EMD and WB9NLZ for their assistance in compiling this list.

This list is believed to be reasonably complete and accurate as of the date of this notice. Corrections and additions may be e-mailed to me at the listed address. I shall be pleased to add to the list any publication omitted if it is of high interest to QRP operators and builders. And, of course, I shall be pleased to correct any errors and update the information listed.

Permission to reproduce this list is hereby granted on condition that a full reference to its source is included.

Good reading, good building, and good operating to you.

L. B. Cebik, W4RNL

Club-Sponsored Journals

1. Name: QRP Quarterly   Issues per year: 4
   Source: QRP ARCI   Cost: $12.00 US*
   Basis: Membership   Pages: 40/issue
   Address: Mike Bryce, WB8VGE
            2225 Mayflower NW
            Massillon, OH 44647 USA

Contents: Construction (circuits, antennas, modifications, test equipment, etc., Tech Ed. WB6TPU), equipment reviews, shop and building tips ("Idea Exchange," WA8MCQ), operating, award, editorial views and QRP philosophy, contest dates and results, and member news (KI6SN)

Notes: *$10 renewal/year; see club list for dues and address in Great Britain; 8.5×11 format

2. Name: SPRAT   Issues per year: 4
   Source: G-QRP Club   Cost: $12.00 US*
   Basis: Membership   Pages: 44/issue
   Address: *Mike Kilgore, KG5F
            2046 Ash Hill Road
            Carrollton, TX 75007 USA

Contents: Ed. George Dobbs, G3RJV; 60% construction each issue (circuits, antennas, test equipment, etc., both basic and advanced, with some pcb layouts) from many different countries; award, operating, contest, G- novice, SSB, VHF, and member columns & news.

Notes: *Membership/subscription dues to be sent according to country of residence; see list of clubs for information on non-US

costs and addresses; SPRAT = "Small Powered Radio Amateur Transmitter", 5.75×8.5

3. Name: QRPp   Issues per year: 4
   Source: NORCAL   Cost: $10.00 US
   Basis: Membership   Pages: 72/issue
   Address: The QRP Club of Northern California
            Jim Cates, WA6GER
            3241 Eastwood Road
            Sacramento, CA 95821 USA

Contents: Ed. Doug Hendricks, KI6DS; over 20 articles per issue, mostly devoted to technical and construction topics including new designs, conversions, improvements, and modifications, featuring NORCAL club projects, such as NORCAL 40(A) and Sierra, with a member profile and some operating features.

Notes: Membership is free, $10 is for QRPp; $15/year foreign airmail; schedule: March, June, Sept., Dec.; Make subscription checks payable to Jim Cates, not NORCAL; 5.75x8.5

4. Name: 72   Issues per year: 4
   Source: New England QRP ARC   Cost: $10.00 US*
   Basis: Membership   Pages: 32/issue
   Address: Jack Frake, NG1G
            P.O. Box 93
            Barnard, VT 05031

Contents: Ed. Dennis Marandos, K1LGQ; a balanced combination of technical articles (both background theory and practical circuits and tips), operating news and advice, and club matters, with general interest features.

Notes: *Renewals: $7.00/per year to Paul Kranz, W1CFI, 26 Mattacomett Path, Harvard, MA 01451

5. Name: Low Down   Issues per year: 6
   Source: Colorado QRP Club   Cost: $10.00 US
   Basis: Membership   Pages: 24/issue
   Address: Rich High, WØHEP (President and Editor)*
            740 Galena Street
            Aurora, CO 80010-3922 USA
            FAX: 303-344-0741 e-mail: CQC@aol.com

Contents: Technical articles; rig profiles and other equipment reviews; overseas QRP operating features; club member profiles ("Check-Ins"); CQC contest news, rules, and forms; QRP philosophy and views; special 2-month advance calendar of QRP operating events and contests

Notes: Seeking more technical articles and QRP-overseas articles. New address as of 9-1-95.

*Send memberships and renewals to: Colorado QRP Club, PO Box 371883, Denver, CO 80237-1883

6. Name: The Five-Watter (T5W)   Issues per year: 4
   Source: Michigan QRP Club   Cost: $ 7.00 US*
   Basis: Membership   Pages: 20/issue
   Address: L. T. Switzer, N8CQA
            654 Georgia Avenue
            Marysville, MI 48040

Contents: Ed. Lowell Corbin, KD8FR; A mix of club, operating, building, and antenna information, along with occasional expressions of viewpoints.

Notes: *New memberships: $7.00 US/VE, $12 DX; renewal dues $5.00 US/VE, $10 DX

7. Name: QRP Recycler   Issues per year: 6
   Source: Valley Forge VHF Society   Cost: $ 9.95 US*
   Basis: Subscription   Pages: 4/issue
   Address: PTM
            Drawer 506
            Devault, PA 19432

Contents: QRP-related ads. The ads themselves are free, and the only charge is for subscriptions. The size is 8.5x11, printed on 100% recycled paper for 100% recycled QRP equipment.

Notes: *The $9.95 subscription price is for 3rd class mail or for e-mail delivery. For 1st class delivery, the price is $13.95/year. The sponsoring society maintains a Web site at http://home.aol.com/QRP1. E-mail to the Society at QRP1@aol.com. A sample issue is on-line at the WWW site.

8. Name: Lo-Key   Issues per year: 4
   Source: CW Operators QRP Club (VK) Cost $14.00 A*
   Basis: Mem/Subscription   Pages: 32/issue
   Address: Kevin Zietz, VK5AKZ
            41 Tobruk Avenue
            St. Marys, SA 5042
            Australia

Contents: Ed. Don Callow, VK5AIL; Two to three construction articles/issue, including advanced ideas, equipment modifications, keyers, etc. (some with parts kits available); awards, contest, and net program news.

Notes: *VK price $10/yr; ZL $12/yr; dx S14/yr: N8ET will accept subscription money at Dayton and forward in order to assist with currency conversion. 5.75×8.5

9. Name: OK QRP INFO   Issues per year: 4
   Source: OK (Czech) QRP Club   Cost: $10.00 US*
   Basis: Membership   Pages: 35/issue
   Address: Petr Doudra OK1CZ (IN: HRUSKA@ig.cas.cz)
            U 1. baterie 1
            16200 Praha (Prague)
            Czech Republic

Contents: Several construction articles (up to 8 brief ones), most with English translations; also general interest reports on QRP activities

Notes: *Cost/yr: 15 IRCs; GBP 5.00; US$ 10.00; DM 15; 5.75x8.5

Independent Magazines/Journals

1. Name: HAMBREW   Issues per year: 4
   Source: George De Grazio, WF0K Cost: $10.00 US
   Basis: Subscription   Pages: +/-50/issue
   Address: P.O. Box 280083
            Lakewood, CO 80226-0083 USA
   Tel: 303-989-5642
            (Answering Machine for credit card subscriptions)

Contents: Home brewing with high QRP interest of everything from power supplies to transmitters, receivers, antenna tuners, with some basic theory, operating, and contest features. Many feature articles to aid the new builder.

Notes: Publisher recently reduced price to make HAMBREW more accessible; will be experimenting with paper quality to ensure readability. 5.75×8.5

2. Name: The Radio Craftsman   Issues per year: 6
   Source: Doug Heacock, AA0MS Cost: No longer issued
   Basis: Subscription   Pages: 8/issue
   Address: P.O. Box 3682
            Lawrence, KS 66046-0682
            e-mail: heacock@kuhub.cc.ukans.edu

Contents: Articles to educate homebrewers about radio electronics, construction techniques. Each issue: review of book and of parts supplier based on ordering experience. Annual lists of parts and kits suppliers. Current (95) series on piece-by-piece radio design.

Notes: Publication ceased in late 1995; listed for reference.

Newsletters

1. Name: QRP Gazette   Issues per year: 6
   Source: QRP Soc of Central PA   Cost: $ 4.00 US

   Basis: Membership   Pages: 4/issue
   Address: Cameron Bailey, KT3A
            P.O. Box 173
            Mount Wolf, PA 17347-0173 USA

Contents: General interest QRP items, club and field activities, meeting agenda, updates on club projects

Notes: "Serving the needs of local QRPers in Central PA"

2. Name: NEIQS Quarterly   Issues per year: 4
   Source: Don Kozlovsky   Cost: $0.00 US*
   Basis: Subscription*   Pages: —/issue
   Address: 28 W 256 Purnell Road
            West Chicago, IL 60185

Contents: Operating news of interest to all QRPers

Notes: *NEIQS = NorthEastern Illinois QRP Society. Newsletter is free to QRPers who have on file with the editor #10 SASEs.

3. Name: NWQ Newsletter   Issues per year: 6
   Source: Bill Todd, N7MFB   Cost: $10.00 US*
   Basis: Membership   Pages: 8/issue
   Address: NorthWest QRP Club
            PO Box 354
            Bay Center, WA 98527

Contents: Columns on QRP DX, Contests, New Members, and Technical. Tech column includes products reviews, hints, mods, along with info on antennas, filters, kits and experimentation.

Notes: *$12 CAN, DX: $15 (US); no annual dues. 8.5×11" size. Newsletter available on club BBS.

4. Name: The Peanut Whistle   Issues per year: 12
   Source: St. Louis QRP Society   Cost: $12.00 US
   Basis: Membership*   Pages: —/issue
   Address: Keith Arns, KC0PP
            2832 Penbrooke Lane
            St. Charles, MO 63301

Contents: News of interest to members.

Notes: *SLQS is a local club for members in the local (St. Louis metropolitan area. Prospective members should attend one meeting before joining.

5. Name: QRP CoBC   Issues per year: 4
   Source: John D. Spittle, VE7QK Cost: $—.— US
   Basis: *   Pages: 2/issue
   Address: QRP Club of British Columbia
            e-mail: jds@freenet.vancouver.bc.ca

Contents: Membership, meeting, activities, and club project news

Notes: *Newsletter distributed via e-mail and available on qrp-l.

6. Name: The Nineties   Issues per year: 6-10
   Source: MFJ 90s Radio Club   Cost: $10.00 US
   Basis: Membership   Pages: —/issue
   Address: Bill Di Meo, KD4LDR, Editor
            5235 Devon Street
            Cocoa, FL 32927

Contents: Articles that concentrate on the MFJ 90xx series of transceivers. Not affiliated with MFJ.

Notes: New editor and subscription basis as of 9-16-95.

7. Name: Lowdown   Issues per year: 12
   Source: Longwave Club of America Cost: $. US
   Basis: subscription   Pages: /issue
   Address: Hi Justin
            45 Wildflower Road
            Levittown, PA 19057

Contents: 1750 meter (LOWFER or VLF) activity, including circuits for home brew. With a 1 watt and 50' antenna limit, 1750 meter work has to be qrp.

Notes: Contact Hi Justin for further information on Lowdown. Do not confuse this journal with the CQC journal.

ARRL Publications for QRP Enthusiasts

Contact the American Radio Relay League, Inc., 225 Main St., Newington, CT 06111 (860) 594-0200, email: **kcapodicasa@arrl .org** (Internet), MCI: 215-5052, for information about ARRL products, services and benefits. Should you choose to place credit card publication orders via the Internet, you may email to: **Ltardette@arrl.org**. Or if you prefer, email your phone number to **Ltardette@arrl.org** and we can call you back for your credit card information.

The prices cited do not include shipping and handling. Shipping and handling charges are as follows:

Amount of Order	ADD
Up to $20.00	$4.00
$20.01 - 30.00	5.00
30.01 - 40.00	6.00
40.01 - 50.00	7.00
50.01 - 75.00	8.00
Over $75.00	9.00

Please include your name and shipping address when placing publication orders. MasterCard, VISA, American Express, and Discover cards accepted. In the US, add the above amounts to your order to cover shipping and handling. Add an additional $1.50 to the US rate for shipment outside the US. US orders will be handled via UPS or comparable service where UPS delivery is not possible. International air and other specialty forwarding methods are available. Please call or write for information.

File updated: February 23, 1996

W1FB's QRP Notebook by Doug DeMaw is packed with construction projects for QRP transmitters, receivers and accessories. This second edition is the completely rewritten successor to Doug's popular *QRP Notebook*, and features totally new circuits. Learn the inside secrets from this veteran builder, writer and former *QST* Technical Editor. Most of the projects feature printed circuit boards that are available from a commercial source. Gain understanding of circuits. Experience firsthand the thrill of making contacts using equipment that you built. 2nd ed, c1991, 184 pages, #3657 $10

W1FB's Design Notebook: Practical Circuits for Experimenters is just the book for the avid builder of Amateur Radio equipment. This plain-language book is filled with simple, practical projects that can be built using readily available components and common hand tools. There are explanations of how the various circuits work—without heavy mathematical analysis. 1st ed, c1990, 200 pages, #3207 $10

Your QRP Operating Companion shows that you don't need special rigs or expensive equipment to enjoy the excitement and challenge of low-power operating. Ragchewing, DXing, contesting all are more enjoyable with QRP. Includes operating tips, lists of QRP clubs and organizations, net and calling frequencies, and much more. 1st ed, c1992, 96 pages, #3762 $6

Low-Profile Amateur Radio is for the ham who lives where antennas are frowned upon. You'll see that you don't need a house with acreage to enjoy your favorite hobby. One practical solution: hide your antennas. Another: operate with low power. This book tells you how to get on the air using these techniques and others

without calling attention to yourself. 1st ed, c1993, 128 pages, #4114 $8

The ARRL Handbook

Each year's *ARRL Handbook* is packed with new projects and updated information. Whether you're an Amateur Radio beginner, an experienced operator, electronic technician, engineering student or engineer, you'll find each chapter of the *ARRL Handbook* a standalone "mini-book" that will cover your favorite topics and provide invaluable reference material, fascinating facts and some great do-it-yourself projects.

In the Transceivers chapter, check out the multiband QRP transceiver from Wayne Burdick, N6KR, and the NorCal QRP club: Operate 160 through 10 meters with plug-in band modules. Try a VLF transceiver (no license required!) or a QRP transmitter built from a single IC.

The *ARRL Handbook* includes a 3.5-inch, 1.44-MB IBM-compatible diskette with a variety of standalone applications and programs used with projects in the book. *TISFIND*, a Windows application from the ARRL's Technical Information Service, provides you with the names and addresses of nearly 900 Amateur Radio vendors and organizations. Your frustrating hunts for suppliers are history!

If it's ham radio, it's in *The Handbook*.

The ARRL Radio Buyer's Sourcebooks are for anyone who buys, sells or owns Amateur Radio equipment. Two volumes are available: *The ARRL Radio Buyer's Sourcebook* covers selected *QST* Product Reviews from 1981 through 1991 and a few golden oldies. *The ARRL Radio Buyer's Sourcebook Volume 2* contains all *QST* Product Reviews published in 1991 and 1992. Both books explain what radios do, how well they do it, where to get them serviced and where to find articles about modifications. Handy comparative feature and performance charts cover equipment reviewed in the books. Each contains a history of Amateur Radio technology and a glossary of radio features and terms. Heading for a hamfest or ham dealer? Don't leave home without both *Radio Buyer's Sourcebooks*.

The ARRL Radio Buyer's Sourcebook, 1st ed, c1991, 384 pages, #3452 $15

The ARRL Radio Buyer's Sourcebook Volume 2, 1st ed, c1993, 240 pages, #4211 $15

The ARRL Antenna Book is the definitive source for information on state-of-the-art antenna and transmission line theory and construction. The book presents the best and most highly regarded coverage of antenna fundamentals, propagation, transmission lines, Yagis and quads, as well as all popular wire antenna designs. You'll find a new chapter on HF Yagi Arrays based on the latest computer modeling software. The Radio Wave Propagation chapter has been revised to include comprehensive statistical data on the range of elevation angles needed for communication from all areas of the US to important DX locations. Included with this edition is a 1.44-MB 3.5-inch diskette for the IBM PC/XT/AT and compatible computers with software by K6STI, W1FM and N6BV for Yagi analysis, propagation prediction, transmission-line evaluation, and more.

About the American Radio Relay League

The seed for Amateur Radio was planted in the 1890s, when Guglielmo Marconi began his experiments in wireless telegraphy. Soon he was joined by dozens, then hundreds, of others who were enthusiastic about sending and receiving messages through the air—some with a commercial interest, but others solely out of a love for this new communications medium. The United States government began licensing Amateur Radio operators in 1912.

By 1914, there were thousands of Amateur Radio operators—hams—in the United States. Hiram Percy Maxim, a leading Hartford, Connecticut, inventor and industrialist saw the need for an organization to band together this fledgling group of radio experimenters. In May 1914 he founded the American Radio Relay League (ARRL) to meet that need.

Today ARRL, with more than 170,000 members, is the largest organization of radio amateurs in the United States. The League is a not-for-profit organization that:

- promotes interest in Amateur Radio communications and experimentation
- represents US radio amateurs in legislative matters, and
- maintains fraternalism and a high standard of conduct among Amateur Radio operators.

At League headquarters in the Hartford suburb of Newington, the staff helps serve the needs of members. ARRL is also International Secretariat for the International Amateur Radio Union, which is made up of similar societies in more than 100 countries around the world.

ARRL publishes the monthly journal *QST*, as well as newsletters and many publications covering all aspects of Amateur Radio. Its headquarters station, W1AW, transmits bulletins of interest to radio amateurs and Morse code practice sessions. The League also coordinates an extensive field organization, which includes volunteers who provide technical information for radio amateurs and public-service activities. ARRL also represents US amateurs with the Federal Communications Commission and other government agencies in the US and abroad.

Membership in ARRL means much more than receiving *QST* each month. In addition to the services already described, ARRL offers membership services on a personal level, such as the ARRL Volunteer Examiner Coordinator Program and a QSL bureau.

Full ARRL membership (available only to licensed radio amateurs) gives you a voice in how the affairs of the organization are governed. League policy is set by a Board of Directors (one from each of 15 Divisions). Each year, half of the ARRL Board of Directors stands for election by the full members they represent. The day-to-day operation of ARRL HQ is managed by an Executive Vice President and a Chief Financial Officer.

No matter what aspect of Amateur Radio attracts you, ARRL membership is relevant and important. There would be no Amateur Radio as we know it today were it not for the ARRL. We would be happy to welcome you as a member! (An Amateur Radio license is not required for Associate Membership.) For more information about ARRL and answers to any questions you may have about Amateur Radio, write or call:

ARRL Educational Activities Dept
225 Main Street
Newington CT 06111-1494
(860) 594-0200
Prospective new amateurs call:
800-32-NEW HAM (800-326-3942)

You can also contact us via e-mail: **ead@arrl.org**
or check out our World Wide Web site:
http://www.arrl.org/

ஐ Invitation to Membership ೞ

Class of License	Call Sign	Date of Birth
Name		
Address		
City, State, ZIP		

Membership Class

	❑ Regular		❑ Family ❑ Blind	❑ 65 or older with one time Proof of Age in the US and Possessions
	US AND POSSESSIONS	ELSEWHERE		US
❑ 1 year	$31	$44	$5	$25
❑ 2 years	59	85	10	48
❑ 3 years	83	122	15	67

A member of the immediate family of a League member, living at the same address, may become a League member without *QST* at the special rate of $5 per year. Family membership must run concurrent with that of the member receiving *QST*. Blind amateurs may join without *QST* for $5 per year.

If you are 21 or younger, a special rate may apply. Write HQ for details.

Payment enclosed ❑

Charge to: ❑ VISA (13 or 16 digits) ❑ MasterCard (16 digits)
          ❑ AMEX (15 digits) ❑ Discover (16 digits)

Card Number _____

Card good from _____ to _____
(EXPIRATION DATE)

Signature _____

If you do not wish your name and address made available for non-ARRL related mailings, please check this box. ❑

QRP-PWR

THE AMERICAN RADIO RELAY LEAGUE, INC

225 MAIN STREET   NEWINGTON, CONNECTICUT 06111 USA   860-594-0200   FAX: 860-594-0303

You still can't find it ??
ARRL 1995 Periodicals
CD-ROM to the rescue...

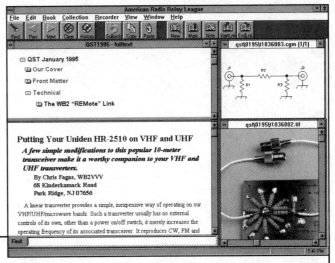

You know *QST* and other ARRL periodicals are invaluable resource tools. You hoard your back issues and refer to them over and over again. You panic because someone "straightened up" and now you're missing issues. Or even worse, your collection takes up so much room, your family has given THE ultimatum: Either the magazines go or they do. But the worst part is that you still can't remember which elusive issue had that juicy project or the essential information you need right now.

If you've got a computer with CD-ROM drive, we've got the solution to your problems: the *1995 ARRL Periodicals CD-ROM*. That's right, we've compiled all 1995 *QST*, *NCJ* and *QEX* issues into one value packed CD-ROM. And that's not all. Having the information at your fingertips is one thing, but we've also included a number of special features to make your hunting expeditions obsolete.

The *1995 ARRL Periodicals CD-ROM* includes the following:

• The full text of every *QST*, *QEX*, and *NCJ* article—including your favorite technical and general interest articles, columns, product reviews, and New Ham Companion features. Every word! Plus, every drawing, table, illustration and photograph (many in color). More than 2000 images in all!

• More than 1000 advertisement images, indexed alphabetically by vendor and product, in special ad sections created for each periodical.

• A powerful search engine that lets you find desired information quickly by entering article titles, call signs, names or just about any other word. Imagine searching for all occurrences of "antenna" or "FM" or any other topic of interest—even your own call sign!

• Advanced search features to help you narrow your search—after all, there are more than 1.8 million words on this

CD-ROM! It's easy to try wildcard searches (**KB1*** finds all call signs starting with KB1); Boolean searches (**VHF and contest** finds all articles with the words VHF and contest near each other); and proximity searches (**ARRL within 2 words before BBS** finds occurrences like ARRL BBS, ARRL HQ BBS, ARRL Headquarters BBS).

• *Windows* printing and Clipboard support, so you can print out articles or share them with other *Windows* applications.

• Tools to create bookmarks at often-used articles; to make your own hyperlinks to jump between spots that you define; or even to record your path as you navigate through a series of articles or issues. You can also annotate the text with personal comments that can be stored at any spot in the text and retrieved simply by clicking an icon.

AVAILABLE NOW!

Minimum System Requirements

- 386, 486 or Pentium™ IBM PC or 100% compatible (486 or better recommended)
- 4 Mbytes of RAM (8 Mbytes recommended)
- Hard disk with at least 10 Mbytes of free space
- Microsoft Windows™ 3.1 or higher
- 640×480, 256-color graphics
- CD-ROM drive (double speed or faster recommended)
- Mouse or equivalent pointing device

Don't waste another minute hunting for information. Order your 1995 ARRL Periodicals CD-ROM today. You'll be glad you did. ARRL Order No. 5579 - Retail $19.95 plus $4 shipping/handling for ARRL Members, $29.95 plus $4 shipping/handling for nonmembers.

ARRL 225 Main Street • Newington, CT 06111-1494   tel: 860-594-0250 fax: 860-594-0303

e-mail: pubsales@arrl.org   World Wide Web: http://www.arrl.org/

Notes

Notes

Notes

Notes

FEEDBACK

Please use this form to give us your comments on this book and what you'd like to see in future editions, or e-mail us at **pubsfdbk@arrl.org** (publications feedback).

Where did you purchase this book?
☐ From ARRL directly   ☐ From an ARRL dealer

Is there a dealer who carries ARRL publications within:
☐ 5 miles   ☐ 15 miles   ☐ 30 miles of your location?   ☐ Not sure.

License class:
☐ Novice   ☐ Technician   ☐ Technician Plus   ☐ General   ☐ Advanced   ☐ Amateur Extra

Name _____   ARRL member? ☐ Yes ☐ No

_____ Call Sign _____

Daytime Phone (   ) _____ Age _____

Address _____

City, State/Province, ZIP/Postal Code _____

If licensed, how long? _____

Other hobbies _____

For ARRL use only	QRP PWR
Edition	1 2 3 4 5 6 7 8 9 10 11 12
Printing	1 2 3 4 5 6 7 8 9 10 11 12

Occupation _____

From _____

_____

_____

EDITOR, QRP POWER
AMERICAN RADIO RELAY LEAGUE
225 MAIN STREET
NEWINGTON CT 06111-1494

please fold and tape